AGRICULTURAL ECOLOGY

BY

GIROLAMO AZZI

Professor of Agricultural Ecology in the
University of Perugia

CONSTABLE & COMPANY LTD
10–12 ORANGE STREET LONDON WC2

PUBLISHED IN THE U. S. A.
BY ESSENTIAL BOOKS,
FAIR LAWN, NEW JERSEY

LONDON
PUBLISHED BY
Constable and Company Ltd.
10–12 ORANGE STREET, W.C.2

CANADA
Longmans, Green and Company
TORONTO

SOUTH *and* EAST AFRICA
Longmans, Green and Company Ltd.
CAPE TOWN   NAIROBI

AUSTRALIA
Walter Standish and Son
SYDNEY

First published 1956

Printed in Great Britain by Richard Clay and Company, Ltd.
Bungay, Suffolk.

PREFACE

When, in the second half of the last century, the teaching of agriculture was brought to a university level, a number of subjects were borrowed from other faculties already in existence : physics, engineering, medicine, law, etc.

With regard to the physical environment, climate and soil, the study of the atmosphere was assigned to physicists—which led to the creation of *Agricultural Meteorology*—and that of soil to geologists—which led to the creation of *Agricultural Geology*, later transformed into *Geo-pedology*.

Agricultural meteorology, as it is professed, has as its object : the study of statistics as applied to meteorology, the study of atmospheric factors, the dynamism of air masses, weather forecasting; and a whole series of problems which concern agriculture in relation to particular meteorological factors; for example, the forecast of minimum temperatures so as to make possible the timely adoption of anti-frost measures, meteorological indications for the application of anticryptogamous substances, and quite recently the study on rain-making (a highly interesting problem, undoubtedly, but still very far, it seems, from practical everyday application).

Geology is concerned with geological formations, stratigraphy, lithology, mineralogy, crystallography ; pedology deals with the transformation of rocks into soil, of their evolution (including their degradation) under the action of climatic and biological factors.

Between agricultural meteorology and pedology there exists a deep rift which agriculture ecology has tried to fill, for what particularly interests the agronomist is not so much the manner in which soils were formed but their behaviour towards different crops. And this is a problem of a biological nature.

Moreover, the causes and the processes of formation of clouds, of mists, fogs, etc., which are the concern of the physicist, can also be of interest to the agronomist, who must possess a knowledge of the elements of meteorology (as also of geology); but with regard to the atmosphere the fundamental problem is that of the effects of meteorological factors on the develop-

v

ment and yield of cultivated plants. Here again it is a
question of studies of a biological nature.

The meteorological and pedological factors affecting yield
act on plants as a whole, so that one would not know how to
separate them one from the other in order to consider each
singly in an absolute manner.

While researches on the different meteorological and pedological components constitute distinct subjects from a *non-
biological* point of view, their study in relation to the yield of
plants necessarily converges on a single branch of science :
Agricultural Ecology.

This is why agricultural ecology, to which from 1920 we have
given a clearly defined outline, in reconstructing the indivisible
unity of the physical environment, fills a gap within the framework of agricultural science.

The concepts and principles on which it is based are, we
believe, completely new.

It has, however, been possible to insert harmonically within
our framework the ideas of :

B. I. BROUNOV—Parallel observations on the development of
the plant and the trend of the meteorological factors ;
divisions of the vegetative periods into sub-periods.

G. GASSNER—Transformation of winter forms of cereals into
spring forms by low temperature treatments.

W. GARNER and H. A. ALLARD—Photoperiodism.

T. D. LYSSENKO—Vernalisation and stadial theory.

N. I. VAVILOV—Law of homologous variations and centres of
origin of cultivated plants.

*   *   *   *   *

The application of our new concepts will be able to furnish
the basis for much research and important publications from a
scientific and practical point of view.

It is sufficient to indicate : the necessity to take up the study
of soils in their new prospective ; the determination of meteorological equivalents which have so far been calculated for a very
limited number of plants ; the vast and practically unexplored
sector of ecological characteristics based on the theory of
" velocity–mass–structure " and further the study of factorial
combinations ; the organisation of geographical trials (not only
for wheat as is the case for those already undertaken, but also

for other cultivated plants); finally the differential analysis of yields which will give us the possibility of discovering the laws which govern the complex relationships between plant, physical environment and yield.

Agricultural ecology gives a measured representation of the physical environment which is necessary for the solution of the majority of the problems concerning agriculture from the agronomical, economical and genetical point of view.

The methods I propose could contribute also to the development of studies concerning the environment in relation with the problems of forestry production, animal husbandry and physical and intellectual activity of man. This could advantageously lead to a co-ordination of the four branches of research : agricultural ecology, animal ecology, forest ecology and human ecology.

I hope this English edition of my work will afford opportunities for a widespread and fruitful collaboration with colleagues of Great Britain, the Commonwealth, the United States and of all other English-speaking nations.

Although based on a solid framework, there are naturally many gaps to be filled, much correction to be introduced and certain points to be modified; it is certain that many publications which I could usefully have employed in this book have escaped my attention, but it is my sincere hope that the horizons which are now disclosed will favour an active collaboration with colleagues all over the globe.

My warmest thanks go to Dr. P. S. Hudson, Director of the Commonwealth Bureau of Plant Breeding and Genetics, Cambridge, who was kind enough to present me to the publishers, to Dr. George Ordish for his accurate revision of the text, to Dr. Enzo Fano for the translation from the Italian into English, and to the many colleagues who furnished valuable material and took part in the geographical trials.

My congratulations and sincere appreciation to Messrs. Constable & Co., Ltd., and to the printers, for the handsome and perfect presentation of this edition.

G. Azzi

Perugia,
   July 1955

CONTENTS

Part I
AGRICULTURAL CLIMATOLOGY

Part II
THE SOIL-UNIT AND THE CLIMATE–SOIL COMPLEX

ix

Part III
THE YIELD AND ECOLOGICAL CHARACTERISTICS OF CULTIVATED PLANTS

Part IV
FACTORIAL COMBINATIONS AND DIFFERENTIAL ANALYSIS OF YIELD

INTRODUCTION

THE branch of science known as Agricultural Ecology is of very recent origin : it is first mentioned in a report presented to the " Accademia dei Lincei " by a Commission of Enquiry composed of Messrs. L. Luzzatti, L. De Marchi and R. Pirotta. The Commission reported on my scientific activities as follows : " This branch of science (Ecology) which can undoubtedly aspire to become an independent study in the biological field, has a purely scientific character and scope in that it considers the plant as an organism thriving in its environment, and it can have great practical significance when dealing with plants cultivated by man for his own requirements : it then becomes Agricultural Ecology."[1]

Following up this report, the Ministry of Agriculture started a Service of Agricultural Meteorology on an ecological basis (Law no. 500, 7th April, 1921) and created a chair in Agricultural Ecology, the first in the world, at the Istituto Superiore Agrario, Perugia.

In 1940, the Minister of Agriculture appointed me Director of the Royal Central Office of Meteorology and Agricultural Ecology for research on physical environment (climate and soil) in relation to agricultural production (Article 24, Royal Decree dated 29th May, 1941, no. 480).

The " Conférence Internationale du Blé " Rome, 1927, which was attended by the most eminent personalities in the agricultural world, recognised and highly praised my work " Le climat du blé dans le monde " and unaminously adopted the following resolution : " The Conference considers the report presented by Prof. G. Azzi : ' Le climat du blé dans le monde ', published by the International Institute of Agriculture, as the basis for studies on wheat from an international point of view. Such work is highly important for mutual understanding and international progress." (Actes de la 1ere Conférence Internationale du Blé, pp. 96–97, Rome, 1927).

[1] Report in the Official Gazette of the Accademia dei Lincei, Vol. XXIX, 5th Series, Part II, 1st Quarter—Deliberation of 4th June, 1920.

In November of that year, the " Conseil International Scientifique Agricole ", following up the work of the conference, voted in favour of the proposals made by the joint Commissions of Agricultural Ecology, Applied Meteorology and Genetics, for the creation of a centre for the co-ordination of research into Agricultural Ecology and Genetics at the International Institute of Agriculture. I was elected Life President of this institution.

. . . . .

The study of Agricultural Ecology has from 1929, when I went abroad to establish for the first time a course in the subject at the Faculty of Agriculture, University of Buenos Aires, up to the present day, spread to the following countries : Albania, Algeria, Argentina, Brazil, Bulgaria, France, French Indo-China, Greece, Hungary, Jugoslavia, Mexico, Morocco, Peru, Portugal, Roumania, Spain, Tunis, United States, Uruguay, U.S.S.R. and Venezuela.

I have had the good fortune to visit in an official capacity most of these states and to illustrate my ideas with a series of lectures, thus creating the framework for a collaboration which continues to prosper and expand. Experimental institutes, new services and University Chairs are being created and the establishment of Agricultural Ecology, in contrast to other out-dated disciplines which are destined to disappear, can be witnessed throughout the world.

The possibility, therefore, of collaboration between colleagues in different countries and of developing a single plan for the international organisation of teaching and research on physical environment, climate and soil, in relation to agricultural production, is becoming more and more a concrete reality.

Without excluding the necessity for further modification and perfection, Agricultural Ecology has, in the brief space of a quarter of a century, assumed a concise and highly personal form, with its lines and contours neatly traced.

Founded on a solid rational basis, the subject, both in its field of action and in its scope, occupies a clearly defined position in the sphere of agricultural science and differs entirely in principles, methods and range from the general ecology of the naturalists.

. . . . .

A speculative science in concept, but a highly practical one in farm management, Agricultural Ecology gives a picture of the existing bio-physical relationships of plants and animals. It places the evaluation of yields on an objective scientific and rational basis, by the perfect co-ordination and analysis of all the factors concerned.

While, on the one hand, Agricultural Ecology, in its concept and methods, is based on pure science and on a philosophical system of thought, on the other it comes into direct contact with the farmer's problems, and so in use secures that collaboration between thought and action which so greatly helps towards the diffusion and realisation of ideas.

DEFINITION

Agricultural Ecology is the study of the physical characteristics of environment, climate and soil, in relation to the development of agricultural plants, and to the yield of such plants from the quantitative (amount of the product), qualitative (quality of the product) and generative (characters of the seed) points of view.

If environment had no effect on a plant, one plant grown from a single small seed would (and I hope I shall be forgiven if I use my imagination a little !) fill the universe with its mass ; on the contrary, if there were complete antagonism between plant and environment, the plant would not be able to thrive at all.

So between plant and environment there exists a natural divergence integrated by the yield which is the final result of the more or less contrasted relationship between them.

We begin from the yield which represents and integrates the action of all factors that have influenced the plant organism during development, and then go on to determine these factors.

These may be divided into two groups :

(1) *Extrinsic :* factors concerned with environment, both natural and artificial.

(2) *Intrinsic :* characteristics of the plant.

Excesses and deficiencies of temperature and of rainfall (that is, thermic and pluviometric conditions), the relative length of day and night, atmospheric and soil humidity, solar radiation, topographical conditions, the many diseases and insects, soil composition, water content and state of aggregation (all variable within the widest limits), the different types of rotation, and the many formulæ for fertilisers are all so many factors, so many variables affecting yield.

In studying the action of these components on yield, we find that the same yield can be obtained with quite distinct groupings of factors. This is because it is possible for the factors to combine in many different ways, and thus the most unexpected compensating effect may result.

In the study of the bio-environmental relationships it is not possible to consider each single factor independently, but all must be treated as a function of all the other factors which influence the yield.

If we consider a law in physics such as that referring to the relationship between volume and pressure of gases (Boyle's Law), its validity is universal despite disturbing causes of small magnitude. In biology, on the contrary, we have disturbing causes as in physics, but they can be of large magnitude—not infinitesimal, as in physics—and display such intense action as sometimes to veil the expression of the law relative to the relationship between two well-defined factors. This explains the variability and instability of the normal factors making up yield.

The action of each factor on the plant must therefore be carefully studied and the effect of each measured as a function of all the other factors.

This conception consequently sharply distinguishes the problem of factorial combinations in physics from that of factorial combinations in biology, and starting from the synthesis, which is the yield, it moves to an analysis (determination of causal complements). We thus build up a system based on a series of well-defined concepts which represent the backbone of such a system; they are :

(1) Meteorological equivalents and climatic axes.

(2) Soil-unit and soil series.

(3) A Climate–Soil complex as a representation of physical environment (climate and soil) considered as an inseparable whole.

(4) Ecological characteristics (morphological and physiological) correlated with the different degrees of produc-

tivity and resistance, which are the two fundamental components affecting yield.

(5) Factorial combinations (geographical trials and differential analyses of yield) which is a new basis for agricultural research.

. . . . .

The spectacular polymorphism presented by the various agricultural species and the large number of factors affecting the physical and biological environment can combine in the most varied proportions, and so influence the yield. This had, until recently, made the solution of the problem of the environmental relationship in all its intricate complexity practically impossible. To-day Agricultural Ecology makes a considerable contribution towards the solution of this problem.

The polychrome and intricate puzzle falls into place in a neatly ordered pattern; from the tangle of the combinations of yield factors, clear and well-measured elements spring forth which give a good picture of the positive and negative points of the environment. These will provide some idea of how to attain the highest and best-quality yield under the most varied environmental conditions.

PART ONE

AGRICULTURAL CLIMATOLOGY

CHAPTER I

THE CONCEPT OF METEOROLOGICAL EQUIVA-LENTS AND AGRICULTURAL CLIMATOLOGY

(Bio-atmospheric Units)

ATMOSPHERIC factors may be divided into two groups :

(1) Variable (temperature, rainfall, etc.).
(2) Non-variable.

By this latter term we mean those factors, such as the relative length of day and night, which, it is true, vary from place to place and from season to season but which, once place and date are fixed, remain constant.   As far as we are concerned, there-fore, these factors may be considered non-variables, and are so classified.

.   .   .   .

Suppose we have two varieties of wheat, A and B, for which, by means of geographical trials, it has been possible to establish the mean yield for favourable years (that is, those years with sufficient rainfall), and for unfavourable years (that is, drought years).   We have :

	Variety A.	Variety B.
Yield in favourable years	42	31
„ unfavourable years	8	15

Which of the two varieties should we use in a region where drought alone reduces the yield ?

If it were possible to make long-range weather forecasts to include the period from the moment of sowing to the reaping of the harvest, there would be no doubt as to the choice.   We would give preference to variety A if the forecast were favour-able, and to B if it were unfavourable.

However, weather forecasting is usually limited to a period of 24 hours, and in particular cases to a few days (such as timing the arrival of cyclones in the U.S.A.), so that only rarely is it possible to use a weather forecast to overcome

3

unfavourable meteorological conditions. This is done, for instance, in the campaign against frosts, it being possible to determine the dew-point at nightfall, and so foretell the minimum temperature expected the following morning, and in this way to take counter-measures in time (such as smoke or orchard heating).

Adaptation of agricultural activities to contingent weather conditions by the artificial modification of certain meteorological situations, can thus be realised in a few cases only.

Agricultural Ecology, instead of trying to combat adverse meteorological conditions, furnishes the means by which crop cultivation may be adapted to climate (i.e. mean weather conditions).

In order to be able to choose between the two wheat varieties A or B it is essential to know, for the particular locality, how many times drought occurs over a period of 10 years and how often the conditions are favourable over the same period.

It therefore becomes necessary to calculate the quantity of rainfall which is sufficient for the plant, and the amount which is to be considered insufficient. This, until now, could not be done, but the concept of " meteorological equivalents " makes this distinction possible. Their adoption not only simplifies the solution of all bio-atmospheric problems, but also solves the highly complex ones which, formerly, had been regarded as practically insoluble.

By Meteorological Equivalents, both thermic and pluviometric, is meant the degrees of temperature and the mm. of rainfall which distinguish normal conditions from those defined as abnormal, both on account of excess and insufficiency.

The equivalents for insufficient and for excessive rainfall for wheat, for instance, in the month preceding earing are given as 40 and 116 mm. respectively. We thus have :

(1) Normal or favourable conditions for the values (mm. of rainfall) found between the two equivalents (40 and 116 mm.).

(2) Abnormal or unfavourable conditions arising through lack of rain (below 40 mm., the equivalent for drought).

(3) Abnormal or unfavourable conditions through excess of rain (above 116 mm., the equivalent for excess).

To enable the reader to understand clearly the process adopted for the determination of equivalents, I will put a number of questions, the answers to which will be quite obvious.

When the total precipitation in the month before earing of wheat is equal to 0 mm., it is unnecessary to ask if there has been drought or not. (Bear in mind that the water requirements of the plant in this period are very high.)

With 1 mm. of rainfall may we speak of sufficient rainfall? No, since this quantity is insignificant. With yet another mm. may we state that we have reached sufficiency? Again the answer is No. Thus we can go on adding 1 mm. each time and still remain at a stage of insufficient rainfall for the needs of the plant.

However, it will be obvious that at some point on the rising scale the amount of rain must be definitely sufficient, but we shall never be able to mark the actual point when, by the addition of 1 mm. of rain, we have passed from a condition of rain deficiency to one of rain sufficiency.

The method I propose makes it possible to break up this continuous series of increasing rainfalls and definitely separate a sufficient from an insufficient amount of rain.

For these determinations we used the figures in the files of the Central Office of Meteorology and Agricultural Ecology. Collection of these data was begun in 1881, and 250 stations well distributed over Italian territory have sent in, every 10 days, observations on the state of the various crops in regard to meteorological conditions; at harvest time they gave details of quantity and quality of the product, together with the factors which acted both favourably and unfavourably on yield.

From over half a million reports—a really imposing mass of figures—we have extracted those few (few in relation to the massive documentation) facts which were of value, and have used them to define the different bio-atmospheric relationships.

The voluminous data thus utilised made it possible to represent the effect of a single meteorological factor (rainfall, for instance) as a function of all the other factors acting on the yield under the most varied conditions, a result which could not have been obtained from information limited to a restricted area. By the most varied conditions is meant the complete range of soils from the best to the worst, from the most favourable thermic conditions to those limiting yield by reason of excess or deficiency, etc.

For the evaluation of bio-atmospheric relationships two groups of years with an equal number of cases in each must be considered :

(a) Those with abundant harvest when evidently no one factor seemed to act preponderantly in a negative sense on the yield.

(b) Those with poor harvest resulting from excess or deficiency of the particular factor of which we wish to determine the equivalent.

In order to calculate the drought equivalent for wheat in the month preceding earing (the critical period), we take two groups of years : one with very good harvests and the other with poor harvests owing to deficient rainfall, excluding the intermediate situations (good, satisfactory and mediocre), which would complicate the determination without adding anything to the precision of the result.   Fig. 1 shows in the form of a graph the mms. of rain in the month preceding earing on the vertical axis, while the horizontal axis shows the years (time) or the place (station).

The years in which there was a harvest below normal owing to drought are marked by a black dot, and the years in which the yield was plentiful, by an open circle at the corresponding points of intersection of the axes.

Thus at Foggia in 1920 there was a poor harvest owing to only 30 mm. of rain falling in the month preceding earing. We thus trace the parallel, from the point on the horizontal axis corresponding to 1920, to the rain axis, and from the point on the vertical axis corresponding to 30 mm., the parallel to the horizontal axis.   The point of intersection of the two lines thus traced represents the position in the graph relative to the harvest in question.   This point is marked by a black dot.

For the year 1921, with an abundant harvest and a rainfall of 76 mm., by a similar process, we mark an open circle at the point of intersection of the parallels corresponding to the 76-mm. rainfall and to the year 1921.   We proceed thus until we have examined all the cases under consideration.

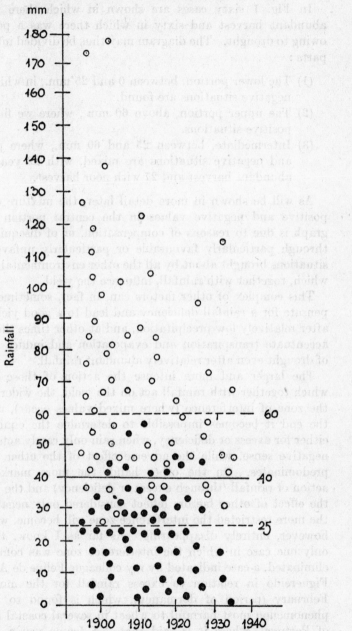

FIG. 1.   EQUIVALENT OF DROUGHT FOR WHEAT IN THE MONTH BEFORE
EARING.

In Fig. 1 sixty cases are shown in which there was an abundant harvest and sixty in which there was a poor one owing to drought. The diagram may thus be divided into three parts :

(1) The lower portion, between 0 and 25 mm., in which only negative situations are found.
(2) The upper portion, above 60 mm., where we find only positive situations.
(3) Intermediate, between 25 and 60 mm., where positive and negative situations are mixed, with 29 years with abundant harvest and 27 with poor harvest.

As will be shown in more detail later, the mixture of both positive and negative values in the central portion of the graph is due to reasons of compensation, or of disequilibrium through particularly favourable or particularly unfavourable situations brought about by all the other environmental factors which, together with rainfall, influence the yield.

This complex of other factors can, in fact, sometimes compensate for a rainfall deficiency and lead to a good yield even after relatively low precipitation, and at other times they may accentuate transpiration and evaporation and induce a state of drought even after relatively abundant rainfall.

The larger and more intense the action of those factors which together with rainfall act on the yield, the wider will be the zone of interference (where mixed values occur), until at the end it becomes impossible to determine the equivalent, either for excess or deficiency, when rain only rarely acts in the negative sense, while the adverse effect of the other factors predominates. On the other hand, the more marked the action of rainfall (through excess or deficiency) and the weaker the effect of other factors (effect considered only negatively), the more restricted the interference zone will become, without, however, entirely disappearing. As far as I know, there is only one case in which the interference zone was completely eliminated, a case indicated by my colleague Felipe de Almeida Figuereido in relation to excess rainfall for the month of February (period of dormancy), which is found to be the phenomenon most harmful to wheat in several coastal regions of Portugal, where it is said that " A foame ven a nado "

(Hunger comes swimming in).   A total of 60 mm. precipitation during this month clearly separates the years with good harvest from those with poor harvest.

We are now in possession of facts which allow us to determine the drought equivalent for wheat in the month preceding earing. To do this, we simply trace a horizontal line, across the mixed zone, which will separate an equal number of abnormal (asymmetric) cases—thus ten above with poor yields and ten below with abundant yields.

This line divides the factors acting on yield into two groups and cuts the rain axis at 40 mm., which thus represents the meteorological equivalent for drought in the month preceding earing for wheat.   The drought equivalent thus clearly separates sufficient from insufficient rainfall.[1]

The Stability of Meteorological Equivalents

Since the equivalent for excess and for deficient rainfall must be calculated as a function of all the other factors (natural and agronomic) which influence yield, it could be supposed that a very large number of cases is necessary to enable this determination to be made.

In practice the number of cases necessary for the determination of the equivalents may be reduced to a minimum.   If, as we have done, we base our calculations on extreme situations only—that is, very abundant or very poor harvests resulting from drought—we thus eliminate the great number of intermediate positions.   The positive action of rainfall on the harvest gradually decreases from the upper portion of the graph towards 40 mm., while the intensity of drought naturally diminishes from 0 mm. to 40 mm.   The contrast therefore between positive

[1] Several colleagues have suggested that it might be possible to utilise the regression coefficient to separate normal from abnormal situations due to either deficiency or excess.   This cannot be envisaged in our concept of meteorological equivalents, as the equivalent for drought undoubtedly separates normal from abnormal situations, but in no way gives a measurement of the yield.   In a locality of rain deficiency with particularly favourable soils and good farming practice, it is possible to obtain what is said to be a relatively low yield.   On the other hand, in localities with poor soils and primitive cultural methods it is, in a season of abundant rains, possible to obtain yields which are considered as good, though still inferior to those in the former case obtained under drought conditions.

and negative conditions is reduced to the lowest terms at 40 mm. (see Fig. 2).

The equivalent, corresponding to a state of neutrality between the two groups of values, can obviously oscillate only within very restricted limits.

The stability of the equivalent, determined as above, is confirmed by the fact that the line of such an equivalent is the

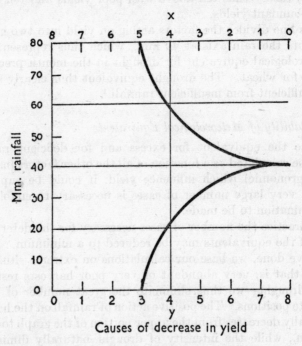

FIG. 2. STABILITY OF THE METEOROLOGICAL EQUIVALENT.

asymptote common to both hyperbole of the two groups of yields, above this line (in the favourable) and below (in the unfavourable) conditions.

Marked on the ordinate of Fig. 2 are precipitations between 0 mm. and 80 mm., since we need to be at a distance from the equivalent for excess, and so avoid a possible cause of error, and also to be able to find that, other conditions being constant, the yield increases approximately with increases in available water.

The upper portion of the graph is divided into eight parts, corresponding (from right to left) to the following eight (negative) causes of possible decreases in yield :

(1) Exhausting preceding culture.
(2) Shallow working of the soil.
(3) Imperfect drainage.
(4) Lack of fertilisers.
(5) Disease.
(6) Poor soil.
(7) Insect pests.
(8) Mountainous and hilly topography.

In the same way, the lower portion of the graph is divided into eight parts, corresponding to the eight causes of decrease in yield which we have written in from left to right.

Let us now trace a line xy through the diagram. This line and the line of the equivalent divide the graph into four sections. The two top sections will include for the most part good yields, while in the two sections below low yields predominate.

Referring to the upper half of the graph, let us now draw a horizontal line at 60 mm.; at the point of intersection with xy we mark (from the many observations made in Umbria) a yield of 20 quintals.

Moving up the xy axis, we reach the point of intersection with the 70 mark, and, since water conditions are improved, the yield will consequently be greater. To find the same yield of 20 quintals we shall have to move a little to the left, so as to compensate for the improvement due to increased precipitation, with a worsening of the general conditions of the environment.

Higher still on xy, and with a still further increase in the quantities of available rainfall, we shall have to move still further left, touching, for instance, the sum of adverse factors at the 5 mark (on the 80-mm. abscissa).

Below the point of intersection of 60 mm. with xy, we move down the xy axis and reach the point of intersection with the 50-mm. mark; the yield naturally decreases owing to the smaller quantities of water available, and to obtain the yield of 20 quintals we must move to the right, thus reducing the environmental adverse factors.

Once having reached the 40-mm. mark, in order to retain the equilibrium for a yield of 20 quintals we shall have to move right as far as the zero of the series of adversities and mark in, at that point, a yield of 20 quintals. This yield would move outside the boundaries of the graph (moving right) and tend towards infinity, since any further decrease in precipitations below 40 mm. (drought equivalent) would obviously lead to a decrease in production.

Similarly, in the lower part of the graph a horizontal line is traced corresponding to the 20-mm. mark. At the point of intersection with the xy axis we find a mean yield of 9 quintals. If we move lower, to the 10-mm. mark, production will diminish and to maintain the level of quintals we shall have to move left, compensating the conditions with a decrease in the action of the negative factors of the environment.

On the other hand, if we move up to 30 mm., the product will increase, and to maintain the yield at 9 quintals we must move to the right, and so compensate the improved rainfall conditions by an increase in the negative action of the environmental factors.

Going up still further to the 40-mm. mark, we have to reach the maximum sum total of adversities to keep to the 9 quintals level. Beginning from this point, the value 9 remains constant, in that a further increase in precipitation above the drought equivalent would lead to an increase in yield.

The curves which join the yields 20 quintals and 9 quintals are therefore two typical hyperbole which have the equivalent axis as a common asymptote : this confirms the stability of the equivalent and furnishes a clear geometrical evaluation of the phenomenon.

The two curves converge on the right-hand side of the graph on the 40-mm. mark of the abscissa, and the difference between the unit yields—20 quintals and 9 quintals, respectively— measures the positive and negative effect of the total absence or presence of the eight adverse factors considered.

.   .   .   .   .

We are now in a position to answer the question of the choice between the two varieties of wheat A and B for a given locality.

If in this zone, over a 10-year period, we have three years with total precipitations in the month preceding earing below 40 mm. (equivalent for drought), we have :

Variety A.	Variety B.
$42 \cdot 0 \times 7$ years $= 294 \cdot 0$ quintals	$31 \cdot 0 \times 7$ years $= 217 \cdot 0$ quintals
$8 \cdot 0 \times 3$,, $= 24 \cdot 0$,,	$15 \cdot 0 \times 3$,, $= 45 \cdot 0$,,
Annual mean : $31 \cdot 8$,,	Annual mean : $26 \cdot 2$,,

Variety A will therefore be the first choice, presenting a mean yield of $31 \cdot 8$ quintals as against $26 \cdot 2$ quintals of variety B. If, however, the drought frequency is equal to seven, there having been only three favourable years in a 10-year period, we have :

Variety A.	Variety B.
$42 \cdot 0 \times 3$ years $= 126 \cdot 0$ quintals	$31 \cdot 0 \times 3$ years $= 93 \cdot 0$ quintals
$8 \cdot 0 \times 7$,, $= 56 \cdot 0$,,	$15 \cdot 0 \times 7$,, $= 105 \cdot 0$,,
Annual mean : $18 \cdot 2$,,	Annual mean : $19 \cdot 8$,,

In this case we shall prefer variety B.

. . . . . .

The meteorological equivalents, through their very construction, can obviously not be applied to single isolated cases, it being possible, as already seen, to have abundant yields with rains below the equivalent and low yields with rainfall above it. Equivalents are not a measure of the amount of the yield, which is a resultant of a more complex situation (see Differential Analysis of Yield, page 365), but can be used only in the evaluation of the frequency of favourable and unfavourable pluviometric and thermic situations.

Climate is thus schematically represented by the frequencies of favourable (normal) and unfavourable situations, through excess and deficiency of temperature and rainfall.

CHAPTER II

DIVISION OF THE VEGETATIVE PERIOD INTO SUB-PERIODS

DURING its life cycle the plant undergoes continual changes in volume, weight, form and structure, so that its needs and its sensitivity towards environmental factors also vary continuously.

Thus the relationships between plant and environment, and hence the equivalents, should theoretically be determined for each moment of the vegetative cycles—a hard task indeed! With the division of the vegetative period into sub-periods, it becomes possible to find a simple solution to a problem which at first sight might seem quite insoluble.

In fact, however much an organism may appear to show a continuous series of variations from germination to the maturity of fruits or seeds, these mutations are not gradual and continuous. We find relatively short intervals during which the plant undergoes profound modifications, with the disappearance of certain organs and the formation of new ones; then it will remain morphologically and physiologically unaltered until a new phase starts and new transformations take place. We thus have the various phases of development (sprouting, budding, earing, setting, etc.) and the intermediate periods or sub-periods which come between successive phases. During each sub-period the structure and requirements of the plant remain practically constant or vary in a single direction. Theoretically we may visualise the beginning and the end of the vegetative cycle as two points situated at different heights and joined together by a staircase. Between one step and the next there is a certain difference in level, while the surface of each step is flat.

It thus becomes evident that the equivalents for excess and deficiency will have to be determined for each of the sub-periods into which the vegetative cycle is divided.

In order that any one species may be cultivated in any one locality, it is essential that :

(1) There be sufficient time in the season for the plant to complete its development from sprouting up to full maturity of fruits and seeds.

(2) During this period adverse atmospheric conditions do not reach such an intensity that they will lower the yield below reasonable expectations.

Importance of Phenology in Ecological Research

Phenology—the study of periodical phenomena in animal and plant life in the biosphere—is without doubt a most interesting branch of biology, for it furnishes us with data which can be used for important scientific research.

However, we have limited the study of periodical phenomena to the determination of the different phases of vegetation from sowing (or budding) up to harvest; this, as already stated, enables us to divide the vegetative cycle into separate periods, which we will discuss later.

Phenological evaluations, and the dates at which the different vegetative phases develop from sowing (or budding) to reaping, are an integral part of the information required for the determination of both the natural and agricultural factors which have reacted to produce any given yield of cultivated plants.

Thus phenology, as applied to agriculture, is an integral part of agricultural ecology.

At the polar and the equatorial limits of distribution of wheat we find that there is a short period which the plant fully exploits, giving it a bare chance of developing and just ripening its seed. In this case the dates for sowing and reaping are fixed and cannot vary, since throughout the remaining part of the year thermic conditions are decisively incompatible with the development of the plant, owing either to deficiency or excess.

Moving away from the polar limits, temperature becomes more and more favourable for crop production, and it becomes possible to sow earlier and to harvest later and to cultivate both early and late varieties.

In the Mediterranean region, for instance, the early variety

of dessert grapes " Chasselas doré " is picked in August, while
the late " Pizzutello " mature at the end of October.

In such districts there is a period after the reaping of winter
cereals, for instance, with very high temperatures before the
next cereal sowing can be made, which could be utilised for
another harvest.

The studies and research carried out by F. Schnelle in the
territory of Hessen on questions of phenology might well be
referred to here.   In this locality after the harvesting of winter
turnips, barley and winter rye, there remains a summer–
autumnal period which can be utilised for a second harvest of
fodder plants and vegetables.   This interval ceases to be of
use when the mean temperature falls below 9° C.

Schnelle puts the problem of catch crops on a practical basis,
indicating the most adaptable species in relation to the length
of the available period.   In a series of maps he gives the
harvest isophanes (see page 39) for the three plants mentioned
above, the length of the available interval, and the temperature,
rain and solar radiation during this interval.   These figures
representing the ambiental meteorological situation during the
utilisable interval help in the choice of the most convenient
catch crop to be adopted.

In those regions of northern Italy where rice is cultivated,
very early wheats, such as the variety " Mentana ", are capable
of reaching full maturity in the first half of June, thus enabling
growers to obtain a second harvest by sowing equally early
varieties of rice immediately after the wheat harvest.   These
are able to mature in good time—towards the end of September
or early in October.   In even more favourable conditions it
becomes possible, as we shall see, to have two wheat harvests a
year (certain regions in Kenya), three successive yields of maize
(Venezuela) and, for woody plants, two complete cycles in a
year—for instance, the vine in the State of Minas Geraes.

With more and more favourable environmental conditions,
a state is reached in which it is possible to sow herbaceous
plants in any period of the year (as for example cassava in the
Amazon), while with woody plants it is not uncommon to see
on the same branch blooms and fruits in all stages of development and maturity (as on the peach in Ceylon).

With variations in distribution of temperature, rainfall and length of day, the period of sowing and harvesting and the dates of individual phases of development can therefore vary considerably, from one point to another in the area of distribution of a species.   Similar conditions can also be found in a much more restricted area when rapid changes of altitude occur.

*   *   *

The phases which serve to divide the vegetative period into sub-periods may be very evident, or hidden.   Visible phases include : germination, beginning of tillering (for cereals), budding (for woody plants), blooming, seed setting and the beginning of maturity.

*   *   *

Earing constitutes a most important phase, inasmuch as it separates a sub-period of rapid development, during which the needs of the plant in respect of water are very high, from the sub-period of maturity, when the plant, after having reached its maximum weight, begins to dry up, so that its water requirements become more and more reduced.

But what point are we to take as that of earing ?   In reality, moving from one plant to another (and from one culm to another of the same plant), there may be a difference of a week or more between the appearance of the first and last ear.

Various stages of this phase could be singled out : for instance, the appearance of the very first ears ; of one quarter of the ears ; of one half of the ears ; or when three-quarters or all, or almost all, of the plants have eared, and so on.

In order to avoid errors of evaluation and to render the calculation easier, it is found convenient to accept as the date of earing the moment when the field or plot appears to be covered with ears.

In the same way, we shall talk of the flowering of a tree when the plant appears to be covered by blossoms with their corollas open ; and of blackening (for the grape) when the majority of bunches assume that colour, and so on.

The date of appearance and the rhythm of succession of the phases of development are strictly correlated to temperature, humidity and, as we shall see later on, to the relative length of

C

day and night.   If we have perfect knowledge of these factors, it becomes possible to calculate the probable date of each phase with close approximations for separate varieties of a species.

I quote here the phenological figures for various plants, not only of the temperate zone, but also of the tropics, not wishing to restrict the picture to the limited political borders of this or that nation.

Besides indicating the phase of development and the sub-periods in the life of the plant, it has here been considered opportune to add short comments and illustrative notes which will serve as an introduction to the study of bio-atmospheric problems by the ecological method.

WHEAT, RICE and other Cereals

The vegetative period for wheat can be divided into the following sub-periods :

(1) from sowing to the beginning of the winter rest period;
(2) from the beginning of the resting period to the resumption of activity in spring (under appropriate conditions of temperature and climate this sub-period constitutes the tillering phase);
(3) from the resumption of growth to earing;
(4) from earing to complete maturity.

This same division can also serve for oats, barley and rye.

In localities situated around the top limit of temperature, the cultivation of wheat and its development are limited to the coldest period of the year; while in situations around the low-temperature limit the wheat-plant completes its cycle in the warmest period.

The following is a typical example for Assuan (tropical sector) and for Vladivostok (polar sector).

	Assuan.		Vladivostok.	
Sowing	December	18·3° C.	June	13·8° C.
	January	16·0° C.	July	18·9° C.
	February	17·4° C.	August	20·8° C.
Harvest	March	22·6° C.	September	16·4° C.

During other months in Assuan higher temperatures (excessive) than those observed in the four months between December and March are present, while in Vladivostok the remaining eight months of the year have lower temperatures (harmful through deficiency) than those observed in the period between June and September.

In the equatorial mountainous region the biological cycle of wheat and the appropriate moment for sowing and of the successive phases of growth are subordinated to rain distribution (in consideration of the fact that temperature never reaches the limits for deficiency or excess), so that development of spring varieties of wheat is possible at any time of the year. In British East Africa, under such conditions, two successive cycles may be obtained in a twelve-months period, thus fully exploiting the alternation between the two rainy and the two dry seasons.

Wheat is sown in April, at the beginning of the rainy season, and development reaches completion in the dry season, so allowing for a first harvest in September. In November, at the beginning of the second wet season, wheat is again sown, and the second harvest is gathered in March.

Two successive harvests of rice are also obtained in the Barlovento region (Venezuela), without irrigation, and with a total production of 30 quintals per hectare of grain per year :

First Harvest.   Sown in the months July–August and reaped in September–October, utilising the normal summer rains, common to the whole of Venezuela.

Second Harvest.   Sown in November and reaped at the end of January and beginning of February, utilising the winter rains which occur only in certain sectors of the Republic.

We record here the rainfall in mm. for the various months. The monthly temperatures vary between 24° and 28° C.

1	July	.	.	286 mm.	First sowing
2	August	.	.	157	
3	September	.	.	163	
4	October	.	.	154	First harvest
1	November	.	.	228	Second sowing
2	December	.	.	279	
3	January	.	.	147	
4	February	.	.	66	Second harvest

Rainfall is more or less the same for the two cycles : 760 mm. for the first, 720 mm. for the second. These are just sufficient for the dry cultivation of rice; consequently the harvests are never very abundant, the mean for each being 15 quintals per hectare.

POTATO

This plant also has four sub-periods :

(1) from the planting of the tubers to sprouting;
(2) from sprouting to the initial formation of the tubers, which at this time are the size of a pea ;
(3) from the initial formation of tubers to flowering;
(4) from flowering to harvest.

In the third sub-period—from the formation of tubers to flowering—the potato, as we shall see later on, is particularly sensitive to partial or total lack of water, which at this time is of decisive importance in determining the yield.

VINE

For the vine we have the following sub-periods :

(1) from the end of the vintage to the initial stages of budding;
(2) from the initial stages of budding to the first sign of blooming;
(3) from blooming to setting (the corolla falls and the small newly set fruits appear);
(4) from the appearance of the fruits to the beginning of maturity (change of colour of the fruits);
(5) from beginning to complete maturity;
(6) from full maturity to the end of the harvest.

The photographs in the text (Figs. 3a–h) give a clear idea of the morphological changes in successive phases of development of the vine, and do not call for further explanation.

It is generally accepted that the successive annual cycles in the development of the vine are separated by a well-defined intermediate period of rest which is marked by the falling of the leaves and complete stoppage of growth. This occurs in those countries where temperature varies within very wide

(a)

(b)

(c)

(d)

(a) The start of budding.
(b) Advanced budding.
(c) Leafing.
(d) Appearance of inflorescence.
(e) Flowering.
(f) Fruit setting.
(g) Beginning of maturing.
(h) Maturity.

Fig. 3. Development of the Vine.

limits, falling below the limit compatible with development of
the plant during winter.

The position is quite different in the tropics, where temperature remains constantly high and always well above the limit
for growth.   In this case, as I have personally observed, the
period of rest can be practically suppressed.   An example can
be found in the region of Montes Claros (State of Minas Geraes,
Brazil), where the variety "Isabel" (*Vitis labrusca L.*) has two
successive cycles with two quite distinct harvests in one year.

Figures are given below for temperature and monthly rainfall
in this region for the years 1927–36 :

Months.	Mean temperature, ° C.	Rainfall in mm.
January . . .	24·4	155·1
February . . .	24·2	119·4
March	23·9	113·3
April	23·7	27·1
May	21·4	5·2
June	20·0	3·5
July	19·4	0·5
August	21·1	3·7
September . . .	23·5	11·9
October . . .	25·0	57·6
November . . .	24·2	166·8
December . . .	24·5	277·7

As is clearly seen from the table, the temperature never falls
below 19° C. even in the coldest part of the year, so that
vegetation, since there is always plenty of moisture in the
soil, thrives continuously without any interruption in its cycle.
The first harvest—the more important—is gathered at the
beginning of February : the grapes are often damaged by the
hot and humid conditions and for this reason "Isabel"—highly
tolerant and resistant to meteorological adversities and to
Peronospora (mildew)—is the only possible variety.

Around the middle of March, after the harvest, the young
green branches are pruned.   After a fortnight the plant buds
again, and develops regularly right up to complete maturity at
the end of July and the beginning of August, the month in
which a second harvest is taken.

The August yield is not so abundant as that of the preceding
harvest.   However, in spite of the lower temperature (we are

in the southern hemisphere) during ripening, the August yield
gives musts richer in sugar—a fact which is no doubt due to the
absence of abundant rainfall, for this latter, although increasing
the yield, lowers the quality of the February harvest.

In September the plants are again pruned, and after a fortnight this leads to the appearance of new buds, and these subsequently lead to the principal harvest at the beginning of
February.

In this way a most interesting phenological situation is
created which is summarised in the following tables. These
give, for each of the summer and winter vegetative cycles,
figures relative to the time of pruning, budding and of harvest,
together with mean temperatures and the sum of precipitations
in the two intervals : budding to first stages in maturity, and
first stages in maturity to harvesting.

First Vegetative Cycle

Pruning	15th September
Budding	5th October
Harvest	3rd February

	Temperature, °C.	Precipitation, in mm.
Budding—Maturity (Oct.–Dec.) .	24·6	134·0
Maturity—Harvest (January) . .	24·2	155·1

Second Vegetative Cycle

Pruning	15th March
Budding	1st April
Harvest	4th August

	Temperature, °C.	Precipitation in mm.
Budding—Maturity (April–June) .	21·7	12·0
Maturity—Harvest (July) . .	19·4	0·5

OLIVE

The vegetative cycle of the olive, according to Briccoli is
sub-divided as follows :

(1) from the end of the harvest to the first stages in blooming ;
this comprises, in effect, two sub-periods :

(a) from the end of harvest to the resumption of development in spring ;

(b) from the resumption of growth in spring to blooming.

However, the lack of a real and effective period of winter rest and the overlapping of the last picking of olives with the resumption of rapid growth in spring, means that such a sub-division is very difficult to make in Southern countries :

(2) flowering : from the beginning of flowering to first setting ;
(3) from first setting to blackening ;
(4) from blackening to complete maturity ;
(5) from the beginning to the end of the harvest.

With regard to the hidden phase (see page 34), I would like to recall a series of experiments carried out by Marcucci, from which the following conclusion can be drawn : during the interval of latent life (namely, that period in which the maximum slowing up of the vital activity coincides with a lack of apparent morphogenetical activity) the undifferentiated buds which are not yet defined as floral or foliar are not completely dormant.

These buds are in fact susceptible to the influence of environmental factors (particularly temperature and humidity), and the consequent biochemical reactions set up by such influences display, in more advanced stages of the biologic cycle, an evident effect in the growth, development and finally the yield of the plant.

Consequently the reactions which are produced in the period of dormancy through the stimulus of environmental factors help to single out phases which, as they remain hidden and not immediately discernible by ordinary means, are called " crypto-phases ".

APPLE

We can distinguish the following sub-periods :

(1) from the end of harvest to the appearance of the first buds ;
(2) from the appearance of the first buds to flowering ;
(3) from the first stages in flowering to complete setting (appearance of small newly formed fruits) ;
(4) from the completion of set to the beginning of maturity ;
(5) from maturity to picking ;
(6) from the beginning to the end of the harvest.

Fruit trees in general have definite water requirements, which must be taken into account in order to obtain the maximum benefits from pruning, and more especially from irrigation.

In the interval between the completion of setting and the first stages of maturity the plant needs large quantities of water, not only because of the rapid growth of the great mass of fruit, but also for the nourishment of next year's flower buds, which begin to form at this time; and consequently this period assumes a critical importance (see page 53). It is found in the first half of summer.

In the second half, on the other hand, when the fruits have reached their maximum weight and the flower-buds have completed the first stages of development, a stoppage of wood growth becomes essential, and this is effected by a lack of rainfall or a lowering in temperature. In 1909 at the Apple Station of Pensa (Russia) there was abundant rain in April–July, little in August and in the first half of September, while in the second half of this month and for the whole of October there was total drought : in these conditions the floral buds developed magnificently and, reaching the size of hazel nuts, could be clearly seen on the trees.

But in 1912 the continuous rain, protracted well into the autumn, did not allow the necessary stoppage in the second half of the summer to occur; in the autumn the branches and leaves had greatly increased their mass, the floral buds were minute and poorly developed and could hardly be distinguished from the leaf-buds : only their position enabled them to be identified. Consequently to get good fruit-buds for the next year's crop it is necessary, after a period of growth in the first part of the summer, to have a period of rest, which, as already said, is obtained by means of a period of water deficiency or of low temperatures.

The positive action of the preceding year's rainfall on the harvest, because of its effects on the formation of the flower-buds, has been studied by the Russians Semadeni, Widdimov and Krassitchkow, and shown to be true not only for the *Pomaceae*, but also for the hazel, cherry, strawberry and raspberry.

Strawberries and gooseberries give high yields only when the rains of the preceding summer have been sufficient for the formation and development of the fruit-buds.

We will now consider some of the crops of tropical and sub-tropical regions.

CASSAVA

The biologic cycle of the cassava may be divided into five sub-periods :

(1) from planting to budding (propagation from shoots);
(2) from budding to the first stages in the thickening of the roots ;
(3) from the first stages in thickening to the maximum development of the root, this stage coinciding with leaf-fall ;
(4) from leaf-fall to the new budding phase (period of rest);
(5) from this phase to harvest.

In annual varieties the vegetative cycle ends with the third sub-period. The perennial varieties, left in the ground for 10 years or more, renew the vegetative cycle every year; new roots are added, while those already formed increase their weight continuously to a maximum.

On the other hand, in equatorial and tropical regions, in a damp, hot climate, planting and harvesting may be undertaken in whatever period one wishes, so that cassava constitutes a magnificent food reserve for rural populations. The harvest can be taken at any time during the whole year, as happens in the regions of the Amazon. However, some periods are more suitable than others—for instance, in winter, owing to the lack of rainfall, the roots are drier, and hence richer in flour. Consequently they are able to furnish a more abundant and better-quality product. If the harvest is delayed after the said period there is a certain reduction in the starch content of the crop.

In any case, the extraction of the roots must be avoided at the time of budding, because the starch reserves are then transformed into sugar, which migrates to the aerial parts of the plant.

In choosing the period most suitable for planting, one must avoid adverse meteorological periods because of the extreme sensitivity of the plant at such times.

The adverse meteorological factors are (we refer to Brazil) :

(1) *Excess rainfall.* During the first sub-period this can easily exhaust the shoots so that the crop shows many gaps. When the root is fully developed and approaching maturity, excessive dampness brings on a rot which affects both the quality and quantity of the product. For these reasons, cassava is preferably cultivated on loose and easily drained soils, and planting must never be undertaken in periods of continuous rainfall.

(2) *Drought.* This can be equally dangerous during planting and development. In those regions most prone to this adversity the variety "Manipeba", ideal for its resistance to water deficiency, is cultivated. During the dry, hot summer this variety loses all its leaves, thus entering a rest period, and resumes growth on the return of rainfall.

(3) *Low temperature.* In southern Brazil low temperatures often damage cassava during its development. Frost is the most harmful element in southern Rio Grande, Paraná and Santa Catarina. For this reason the cultivation of cassava in Southern Brazil is confined almost exclusively to summer : this is owing to the fact that in the winter (21st June to 21st September : winter in the southern hemisphere) low temperatures hinder development and causes lesions and necrosis of the tissues. In April, just before the onset of frosts, farmers cut the branches, and preserve them by burying them in the ground : these are then utilised for planting in the following spring.

Planting in spring must be carried out as quickly as possible, in order to avoid the various handicaps which lateness would occasion—i.e. (a) increase in temperature causes the branches to bud, rendering them useless as shoots, (b) late planting may expose the root while not yet ripe to the harmful action of the first frosts during the next autumn.

THE PEANUT

Delolme reports that Bouffil, director of the station of M'Bambey (Senegal), divides the vegetative period of the peanut into three stages :

(1) first vegetative stage : from sowing to the first stage of blooming, with a mean duration of 30 days ;

(2) stage of utilisable blooming : 40–50 days, according to latitude ;

(3) stage of maturation : lasting from 35 to 48 days.

The life cycle of the peanut has a duration which varies from 115 to 128 days, and its development takes place in the rainy season, from June (a little earlier in some sectors) to November, with a maximum intensity in August.

As the soil and the agrotechnical conditions are uniform, and the thermic conditions practically always favourable, the dominating factor influencing the yield is rainfall, as is clearly demonstrated by Delolme. Sometimes the rainy season may be interrupted by dry spells of variable duration, lasting for about one month in certain cases. Under such conditions the yield has been observed to decrease by 50% of the normal. These are, however, sporadic and localised cases, and are never such as to influence the productive index of the zone.

With reference to rainfall, two conditions are important :

(1) the duration of the rainy season ;

(2) the quantity of rain (duration remaining constant).

In order to have a clear representation of bio-pluviometric relationships, it becomes necessary to define clearly

(a) *the time of utilisable rains :* meaning by this term precipitations as a whole, from the moment they are considered sufficient for sowing up to a last group of monthly precipitations of at least 20 mm. ;

(b) *the period of utilisable blooming :* from the initial stages of blooming up to three weeks before the fall of the last profitable rain. This, to be considered such, must be of at least 20 mm. The blooms which open out after this period meet up with a dry season and are unable to complete the development and maturation of their fruits.

The graph (Fig. 4) shows the precipitations from June to

November for the Sine-Saloum district, indicating further, by vertical lines, the time of the first and last sowing and the date of the last utilisable rain. At the bottom of the figure are graphically represented the three stages indicated above, which are naturally delayed or anticipated in relation to the data of sowing (between the first and last sowing there often exists an interval of one month).

Joining together, therefore, the points corresponding to the first sowing and to the beginning of the harvest, with those

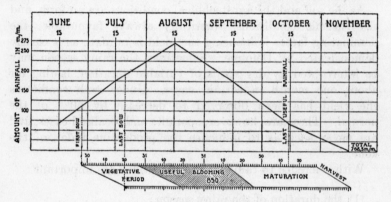

FIG. 4. RAINS AND THE YIELD OF PEANUTS IN SENEGAL.

representing the last sowing and the end of the harvest, we obtain the graphs reproduced in the figure.

Regarding the utilisable blooming stage, we find a surface which corresponds either to a trapeze or to a rhombus, according to the cases considered, and whose area is directly proportional to the yield per hectare (yields from 600 to 1,000 kg. per hectare), as emerges from the table below, where both actual and theoretical figures are given.

Locality.	Theoretical yield in relation to area, kg.	Actual mean yield, kg.
Louga	530	575
Baol	770	835
Sine-Saloum . . .	850	928
Niani-Ouli . . .	970	1,000

The following table gives the figures relative to the duration of utilisable rains and yields per hectare :

Locality.	Rain duration, days.	Yield, kg. per hectare.
Louga	77	575
Baol	88	835
Kaolack	91	897
Niani-Ouli . . .	99	1,000

From this table the direct relationship between the yield and rainy season may be clearly seen.

Besides the duration of the rainy season, as already stated, the amount of rains also affect the yield (and this is an obvious supposition in any case), as is clearly demonstrated by the following figures :

Locality.	Yield, kg. per hectare.	Rainfall, mm.
Niani-Ouli . . .	1,000	960
Sine-Saloum . . .	928	816
Baol	835	683
Thiès	815	661
Louga	575	444

Researches in this field may advantageously be carried out in Europe, where a further limiting factor, besides rain, will be temperature.

CACAO

The cycle of cacao may be divided into the following sub-periods :

(1) from budding to flowering ;
(2) from flowering to the formation of the fruits ;
(3) from the formation of the fruits to the first stages in maturity ;
(4) from maturity to harvest ;
(5) from the beginning to the end of harvest.

Within the normal area of cacao distribution the plant can suffer considerably during the fourth sub-period from excessive moisture, which causes wet rot of the fruits.

Drought, on the contrary, can be harmful at the time of flowering, of fruit setting, as also during the development of fruits (second and third sub-periods).

Consequently, in view of the possible favourable or unfavourable environment, the varieties chosen vary from one zone to another, according to productivity, resistance and adaptability to conditions in the various regions.

In the State of Bahia (Brazil) we thus find three principal varieties : " Commun ", " Pará " and " Maranhão ", which differ from one another in their behaviour under favourable or unfavourable environmental conditions.

Commun has the highest water requirements : it is planted in low, damp ground close to river-banks, where it thrives very well. Under the same soil and climatic conditions it produces more than other varieties (under favourable conditions), and gives a steady yield every year.

Pará is more hardy. It is by preference cultivated in the soils of the interior, which are poorer than those of the alluvial or coastal areas. This variety is more resistant to thermic excesses and to drought than " Commun ". However, under favourable conditions its yield, owing to its lower productivity, is 30% inferior to that of the preceding variety.

Maranhão. This is even more hardy, and is preferred in the less fertile regions of the high plains, where, because of its hardiness, it is better than all other varieties. It is equally resistant to drought, excess heat and to sudden variations in temperature, adapting itself also to poor and relatively shallow grounds. Under favourable environmental conditions it produces a yield which is 40% lower than that of " Commun ", and is thus the least productive of the three varieties considered.

COFFEE

Coffee has the three following sub-periods :

(1) from the completed maturity (harvest) to the following flowering period ;

(2) from the initial stages of flowering to fruit formation ;

(3) from fruit formation to complete maturity of the fruits (harvest).

In Amazonia the unlimited amount of available water and the high temperature throughout the year so act on the coffee plant that we have overlapping of cycles, and at any one time we may find on the same tree buds, flowers and fruits in all stages of growth, from the beginning of development to complete maturity.   Such interference has an undoubtedly negative effect, in that it exhausts the coffee plant in the space of a few years, and makes harvesting laborious, obliging the workers to collect the mature fruits separately one by one.

The normal and economic cultivation of the coffee plant must therefore be practised in regions where the meteorological values and their distribution do not allow of such a luxuriant and uninterrupted growth, but contain it within the limit of normal development in a regular succession of well-defined and separate phases of the biologic cycle.   In the regions around the equator the limiting factor for the economic cultivation of coffee is represented by thermic and water excess, which induce a disorderly growth—a state of anarchy, we could say—in the vegetative framework of the plant.

Very high temperatures, even in the absence of wind, are harmful in the first phases of development and cause the young fruits to fall.   For these reasons coffee does not grow well on the hot slopes under the baking rays of the sun : in such conditions plantations are generally protected by tall shade-plants characterised by a large spreading crown of thick and dense foilage.   In the short interval of thirty days (more or less) during the principal period of flowering, setting and the initial development of fruits, a dry, clear sky is highly favourable.   Lack of rainfall in this period in no way damages the plant, while even very limited quantities cause pollen to be washed away, and consequently reduce setting.   Apart from this short interval, rains act both positively and negatively as follows :

(1) Before the said interval rainfall is advantageous in that it increases the water reserves in the soil, and disadvantageous in that it provokes premature flowering which will not lead to fruit formation, but only exhaust the plants.

(2) After setting, rainfall favours the development of fruits,

and so its effects are useful, but it is also sometimes the cause of " ojo de gallo " (*Stilbum flavidum*, de Cooke)— a disease very harmful to coffee.

This simultaneous positive and negative action makes the determination of the equivalent for excess and deficiency all the more difficult. On information obtained from Mr. Gustavo Brandt of Caracas, I have tried to establish the equivalent for drought in the months preceding the principal flowering phase (February–April). Although the comparison of statistical data between yield and relative quantities of rainfall is not absolutely correct, as the observatory from which the rainfall figures are derived is 30 km. from the plantation, an amount of 40 mm. for the three months February–April appears to be justified. With all due caution, and admitting that in this particular case the positive action of rainfall prevails over the negative, we can adopt 13 mm. as the provisional monthly equivalent for drought in the three months preceding the beginning of the principal flowering period. This, we repeat, is applicable only in those cases in which the positive action of rainfall predominates over the negative.

DATE-PALM

The vegetative period for the date-palm is divided into the following sub-periods :

(1) from the end of harvest to the appearance of the spadix (female inflorescence) ;

(2) from the appearance of the spadix to general anthesis of the flowers ;

(3) from flowering to setting ;

(4) from setting to the beginning of maturity ;

(5) from the first stages of maturity to complete maturity and the beginning of harvest ;

(6) from the beginning to the end of harvest.

However, the Arabs distinguish the four following stages of fruit development :

(a) " Rechim " : the fruits just formed ;

(b) " Beleh " : two months from the beginning of develop-ment—the fruits have reached half of their normal

volume; they are still green in colour and the kernel is
soft;

(c) " Besser " : the fruits have reached the complete development and begin to take colour;

(d) "Temer" : the stage of complete maturity.

The meteorological schedule for this plant is as follows :

Cold. Cold waves during the first sub-period—that of
winter dormancy—do not, even with minima of −4° C., damage
the plant, causing only a few days' delay in the appearance of
the female inflorescence. Once development has begun, however, the return of cold periods and late frosts in spring sometimes damages the female inflorescences, but is particularly
harmful to the plant after setting, causing the newly-formed
fruits to fall. During and up to maturity the date-palm has
very high temperature requirements, so that the limit of expansion in northern regions, according to Lasserre, corresponds
to an annual mean of 19° C. It is in any case certain that even
in the ordinary area of cultivation of this plant thermic deficiencies can delay, or even impede, the full maturity of fruit, so
that the quality of the product is very poor. It is unquestion-
ably insufficiency of heat at the time of maturing which marks
the northern limit of cultivation of the date-palm. I have
personally visited the large palm reserve of Elche in Spain
(province of Alicante), which is truly imposing, with its 18,000
palms. The product is poor, however, and though in part
sold for dessert, the larger portion of the crop is used in jam
manufacture.

The typical region for the date-palm is that of the internal
Sahara oases. Even in Africa temperatures in the coastal belt
are insufficient to produce perfect " caramelisation " of the
fruit.

Rains. The date-palm is extremely sensitive to rain, which
can cause damage at any period; for instance, in Nigeria, where
we find the last date-palm groves, it is the limiting factor. In
fact the fruits ripen in August—the month in which the most
abundant rains occur, and this regularly decimates the few
fruits produced each year.

However, even within the normal area of distribution,
precipitation, even in small quantities, is deleterious during

D

ripening, at flowering time, when the blooms rot, and at the time of pollination, when pollen is washed away.

Thermic Excesses and Scorching by Dry Winds. As already stated, the plant requires high temperatures. During a trip in the Sahara, I was assured by the Military Commander of the Tuggurt Oasis that local farmers were unanimous in their belief that in order to obtain a perfect ripening of the date maximum temperatures should not be less than 45° C. One rarely hears of damage through excessive temperatures, but when these are accompanied by strong, dry winds the damage can be considerable. The negative action of hot, dry winds can be observed in different periods and in different ways :

(1) during setting they cause the newly formed fruits to fall;

(2) in the month of August, during the last stages of development and at the initial stages of maturity, hot, dry winds cause this latter to take place prematurely, and in consequence the produce is composed of small fruits, which are used as fodder for cattle;

(3) high temperatures, together with sirocco winds, favour the spreading of an acarus (Boufaroua) which does considerable damage to the apical buds of the plants.

The Arab proverb, " The date-palm needs its head in fire and its feet in water ", epitomises the ecological framework of the date-palm, which is the agro-botanical prototype of the Saharan oasis of the African interior. Here the deep water wells allow of continued abundant irrigation while the constantly hot atmosphere, dry and clear, is ideal for the formation of flowers, fertilisation and good development of the fruit.

Invisible Phases

In dividing the vegetative period into sub-periods, we have so far based our study on externally visible phases. There are also, however, invisible phases which are highly important in the evaluation of bio-atmospheric relationships, and more especially that of rainfall.

The almond and the water-melon are typical examples, and will serve as illustrations.

ALMOND

The vegetative period of the almond is divided into the following sub-periods :

(1) from flowering to setting;
(2) from setting to the phase (invisible) of maximum weight of the fruits;
(3) from the maximum weight of the fruits to the ripening of the nut;
(4) from maturity to the end of the harvest;
(5) from the end of the harvest to the flowering phase the next year.

The long interval occurring between setting and the complete development of the fruits is not externally characterised by visible phenomena which would allow of a division into two distinct sub-periods.

With the help of extensive research carried out in 1928 it has, however, been possible to divide this interval into two sub-periods, during which the water requirements are very different.

As for the olive, the almond forms its fruits at the end of spring, while the harvest is picked only in autumn, so that these plants thrive throughout the hot, dry summer—a sure proof of an ability to adapt themselves to the dry Mediterranean climate.

A series of determinations were made in which the increase in weight of the fruits of the almond was recorded in order to investigate the bio-environmental situation, and more especially the effect of precipitation on the development of the fruits themselves.

The table set out on p. 36 gives the weights of fruits at different dates. It should be noted that flowering took place during the first ten days of February, and fruit-bearing at the end of the second and beginning of the third week in March. For each determination 100 fruits were taken.

As can be readily seen, there is a continual increase in weight from the beginning of April to a maximum in the first ten days in June, followed by a progressive decrease during the summer, until, at the time of picking, only one-fifth of the maximum figure reached at the beginning of June may be noted. The phase of maximum weight clearly separates the period from

Average Weight of 100 *Almond Fruits*

Date.	Weight, gm.	Date.	Weight, gm.
2nd April . .	20	13th July . .	850
19th „ . .	102	20th „ . .	795
23rd „ . .	198	31st „ . .	700
2nd May . .	300	7th August .	637
8th „ . .	601	13th „ .	540
17th „ . .	780	20th „ .	430
24th „ . .	888	27th „ .	380
31st „ . .	1,000	5th September .	300
9th June . .	1,240	12th „ .	270
16th „ . .	1,105	19th „ .	271
29th „ . .	980	27th „ .	270
6th July . .	900		

setting to harvest into two distinct intervals, the first of which we can call " development " and the second " seasoning ".

The two sub-periods which make up the interval between setting and complete development are therefore :

(a) *Sub-period of Development.*—From setting to the phase of maximum weight the fruits increase continuously and rapidly in weight and volume, so that the plant consumes a large quantity of water. Moreover, the maximum weight is reached at the end of May and the beginning of June, when the soil is still damp from the recent spring rains : drought in this interval (second sub-period) is therefore a rare occurrence.

Using as a basis the observations of the agro-meteorological station of Mineo (Sicily) for the period 1898–1915, we find that drought in the second sub-period (March–May) was recorded only in two years, 1903 and 1914. The effects of lack of rainfall were in this case decisive, causing the fall of the young fruits. In the station report for the first ten days of May 1914 it is specifically stated that " drought has caused the small almonds to drop ". The rains in the February–May period are therefore those which prove to be the most important.

The table on p. 37 gives the figures of total precipitation for the February–May period for the years considered.

In 1903 and 1914, when drought was reported, total precipitation did not reach 100 mm. We can therefore provisionally, and with reserve, take the value 25 mm. monthly as the equivalent for rain deficiency during the second sub-period.

February–May.   Total Precipitation at Mineo, Sicily

Year.	Precipita-tions, mm.	Year.	Precipita-tions, mm.
1898	186	1907	158
1899	123	1908	288
1900	206	1909	210
1901	126	1910	195
1902	323	1911	236
1903	94	1912	149
1904	201	1913	149
1905	175	1914	84
1906	175	1915	183

(b) *Sub-period of Seasoning.*—(Third sub-period). From maximum weight to complete maturity, the weight of the fruits gradually decreases, while the process of drying up, in that it begins from the interior, is not externally visible. Water requirements are much reduced, and gradually reach zero, so that in the region of Mineo, for instance, lack of rain never proved harmful. The year 1907 gave an excellent product; in the second sub-period 158 mm. were recorded, while in the third there was no rain at all. It is quite clear, therefore, that the plant is perfectly capable of maturing its fruits and of giving a good harvest, in quantity or quality, even with a total absence of rain in the third sub-period.

FIG

Figure 5 gives a clear idea of the mode of increase in weight of the fruits of the fig, which in some respects resembles the almond. The curve of fruit weight (100 figs for each determination) can be divided into three parts :

First part : slow development ;
Second part : very rapid development up to the maximum weight (invisible phase) ;
Third part : gradual decrease in weight.

The maximum weight is found at the beginning of maturity. In the ten days (more or less) preceding this phase growth is very rapid, so that this is the critical period in relation to the water requirements of the plant.

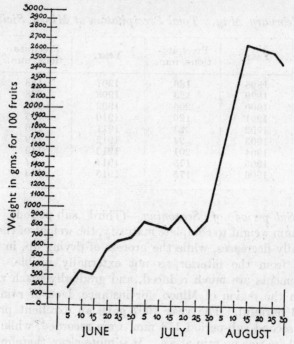

Fig. 5.   The Increase in Weight of the Fig.

WATER-MELON

The vegetative cycle of the plant in relation to bio-environmental factors can be divided into the following sub-periods :

(1) from sprouting to the beginning of development of lateral branches ;

(2) from beginning of development of lateral branches to fructification ;

(3) from fructification to the initial stages of maturity ;

(4) from the beginning to the completion of maturing and harvest.

The last two sub-periods are not distinguishable by simple inspection, as there is no alteration in the external aspect of the fruit.   This makes it impossible to determine where the third sub-period ends and the fourth begins.   However, the following results were obtained by the method indicated.

In order to determine the passage from one sub-period to the next, a series of measurements of the circumference of fruits in cm. was made : at the same time the approximate weights of the fruits were determined.

These measurements show that the curve for growth can be divided into two distinct segments.

(1) *an ascending segment*, which corresponds to the sub-period of development (third) during which the circumference of fruits is doubled every five days ;

(2) *a horizontal or slightly inclined segment*, corresponding to the sub-period of maturity (fourth), during which the increase in circumference is nil, or practically so.

The phase in which the maximum weight is reached, externally invisible, separates the interval between fructification and the harvest into two sub-periods, in the first of which the water requirements of the plant are very high ; in the second the water-melon takes advantage of good, dry weather to complete its maturity. Rain and irrigation are decidedly harmful in this period, and cause cracking of the skin of the fruit and a deterioration of the flesh, which becomes more fibrous and less juicy.

GEOGRAPHICAL REPRESENTATION OF THE PERIODICAL PHENOMENA OF PLANT LIFE

The Isophane Chart

By isophanes we mean the curves which join together all the points at which a given phase of development takes place on the same date. Similar curves may also be constructed for the date of sowing, in spite of the fact that this obviously does not represent a phase of development of the plant, but only the condition necessary for it to begin its biological cycle.

Isophanes for wheat integrate the effect of temperature, precipitation, the duration of the cycle and the dates for the individual phases and cultural operations, so that in it are reflected as a whole the conditions of the physiographic environment which regulate the development of this plant throughout its area of distribution.

Isophane for Sowing of Wheat

It is impossible to bring together the isophanes for sowing in a single chart, since for any one locality there can be three distinct periods of sowing—autumn, winter and spring. This is the case in New Zealand, for instance.

In the equatorial region of the Andes in South America the situation is even more complicated, in that the three periods practically fuse into a single long period of 5 to 6 months. Autumn sowing is primarily considered in this chart (Fig. 6).

There is no doubt that on the whole, as is made particularly evident in the Northern Hemisphere, the curves for sowing are clearly subordinate to the thermic factor, and the form they assume corresponds to the exigencies of latitude, altitude and to the distribution of land and sea.

Between the extreme isophanes, 30th July in Soviet Asia and 30th December in North Africa, there are no less than 5 months difference in the sowing time. In Australia and in South America (south of 20° S.) we observe a progressive putting forward in the date of sowing as we move in the direction of the Pole. In North Chile, for instance, sowing takes place in May, in Central Chile in April, and at the end of March in the southern part of that country.

Although temperature is the most important factor, there are, as already mentioned, other meteorological factors which can have a decisive bearing on the period of sowing, so that the progressive anticipation from the equatorial limit to the Pole and, conversely, the progressive delay as one proceeds toward the Equator, are not already regular and continuous.

In the sub-desert regions of North Africa, where sowing periods are decided by autumn rains, it often happens that the latter arrive late, and thus prolong the summer drought until January or February; this naturally leads to a delay in sowing, independent of any other consideration of an agricultural or meteorological nature.

It must equally be remembered that in those territories where wheat crops are irrigated, the time of sowing is naturally conditioned by the arrival of floods. In Egypt, the Nile floods early, so the isophane for 30th October passes through that country.

As already said, the time of sowing in Ethiopia and Equatorial

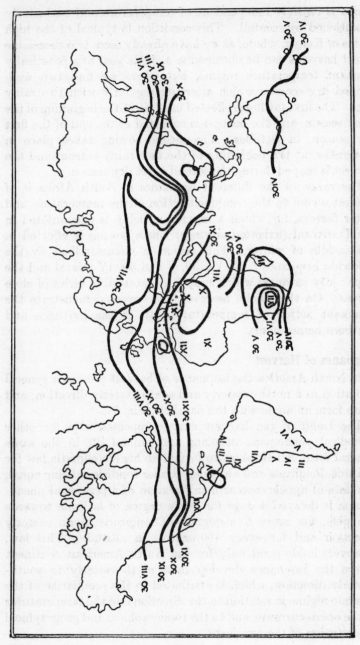

FIG. 6. WORLD ISOPHANES OF WINTER WHEAT SOWINGS.

Africa is entirely independent of temperature and exclusively conditioned by rainfall. This condition is typical of the high plains of Kenya, where, as we have already seen, two successive wheat harvests can be obtained in a single year in a practically constant temperature regime, but where we find two well-defined dry seasons which alternate regularly with two rainy ones. The first sowing is effected in April, at the beginning of the rainy season, and the harvest is collected at the end of the first dry season, in October. The second sowing takes place in November, at the beginning of the new rainy season, and the harvest is reaped during the second short dry season.

The range of the different isophanes in South Africa is of interest owing to the combined action of the temperature and water factors, for which a maximum delay is encountered in the Transvaal (irrigated sowings) where sowing is effected in the middle of winter. This region is circumscribed by the following isophanes : 30. VI, 30. V and 30. IV (Natal and the Cape : dry sowings) which supply an interesting series of close curves. On the whole, however, the curves demonstrate the dominant action of temperature both in the northern and southern hemispheres.

Isophanes of Harvest

In North America the isophanes of harvest present a general evolution in a north-westerly and south-easterly direction, and there form an angle with the parallels (Fig. 7).

The trend of the harvest curves, repeated also for other periodical phenomena of plant and animal life in the same general form, led Hopkins to formulate his bio-climatic law for latitude, longitude and altitude. Other conditions being equal, the date of appearance or manifestation of a periodical phenomenon is delayed 4 days for every degree of latitude towards the pole, for every five degrees of longitude in an easterly direction and for every 100 metres in altitude. This law, however, holds good only for the North American continent where the isophanes develop in a north-westerly to south-easterly direction, which is attributed to the peculiarity of the thermic regime in relation to the direction and the temperatures of the ocean currents, and to the topographical and geographical constitution of the continent.

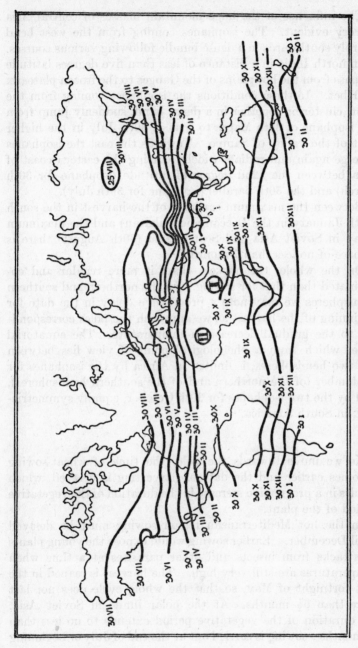

Fig. 7. World Isophanes of Wheat Harvest.

The influence of the huge mountain masses of central Asia is very evident. The isophanes coming from the west bend sharply southwards in a dense bundle following various courses.

In north India in a distance of less than five degrees latitude we pass from the hot plains of the Ganges to the frozen plateaux of Tibet. In these conditions the isophanes coming from the west, clustering together in a dense band, suddenly jump from the isophane of 30th March to that of 30th July in the higher part of the valley of Sampo. Towards the east the isophanes diverge again and radiate widely, cutting the eastern coast of Asia between the 22nd degree of latitude (isophane for 30th March) and the 50th parallel (isophane for 30th July).

Between the maximum earliness of the harvest in the south (30th January in the Deccan and Jukatan) and the maximum delay in Soviet Asia and Scandinavia (30th August) there is a space of no less than 7 months.

On the whole, the harvest chart is more regular and co-ordinated than that for sowing. In the northern and southern hemispheres we may note a progressive delay in the date for beginning of the harvest as we approach the poles corresponding to the gradual decrease in temperature. The equatorial zone, which from a phenological point of view lies between the two hemispheres, is limited in Africa by the isophanes for September (of the northern and of the southern hemispheres), and by the two isophanes for 30th October, equally symmetrically, in South America.

. . . . .

As we move towards the pole, the time of wheat-sowing becomes earlier and the date of harvesting is delayed, which results in a progressive increase in the duration of the vegetative period of the plant.

In the hot Mediterranean region sowing must be delayed until December. Earlier sowing would expose the young plants to attacks from insects and other parasites at a time when temperatures are still very high. The harvest is reaped in the first fortnight of May, so that the whole cycle does not last more than $5\frac{1}{2}$ months. At the polar limit, in Soviet Asia, the duration of the vegetative period extends to no less than 13 months : sowing is carried out at the end of July or beginning of August and the harvest can be reaped only at the end of August or the beginning of September in the following year.

Further descriptions of isophanes will be given later when we deal with weather charts and physiographic zones for maize, wheat and vines (see page 160).

APPROXIMATE CALCULATION OF THE DATES OF THE SUCCESSIVE PHASES OF DEVELOPMENT ON THE BASIS OF SIMPLE METEOROLOGICAL INFORMATION

I should like to give a brief illustration of the possibility of determining, on the basis of simple meteorological observations, the duration of the biological cycle and dates for the successive phases of development of the wheat plant, and we shall now examine this in order to provide a concrete example.

Without entering into a mass of detail, the reader will recall that the time of sowing can be calculated, and with close approximation within reasonably wide limits, if we bear in mind the peculiar characteristics of the individual varieties, the thermic and pluviometric complexes, and the competition with other farm activities.

It is the three phases of sprouting, earing and maturity, which are of greatest interest in relation to adaptation to climatic conditions.

Sprouting

The sowings to which we particularly refer, for the territory of Perugia, take place when the grape harvest has been completed, generally at the beginning of November. To ascertain the duration of the interval from sowing to sprouting, the following table, compiled on the basis of geographical trials, may be utilised :

Wheat : Days from Sowing to Sprouting

Temperature, ° C.	Duration of interval, days.	Temperature, ° C.	Duration of interval, days.
4– 5	35·0	10–11	10·5
5– 6	27·5	11–12	9·5
6– 7	22·5	12–13	8·5
7– 8	19·0	13–14	7·5
8– 9	15·5	14–15	6·5
9–10	12·5	15–16	6·5

If from the time of sowing temperatures remain constant between 7° and 8° C., sprouting would take place on the nineteenth day. At this temperature each day, therefore, represents one nineteenth of the duration of the interval considered.

With variable temperatures during this period, the duration can be calculated by adding up the daily fractions until unity has been reached. The day on which this has been achieved corresponds to the approximate date of appearance of the young plants (sprouting).

Taking 1st November as the date for the beginning of sowing, using the above table, the situation for the year 1951 is illustrated as follows :

November.	Mean temperature, ° C.	Fraction.	Percentage.
1	15·10	$\frac{1}{6\cdot5}$	15·38
2	13·95	$\frac{1}{7\cdot5}$	13·33
3	13·87	$\frac{1}{7\cdot5}$	13·33
4	9·62	$\frac{1}{12\cdot5}$	8·00
5	10·77	$\frac{1}{10\cdot5}$	9·52
6	11·05	$\frac{1}{9\cdot5}$	10·53
7	12·47	$\frac{1}{8\cdot5}$	11·76
8	12·72	$\frac{1}{8\cdot5}$	11·76
			Total 93·61
9	10·90	$\frac{1}{10\cdot5}$	9·52
			Total 103·13

Unity is reached between the eighth and ninth days, which may thus be taken as the approximate date for sprouting.

Earing

Two factors—temperature and length of day—have a decided bearing on the length of the interval between sprouting and earing, as we shall see in greater detail later on. The calculation of the date on which earing takes place is greatly simplified by the fact that the sum of the daily products of length of day in minutes multiplied by mean temperature in ° C. in the interval from sprouting to earing is constant.

The value of this constant for the variety " Mentana " is 931,000.

The following table gives the figures for this variety in 1938 and 1940.

Month.	No. of 10-day periods.	Length of day, minutes.	1938.		1940.	
			Mean temperature, ° C.	Products (in 1,000).	Mean temperature, ° C.	Products (in 1,000).
Nov.	2	615 (10 days)	9·0	55·4	9·2	56·6
,,	3	592 (10 ,,)	7·0	41·4	11·3	66·9
Dec.	1	557 (10 ,,)	6·7	37·3	7·4	41·2
,,	2	549 (10 ,,)	5·1	28·0	5·5	30·2
,,	3	549 (11 ,,)	1·0	6·0	1·7	10·3
Jan.	1	556 (10 ,,)	−1·3	0·0	3·0	16·7
,,	2	575 (10 ,,)	6·2	35·6	8·6	49·4
,,	3	586 (11 ,,)	5·0	32·2	6·2	40·0
Feb.	1	609 (10 ,,)	5·7	34·7	6·3	38·4
,,	2	634 (10 ,,)	2·3	14·9	6·6	41·8
,,	3	665 (8 days in 1938; 9 days in 1940)	4·2	22·3	8·2	49·1
March	1	668 (10 days)	9·3	62·1	6·6	44·1
,,	2	715 (10 ,,)	8·1	57·9	2·2	15·7
,,	3	742 (11 ,,)	11·2	91·4	4·9	40·0
April	1	792 (10 ,,)	8·7	68·9	13·5	106·9
,,	2	800 (10 ,,)	7·9	63·2	13·4	107·2
,,	3	826 (10 ,,)	6·9	57·0	11·7	96·6
May	1	840 (10 days; 8 days in 1940)	10·9	91·6	11·1	74·6
,,	2	856 (10 days)	14·3	122·4	—	—
,,	3	872 (1 day)	21·3	—	—	—
			20th May 21st May	922·3 940·8	8th May 9th May	925·7 935·0

In 1938 the sum of daily products (length of day in minutes by mean temperature) reached in the second 10-day period in May (20th May) 922,300, a figure quite close to the constant. If the product for 21st May is added we read 940,800, so that the constant is exceeded. The date for earing is thus placed between 20th and 21st May.

In 1940 at the end of April the sum of products was notably below the constant, while at the end of the first 10 days of May the constant was considerably exceeded. In order to obtain an exact figure the daily products were determined from the 1st May until 8th May when the figure 925,700 was reached.

Adding the product for 9th May the constant is slightly exceeded and it can therefore be stated that in 1940 the date for earing fell between 8th and 9th May.

Maturity

For the duration of the interval between earing and complete maturity the product of mean temperature by length of interval in days is again constant.

This constant is 816 for the variety " Mentana " and enables one to calculate the theoretical date of maturity.

For the years 1938 and 1940 we find :

Month.	10-Day period.	1938.	1940.
May	1st	10·93° C.	11·13° C.
,,	2nd	14·32	13·25
,,	3rd	21·35	15·91
June	1st	23·65	17·31
,,	2nd	25·80	17·46
,,	3rd	25·65	18·97
Earing :		20th May	8th May
Total temperature :		23rd June, 806° C.	28th June, 813° C.
		24th June, 831° C.	29th June, 832° C.

In these two years " Mentana " should have reached maturity 23–24th June in 1938, and between 28th and 29th June in 1940.

.   .   .   .   .

This is a first attempt at producing a method which will undoubtedly be improved upon, but which even now offers the possibility of calculating by means of meteorological observations alone, with reasonable accuracy, the dates for the various phases of development even for zones in which the plant has not yet been cultivated.

The determination of the dates of the phases of development of a plant for every locality is of fundamental importance, since this renders possible the determination for every locality of the beginning and the end of each single vegetative subperiod, for each of which there are different equivalents. If these dates were not known it would be impossibile to allot the meteorological values (for every locality) to sub-periods (climoscopes).   Thus it would not be possible to utilise the equivalents for representing climate in the agricultural sense as expressed in the frequency of normal or abnormal situations through excess or deficiency of rain or temperature (climatic formulæ).

DEMONSTRATION THAT THE WATER REQUIREMENTS OF THE PLANT VARY FROM ONE SUB-PERIOD TO ANOTHER

To give a clear idea of the variation of the water requirements of the plant from one sub-period to the next, we shall consider a series of experiments on the bean, whose vegetative period is divided into the following sub-periods :

(1) from sowing to sprouting ;
(2) from sprouting to the first stages of flowering ;
(3) from the first stages of flowering to seed setting ;
(4) from setting to the maximum weight of the legume ;
(5) from the maximum weight to drying and complete maturity of the seed.

We have three separate series of experiments :

(1) *Constant Regime for the Whole Cycle of Development*

(*a*) Continual excess of water such as to cause yellowing of the leaves and partial withering of the stems.   When, however, the plant runs the risk of dying, treatment is suspended and then resumed until the symptoms of distress are again apparent.   This treatment is continued throughout the whole vegetative cycle.

(*b*) Constantly dry regime, the plant being furnished with a minimum of water just sufficient to allow it to develop.

(*c*) Constantly favourable water supply (normal).

(2) *Regime of Drought in a Single Sub-period*

For each sub-period there is a group of pots in which a regime of drought is maintained for the particular sub-period, while normal conditions are established for the rest of the vegetative cycle.

(3) *Regime of Excess in a Single Sub-period*

For each sub-period separately there is a group of pots in which excessive humidity is maintained (allowing the water to stagnate), while in all the other sub-periods conditions are kept normal.

E

In this way it becomes possible to measure the relative effects of drought and of excess water in the individual vegetative sub-period.

The following figures give the yields (grams of beans per plant) obtained in each series :

Constant regime

Normal	.	.	.	.	46·0 gms.
Excess	.	.	.	.	7·5 ,,
Drought	.	.	.	.	4·0 ,,

Drought is the more adverse condition of the two and produces the greatest loss. The figures thus give us an adequate idea of the loss ascribable to the two opposite groups of adverse phenomena when acting continuously—i.e. throughout the whole vegetative period.

Drought in Each Sub-period Separately

In order to make the results comparable by eliminating the error arising through the different lengths of the single sub-periods, the loss caused by drought in each sub-period is divided by its length in days.

Thus, for instance, with drought in the second sub-period, from sprouting to flowering phase (which had a duration of 44 days), the product obtained was 6 gms., against the 46 gms. obtained in a normal regime.

The loss was therefore 40 gm., which, divided by the number of days (44), gives a daily loss of 0·9 gm., a measure of the sensitivity of the plant in respect of drought in the second sub-period.

The complete table for every sub-period is as follows :

Sub-period.	Difference from normal (46 gm.), gm.	Duration of sub-period, days.	Daily loss, gm.
(1) From sowing to sprouting .	19·0	5	3·8
(2) From sprouting to first stages of flowering . .	40·0	44	0·9
(3) From first stages of flowering to seed setting . .	34·0	5	6·8
(4) From seed setting to maximum weight of the legume	36·0	34	1·1
(5) From maximum weight to the harvest . . .	18·5	22	0·8

From this it immediately becomes evident that the great decrease resulting from drought in the second sub-period, from sprouting to the flowering phase, is not to be attributed to a particularly high susceptibility on the part of the plant at this time, but rather to the long duration of this sub-period.

The particular susceptibility of the plant in the brief interval from flowering to setting, on the other hand, becomes very clear (third sub-period), while in the fifth sub-period (from the maximum weight of the seed to harvest), in consequence of a natural process of drying up and a continual and proportional decrease in weight, the needs for water are much reduced and the damage which could result from drought in this sub-period is limited.

Consequently the meteorological equivalent for drought in the sub-period from flowering to complete seed-setting will be much higher than that corresponding to the sub-period from the maximum weight to harvest. At this time the quantity of water required by the plant, to allow it to attain normal development, is much reduced, so that the total sum of precipitation required to produce a state of drought must naturally fall to a very low level.

Excess Moisture in a Given Sub-period

The following table incorporates the results :

Sub-period.	Difference from normal (46 gm.), gm.	Duration of sub-period. days.	Daily loss, gm.
(1) From sowing to sprouting .	14	4	3·5
(2) From sprouting to first stages of flowering . .	27	33	0·8
(3) From first stages of flowering to seed setting . .	34	9	3·8
(4) From setting to maximum weight of the legume .	32	24	1·3
(5) From maximum weight to the harvest . . .	19	23	0·8

The greatest damage from excess humidity is found in the sub-period between flowering and seed-setting, and from sowing to sprouting. It becomes evident that the quantity of rain that would prove harmful through excess in the interval between flowering and setting (and from sowing to sprouting) will be less than that which would result in damage to the plant in the interval between maximum weight and harvest; at this time the organism has completed its cycle and is much less susceptible to adversities.

The pluviometric equivalent for excess in mm. from flowering to seed-setting will have to be much lower than the equivalent for excess during the sub-period from the maximum weight to harvest, when the plant, being less sensitive, will require considerable quantities of water to damage it.

We can now summarise in a table the daily losses due to water deficiency and excess :

Sub-period.	Drought, gm.	Excess, gm.
(1) From sowing to sprouting. .	3·8	5·5
(2) From sprouting to first stages of flowering	0·9	0·8
(3) From first stages of flowering to seed setting	6·8	3·7
(4) From seed-setting to maximum weight of the legume . .	1·1	1·3
(5) From maximum weight to the harvest	0·8	0·8

The maximum sensitivity both to deficiency and excess is shown to be in the interval between the flowering phase and setting, while in the last sub-period (from the maximum weight of the legume to harvest) the organism is practically indifferent to variations in humidity.

In the first sub-period, from sowing to sprouting, the losses due to both excess and deficiency would appear to be very high. Such conditions, however, are very rare, as the date for sowing is not fixed and can vary within wide limits, allowing the farmer to wait and choose the most suitable time.

From the foregoing it is quite clear that the equivalents for excess and deficiency must be separately determined for each sub-period. Moreover, the determination of the equivalent for excess will be the more exact the lower the calculated value, while, conversely, the determination of the equivalent for deficiency will be the better defined the higher the value established.

CHAPTER III

SUB-PERIODS OF MAXIMUM AND MINIMUM REACTION

(Critical Periods and Dormancy Periods)

THE different mode of behaviour and the requirements of the plant, with reference to a given factor, during its biological cycle, find their clearest expression in the interval of maximum activity (critical periods) and those of quiescence or of minimum activity (periods of dormancy, or rest).

We define a critical period, in relation to a given factor or phenomenon, as the interval in the biological cycle during which the plant presents the maximum susceptibility to this factor or phenomenon. Variations of the environmental factor are clearly reflected in the yield, and cause the widest fluctuations in production either in the negative or in the positive sense, in relation to the factor considered.

We may similarly define the period of dormancy as the interval during which the plant presents a minimum susceptibility to the effects of external agents. Variations in temperature, humidity, etc., have hardly any effect on the plant, so that variations in yield through the action of any one of these meteorological factors are very small.

From the suspension of growth (in autumn) to the resumption of growth in spring (for herbaceous plants), and from the fall of the leaves to the time of budding for woody plants, is a period of dormancy. The dead, static mass prevails over the dynamic and live one.

When water and sap no longer circulate, or do so very slowly, the organism can successfully resist sudden and large falls in temperature; the buds of fruit trees, well enclosed in the wood and protected by robust resistant scales, are, in fact, hardly affected by drought or frost.

The woody shoots of the vine, for instance, when artificially exposed to a temperature of $-12°$ C. for 8 hours do not seem to suffer at all.

On the return of spring, when leaf and flower, vulnerable in the extreme, emerge from the protective shelter of the scales, a sudden fall in temperature, a gust of wind, a variation in the hydric and hygroscopic regimes are all sufficient to cause irreparable damage in the space of a few minutes.

The critical periods are the moments of maximum sensitivity of the plant, and for the factor temperature these coincide with the time of budding but more especially with the appearance of the flowers and the delicate processes of pollination and of fruit-setting.

From the factor water on the other hand, as can easily be imagined, the critical periods manifest themselves when the weight is increasing rapidly and the processes of transpiration and growth are at their greatest intensity.

In this connection, it is interesting to note the experimental results obtained many years ago in determining the critical period of wheat in relation to rainfall.

The reader's attention is drawn to the following series of four particularly interesting experiments :

First Series. Water requirements of the plant abundantly satisfied

In the 15 days preceding earing the humidity in the soil was allowed to decrease until the plant showed signs of withering. The harvest proved to be very poor.

Second Series. Plants were abundantly irrigated in the 15 days preceding earing

For the rest of the vegetative period water was applied in small quantities and at infrequent intervals; signs of incipient withering were observed. Nevertheless, the harvest was good.[1]

---

[1] Pot experiments are very useful when it is necessary to effect an abrupt passage from a condition of abundant water reserves to a state of drought. It was thus possible, in consequence of the permeability and reduced quantity of soil in the experimental pots, to have great humidity in the soil up to a fortnight before earing, passing then abruptly to drought conditions.

*Third Series. The same procedure as that used for the Second
    Series but with irrigation continued throughout the earing
    phase*

Watering was continued until the straw had turned yellow,
and the yield was superior to that obtained in the Second Series.

Fourth Series. Drought followed by abundant water

A group of plants badly affected by drought appeared to be
having difficulty in their development, and their inflorescences
had just emerged from the leaf-sheaths at the time of earing.
Abundant water had an immediate positive effect. The dry
and apparently dead plants turned green and the culms began
to grow rapidly, developing their leaves and producing normal
ears. The latter, however, in spite of abundant and repeated
irrigation during the formation of the grain and maturity phase
were mainly empty, or had only small quantities of seed of
poor quality.

Maliboga in his experiments caused artificial wilting of barley
plants in pots at different stages of the vegetative period.
The figures below give the yields expressed as a percentage of
that of the control plants which suffered no lack of rainfall :

	Index number of yield.
Control (normal plants)	100
Withering in the period between sprouting and the first stages of development of the plant . .	98
Withering during tillering	95
„ at the time of earing	47
„ during maturity	100

The dominant negative action of drought at the time of
earing clearly emerges, the yield being reduced by no less than
53%.

From the various experiments referred to, the following
general conclusions can be drawn :

(i) The critical period for wheat (and other cereals), with
reference to the factor water, occurs in the period of 15 days
before earing. If moisture in the soil is below the limit compatible with the normal development of the plant, the harvest

will be severely damaged, even if conditions have been favourable throughout the remaining portion of the vegetative period. On the other hand, when water is plentiful during the critical period, there will be a good yield, even if there has been a relative deficiency throughout the remainder of the biologic cycle.

(ii) When the soil lacked water during the critical period, repeated irrigation at the time of earing will promote an energetic and lively resumption of growth; the effects on grain production are, however, practically nil.

(iii) When the plant's requirements have been satisfied throughout the critical period, it is in a position to make good use of additional irrigation up to the moment of yellowing of the straw.

This last very important observation justifies and makes even clearer the concept of the critical period and, in conclusion, the following corollary may be added : when the requirements of the plant have been met throughout the critical period, the plant can utilise further quantities of water until the moment of yellowing of the straw. When, on the other hand, moisture in the soil is below the wilting limit during the critical period, the plant is unable to utilise any further quantities of water which may be placed at its disposal after the said critical period.

An examination of the curve of the weight of the wheat plant throughout its vegetative cycle furnishes a clear illustration of these principles (see Fig. 8).

At the time of sprouting, and for about the next 2 months, the plant increases in weight slowly and gradually. About 3 weeks before earing, however, the curve shoots up, so that in a relatively brief space of time the weight of the plant is more than trebled.

Once it has reached the phase of milk ripeness, the plant ceases its growth, and, in contrast to the preceding period, its weight tends to decrease, so that at complete maturity it is roughly two-fifths of the maximum reached at milk ripeness.

The decrease in weight gives us a good idea and indeed indirect measure of the considerable quantity of water utilised by the plant during the critical period to keep pace with the rapid and intense phenomenon of transpiration, which must accompany the elaboration of the large quantities of plastic substances necessary for the formation and development of the kernel. This is the reason why the critical period for wheat in respect of the factor rain is found to correspond to the earing phase.

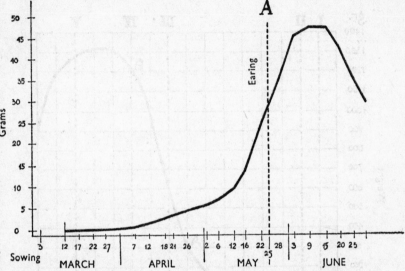

FIG. 8. THE WEIGHT INCREASE OF A PLANT OF SPRING WHEAT.

The drought equivalents in mm. therefore reach their highest values during the intervals of major activity, while in the sub-periods of minor activity, owing to the fact that the requirements of the plant are reduced, the amount of rainfall necessary to assure the minimum of humidity required in the soil will be quite modest.

. . . . .

We affirm once more that the equivalents for excess and deficiency must be determined for each sub-period of development separately.

When considering, however, the problems of agricultural production, it is the critical period in relation to local meteorological adversities which is the prime factor in the study of bio-atmospheric relationships.

The Critical Period of Maize in Relation to Rainfall

To give a general idea of the water requirements of maize, it might be useful to examine the curve for increase in weight obtained when the amount of water in the soil is sufficient to meet, throughout the life-cycle, the needs of transpiration (see

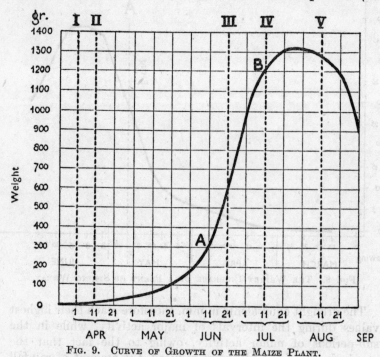

FIG. 9. CURVE OF GROWTH OF THE MAIZE PLANT.

I, Sowing; II, Sprouting; III, Appearance of male inflorescence; IV, Complete setting; V, Milk maturity.

Fig. 9). The curve of growth (increase of weight) may be divided into four portions :

(1) *Stage of Slow Growth.* The plant grows slowly in volume and length even with relatively high temperature. When temperature is very low but still above the limit for growth, or when the soil is too dry, the duration of this period can be considerably protracted (without any immediate harmful effect on the plant), and the plant waits for the favourable conditions which will cause it to resume growth.

(2) *Stage of Rapid Growth.*   With a sudden bend of the curve, the plant passes to a stage of rapid growth and reaches its maximum weight, about 2 weeks before milk ripeness.

(3) *Stage of Slow Decrease in Weight.*   After having reached the maximum weight, the plant begins to dry up and slowly but gradually loses weight, and continues to do so until a few days after milk ripeness has been reached.

(4) *Stage of Rapid Decrease in Weight.*   Until full maturity.

It is evident that the more rapid the increase in weight, the bigger the amount of water consumed and the higher the requirements of the plant in respect of this factor.

Consequently, the critical period for maize in respect to the water factor must be sought in the second stage.   Kiriakov has, in fact, defined the critical period as the interval from 15 days before to 15 days after the appearance of male inflorescences.

．　　　．　　　．　　　．　　　．　　　．

In order to determine the time of the critical period in the different maize zones in Italy, in default of phenological records, the meteoro-agricultural data were examined for the following stations, all taken from the provinces in which maize occupies a regular place in the rotation : Florence and Pisa (Tuscany), Benevento and Caserta (Campania), Mantova (Lombardy), Ferrara (Emilia) and Pesaro (Marche).

To determine the dates of the critical period in the various places, the years were divided into two groups, according to whether the yield was abundant or poor because of drought. For each one of the two groups we calculate the amount of rainfall for successive intervals of 30 days (an interval which corresponds more or less to the duration of the critical period). The interval giving the maximum difference between rainfall in good and bad years will correspond to the critical period.

The following six combinations were considered, each of which had a duration of 30 days :

(1) First, second and third 10-day period in June.

(2) Second and third 10-day period in June and the first in July.

(3) Third 10-day period in June and the first and second in July.

(4) First, second and third 10-day period in July.

(5) Second and third 10-day period in July and first in August.

(6) Third 10-day period in July and first and second in August.

The table below gives the rainfall figures in mm. for Caserta : here we have 12 years with a poor harvest owing to drought, and 7 years with an abundant yield :

Millimetres of Rain—Caserta, Italy

Drought years.	Combinations.					
	1st.	2nd.	3rd.	4th.	5th.	6th.
1887	31·5	50·3	43·3	35·4	41·0	24·5
1894	5·8	5·8	0·3	0·0	0·0	0·0
1901	26·6	15·0	10·5	10·3	20·5	37·0
1902	38·0	36·0	21·0	0·0	2·0	2·1
1916	24·6	0·6	2·2	121·4	122·0	183·3
1919	49·6	35·3	44·8	17·2	17·3	7·2
1922	8·1	18·1	14·8	15·4	5·4	0·6
1923	22·4	46·2	14·0	14·1	0·0	3·0
1927	5·7	0·5	0·5	0·3	0·0	0·0
1931	0·8	0·8	0·8	0·0	0·0	0·2
1935	32·6	18·2	94·7	79·0	78·2	13·5
1938	0·2	0·2	24·5	24·6	25·2	11·7
Mean	20·5	18·9	22·6	26·5	26·0	23·6

Rainfall in Millimetres—Caserta, Italy

Abundant years.	Combinations.					
	1st.	2nd.	3rd.	4th.	5th.	6th.
1911	45·5	44·5	81·0	194·0	104·0	49·5
1918	89·1	91·6	70·5	55·8	3·1	4·0
1926	64·1	82·9	132·8	31·5	96·1	20·5
1930	76·3	88·5	100·0	98·2	84·2	15·2
1932	68·6	68·4	27·1	22·1	22·1	4·0
1933	113·6	142·4	96·4	50·5	22·0	16·8
1936	83·1	71·6	47·5	7·3	5·9	5·9
Mean	77·1	84·2	79·3	65·6	48·2	16·5

The differences between the means of the two groups of years in the different combinations were as follows :

Combination	1st	2nd	3rd.	4th	5th	6th
Difference	56·6	*65·3*	56·7	39·1	22·2	−7·1

It is thus established that the decisive 30-day period in this respect is that which runs from 11th June to 10th July (second combination); for this interval, we find the maximum difference between the two groups of values—namely, 65·3.

The interval for the territory of Caserta between 11th June and 10th July can therefore be considered as the critical period for maize with regard to rainfall.

Proceeding towards the north and to higher altitudes, the time of the critical periods becomes progressively later. Thus at Mantova the critical month is found to be the period between 21st June and 20th July (third combination). The differences in precipitation in the two groups of years are as follows :

Combination	1st	2nd	3rd	4th	5th	6th
Rainfall difference	21·5	29·7	*51·4*	34·2	39·5	18·4

In the mountainous regions around Benevento the critical period coincides with the month of July (fourth combination). The relative figures are :

Combination	1st	2nd	3rd	4th	5th	6th
Rainfall difference	0·8	66·6	81·7	*86·6*	58·9	50·9

Determination of the Equivalent. We can now determine the equivalent for drought in the critical period for maize.

For all stations under examination we calculate the total precipitation for the 30 days corresponding to the critical period and consider both the unfavourable drought years and the favourable ones (see next pages). We shall consider the results relative to 63 years in which there was drought and 63 with favourable rainfall conditions.

These figures are plotted on a graph with two axes crossing each other at right angles, precipitations being represented on the vertical axis and the years on the horizontal one. The years with abundant harvest are marked with an open circle, while those with a poor harvest owing to drought are marked with a black one at the corresponding point of intersection of the axes (see Fig. 10).

Florence

Years with low yield.	Rainfall, mm.	Plentiful years.	Rainfall, mm.
1881	0·0	1887	78·6
1882	33·3	1898	98·7
1883	8·3	1905	90·2
1890	13·2		
1894	21·3		
1923	15·9		
1933	75·4		
1935	3·9		
1936	45·6		
Mean	24·1	Mean	89·2

(The rainfall here considered, as for the other stations, is that corresponding to the 30-day interval for which we find the greatest difference between rainfall in mm. in unfavourable years (drought) and in favourable ones.)

Pesaro

Years with low yield.	Rainfall, mm.	Plentiful years.	Rainfall, mm.
1886	36·9	1887	50·9
1902	49·0	1888	46·4
1907	10·9	1895	85·3
1908	54·4	1896	58·1
1916	5·0	1898	124·7
1917	13·2	1905	140·8
1931	44·5	1913	96·7
		1915	77·4
		1926	47·6
		1929	20·5
		1932	45·5
		1937	119·2
Mean	30·6	Mean	76·1

Caserta

Years with low yield.	Rainfall, mm.	Plentiful years.	Rainfall, mm.
1887	50·3	1911	44·5
1894	5·8	1918	91·6
1901	15·0	1926	82·9
1902	36·0	1930	88·5
1916	0·6	1932	68·4
1919	35·3	1934	142·4
1922	18·1	1936	71·6
1923	46·2		
1927	0·5		
1931	0·8		
1935	18·2		
1938	0·2		
Mean	18·9	Mean	84·3

Ferrara

Years with low yield.	Rainfall, mm.	Plentiful years.	Rainfall, mm.
1882	40·1	1884	82·8
1890	15·5	1891	45·5
1894	15·8	1892	47·6
1902	56·5	1898	120·8
1916	0·4	1899	163·4
Mean	25·7	Mean	92·0

Mantova

Years with low yield.	Rainfall, mm.	Plentiful years.	Rainfall, mm.
1881	7·2	1880	25·5
1889	25·1	1887	142·1
1894	17·6	1898	101·3
1902	30·7	1906	69·3
1909	36·7	1911	47·4
Mean	23·5	Mean	77·1

Pisa

Years with low yield.	Rainfall, mm.	Plentiful years.	Rainfall, mm.
1880	22·7	1881	75·8
1884	106·8	1882	77·6
1885	11·7	1886	138·9
1887	30·1	1893	39·3
1890	24·0	1895	74·4
1891	50·4	1896	83·6
1899	63·7	1898	67·3
1917	2·2	1901	55·3
1918	12·7	1904	15·7
1922	57·1	1905	81·9
1923	56·6	1906	67·0
1927	39·1	1908	84·7
1928	17·0	1909	231·8
1931	7·2	1912	86·6
1935	1·4	1913	95·3
1938	78·5	1914	80·5
1939	4·9	1915	272·8
		1919	40·7
		1920	143·3
		1924	86·8
		1925	12·2
		1926	24·7
		1929	29·1
		1932	70·1
		1933	114·3
		1934	67·7
		1936	101·7
		1937	114·7
Mean	34·4	Mean	86·9

Benevento

Years with low yield.	Rainfall, mm.	Plentiful years.	Rainfall, mm.
1883	3·9	1882	55·5
1892	10·5	1887	135·5
1901	31·5		
1902	0·0		
1903	16·5		
1907	9·5		
1910	0·0		
1912	0·0		
Mean	9·0	Mean	95·5

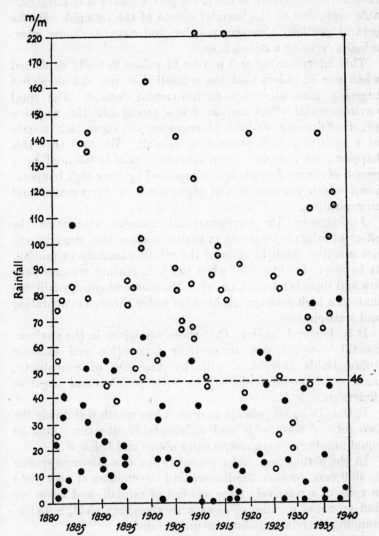

Fig. 10. Equivalent of Drought for Maize during the Critical Period.

F

While in the higher part of the graph we find exclusively favourable situations, in the lower part we have only unfavourable ones, due to the harmful effects of the drought. In the central portion, however, positive and negative cases intermingle, creating a mixed zone.

This intermingling and mixing of values is easily explained when one considers that the rainfall does not act alone but together with all other environmental factors. The total environmental effect can at times accentuate the negative effects of drought, and this phenomenon can show itself in spite of a relatively high amount of rainfall. We find that this happens, for instance, when abundant rain is followed by a period of strong dry winds accompanied by very high temperatures which accentuate the phenomena of evaporation and transpiration.

Analogously, the environmental complex attenuates the effect of rainfall deficiency in such a manner that drought will not manifest itself in spite of the relative scarcity of rainfall. It happens, for instance, when the temperature remains very low and there is no wind, i.e. when the meteorological conditions limit in a high measure the losses of water through evaporation and transpiration.

It is, however, evident that these variations in the environmental complex due to extreme favourable and extreme unfavourable conditions will, by the law of probability, occur with equal frequency in both positive and negative directions.

It thus becomes possible to draw a line which will divide the two sets of favourable and unfavourable situations into an equal number of asymmetric cases above and below it.

In the actual case under consideration the line corresponds to 46·0 mm. Above the line we find eleven cases of poor yield in spite of a relatively large amount of rainfall, and below we find an equal number of cases with abundant yield, notwithstanding the relatively low amount of rainfall.

46·0 mm. therefore represents the pluviometric equivalent for drought during the critical period for maize, and can well serve to determine the frequency of drought in any station at that time. All that is necessary is to note how many times over a considerable period of years the sum of precipitations in the 30 days period from 15 days before to 15 days after the appearance of male inflorescences has been below 46 mm.

In the territory of Perugia the critical period is from the 21st June to 20th July.

The rainfall data relative to this interval for the years 1891 to 1940 are given below :

Rainfall—Perugia.   *21st June to 20th July*

Year.	Mm.	Year.	Mm.	Year.	Mm.
1891	4·9	1908	174·0	1925	61·5
1892	30·9	1909	36·7	1926	91·5
1893	25·3	1910	63·6	1927	1·8
1894	3·9	1911	44·0	1928	13·0
1895	14·6	1912	65·3	1929	19·2
1896	50·3	1913	137·2	1930	81·7
1897	81·0	1914	47·9	1931	27·2
1898	46·7	1915	95·8	1932	118·2
1899	90·9	1916	0·0	1933	38·1
1900	85·3	1917	21·1	1934	47·8
1901	21·5	1918	29·7	1935	0·8
1902	45·0	1919	69·8	1936	36·1
1903	42·1	1920	21·8	1937	100·0
1904	36·5	1921	16·9	1938	2·4
1905	68·6	1922	0·0	1939	0·8
1906	17·5	1923	18·4	1940	137·6
1907	2·4	1924	49·5		

Counting the times in which the monthly total of rainfall is inferior to the drought equivalent (46·0 mm.) we find twenty-nine cases out of fifty.

Hence the frequency of drought in the territory of Perugia for maize during the critical period is 58% (5·8 times in 10 years).

We repeat that the equivalent does not serve to determine the presence or absence of drought for particular cases, but only to calculate the frequency of the phenomenon as a whole (over a period of time).

In 1903, for instance, in spite of the total precipitations being inferior to the equivalent, there were no ill effects and the harvest was abundant : the conditions of the total environmental complex were actually very favourable, and so neutralised the effects which insufficient rainfall would normally have produced.

In 1924, on the other hand, there was drought, and the

resulting harvest was below normal, in spite of the 49·5 mm. of rainfall during the critical period : the adverse conditions of the environmental complex proved such that they overcame the beneficial action of the rain.

These occasional variations in the environmental complex are, however, found with equal frequency both in favourable and in unfavourable directions so that the frequency of drought remains practically unaltered.

If it were possible to effect long-range weather forecasting and know from the moment of sowing what the meteorological conditions during the vegetative period would be, it would in some cases be possible to adapt the necessary agricultural operations to the weather by changing the time of sowing, or by choosing an earlier or later variety, and so make the critical period coincide with the most favourable interval possible.

However, it is not possible to foretell the weather over long periods, and so operations have to be adapted to the general climatic conditions, and for such purposes the equivalents offer an excellent basis and make it possible to determine how many times drought is likely to occur over a 10-year period. We thus get a concrete basis and an accurate measure which enable us to take those precautions which will best serve to diminish the effects of the adverse phenomenon.

A knowledge of critical periods is of particular importance for making agricultural operations better adapted to the atmospheric environment. This can be achieved by following one of two methods :

(1) regulate the time of sowing or choose a variety with a degree of earliness such that its critical period will coincide with the interval during which the frequency of the adverse phenomenon is at a minimum ;

(2) concentrate in the critical period that treatment which tends to diminish the intensity of the adverse phenomenon ; thus for instance, when water (rainfall) is scarce, irrigation will by preference be carried out during the critical period, so as to obtain the greatest benefit from it.

The application of the hoe during the critical period leads to a yield of 27·0 quintals per hectare of maize, while under the same conditions, but applying the hoe a little after the critical period, the yield proved to be 6 quintals less.

CHAPTER IV

THE METEOROLOGICAL EQUIVALENTS FOR SOME HERBACEOUS PLANTS

WE will now consider some plants which are not cultivated for their fruits or seed, but for their stems, leaves or roots. In such conditions the bio-meteorological relationships present some special characteristics, as we shall now explain.

We give now the equivalents for hemp (stem and fibres), sugar-beet (roots), potato, lucerne (stems and leaves) and cotton (fibre).

HEMP

The vegetative period of this plant is divided into three stages :

(1) from sprouting to the beginning of the phase of rapid growth (stage of slow growth);
(2) from the beginning of rapid growth to flowering (stage of rapid growth);
(3) from flowering to seed maturity (linear growth practically ceases).

A direct relationship is noted between the total yield of fibre and the total sum of precipitations in the five 10-day periods preceding the one in which the plant is cut. The equivalent for drought in this interval, which corresponds fairly closely to the second stage, is about 34 mm., while in the first stage, owing to the slowness of growth (from sprouting to the beginning of rapid growth), the equivalent, according to Briccoli, is only 20 mm.

Although it completes its cycle during the hottest season, the water requirements of hemp are relatively modest. This is due to the fact that hemp is almost exclusively sown in rich and deep soils which are well tilled and manured generously, so that they are in a position to absorb a large quantity of water and preserve it for a long time.

If hemp were cultivated in all kinds of soil, including the poorer ones and those affected by drought, the equivalent for rainfall deficiency would naturally be much higher. Its low value is due entirely to the exceptionally favourable soil and agricultural conditions under which it is grown. This equivalent, not being a function of the complete range of soil types from the best to the worst, clearly assumes the character of a special or partial equivalent.

SUGAR-BEET

The same considerations can be made for sugar-beet for which, as is well known, the best soils are reserved, with a consequent decrease in the equivalent for drought.

The vegetative period of the plant can be so sub-divided :

(1) sowing and sprouting;
(2) prevalent development of epygeous portions;
(3) prevalent development of the root.

It is this third sub-period (June–August) which is the most important in respect of the quantitative product.

The monthly equivalent for rainfall deficiency calculated from meteoro-agricultural data at Pisa, Bologna, Vicenza, Castel d'Ario, Sermide, Arezzo and Alexandria is practically identical with that for hemp—namely, 35 mm.

POTATO

The potato is particularly sensitive to deficiency or excess of rainfall in the interval occurring between planting and the beginning of growth, as is well demonstrated by the Briccoli experiments, later followed on the same lines by Qafzezi for similar trials with the bean.

Briccoli reports the following results :

	Weight of tubers per plant, kg.	Soil humidity, per cent.
(1) Without irrigation (dry regime).	0·552	7·2
(2) With four lots of irrigation (normal regime) . . .	1·152	13·3–22·6
(3) With continued application of water (excessive humidity) .	0·504	22·6–26·5

The negative effects of both deficiency and excess moisture in the interval from planting to sprouting are quite evident.

In the general framework of natural economy, however, it is the summer drought which causes the greatest loss and whose negative action is shown, especially when this occurs from the initial stages of the formation of tubers up to flowering (in the penultimate month before the harvest), as Viggiani first asserted.

For this interval the drought equivalent is 35 mm.

This value, practically the same in the summer period as that found for hemp, sugar-beet and potato, suggests that resistance to drought, especially as regards the intrinsic characteristics of these species, is not so much due to their morphological constitution, as to particular characteristics of the plasma (glucid content, amount of colloidal substances, etc.).

Excess moisture in all periods other than that between sowing and sprouting is rarely harmful in the Mediterranean zone, while in the countries of Central Europe, with a regime of summer rains, it is the most damaging meteorological phenomenon.

However, in Italy excessive rainfall also can directly harm the plant in the last month of the vegetative period, when the aerial portions are already inactive and the considerable quantities of water in the soil give rise to the rotting of tubers.

Such an occurrence is sometimes reported in the Ligurian Apennine ranges when monthly precipitations exceed 102 mm.

Indirectly, rainfall, especially in the interval between sprouting and flowering, when the development of the aerial portions is quick and vigorous, becomes damaging and creates wet–hot environmental conditions favouring attacks of *Phytophthora infestans*, the equivalent for excess in this case being 90 mm.

LUCERNE

Lucerne, unlike the plants we have just examined, is perennial, and remains in the ground from 2 to 6 or 7 years (this last under most favourable conditions), and furnishes a number of cuts which under the most adverse conditions is reduced to two, while in the best soils and in rainy years it reaches five.

Let us now examine the drought equivalent for this crop in Central Italy.

For lucerne the period in which normal growth can take place in Umbria is from April to October.

In March and November mean temperatures are already insufficient (7·9° and 8·2° C., respectively). The thermic limit for growth can be put at 9° C., which agrees with the figure established in Germany by Schnelle.

The first cutting is made towards the end of May, the second at the beginning of July and, lastly, the third in the second decade of August. The most favourable month is, without doubt, June, for it usually has high temperatures and sufficient rainfall. In July and August, although temperature is even higher, rains are scarce and drought can often impede normal development, and delays the third cutting.

The quantity of hay produced decreases progressively from the first cut onwards. Hay production per ha. is the following :

First cut	.	.	.	.	39 quintals per ha.
Second cut	.	.	.	.	29 ,, ,,
Third cut	.	.	.	.	19 ,, ,,
Fourth cut	.	.	.	.	8 ,, ,,

As already stated, the first cut is taken at the end of May or beginning of June, and the rainfall in the two months April–May acts decisively on the quantity cut.

From the records of the meteorological observatory attached to the Institute of Agricultural Ecology at the University of Perugia, I have taken data relative to weather conditions (precipitations) and fodder production.

For the first cutting this is given in Table on p. 74.

Taking a general mean of the years with a harvest decidedly superior to what is normally obtained, we find 175 mm. for the bimester April–May (87 mm. monthly), while in the years with a poor harvest the sum of precipitations falls to 89 mm. (44 mm. monthly).

If these figures are brought on to the plane of two orthogonal axes, one corresponding to rainfall and the other to years or stations (as has already been done for wheat and maize : see page 7 and page 65), the horizontal demarcation line is 54 mm. per month, which neatly separates years in which there was drought from those with sufficient rainfall. This figure can thus be accepted as the monthly equivalent for drought for lucerne in the 2-month period under consideration (partial equivalent).

In the years presenting a good and abundant second cut, which occur with a frequency of 54% (5·4 times in 10 years), mean precipitation in the month of June is 86 mm., while in the years with a mediocre and scarce harvest, which in the zone

Harvests and Rainfall, Perugia

Year.	Harvest.	Rainfall, mm.		
		April.	May.	Total.
1883	Abundant	132	128	260
1884	,,	105	20	125
1893	Scarce	60	50	110
1899	Abundant	110	69	179
1901	,,	56	47	103
1902	,,	58	94	152
1903	,,	84	35	119
1906	Very good	126	56	182
1908	Scarce	68	14	82
1909	,,	12	48	60
1910	Good	82	134	216
1913	Very good	184	53	237
1915	Very abundant	96	62	158
1922	Scarce	92	3	95
1924	,,	57	38	95
1926	Good	140	48	188
1931	Very good	58	109	167
1933	Moderate	48	59	107
1935	Scarce	21	68	89
1937	Good	144	59	203
1938	,,	79	99	178
1939	,,	25	129	154

under consideration happens with a frequency of 46% (4·6 times in 10 years), the precipitation in the month of June is reduced to a mean of 33 mm.

With the same procedure as that adopted for the first cutting the equivalent for deficiency for the second cutting is 48 mm.

The diminished necessity for water found at the time of the second cut as compared to the first is directly related to the successively reduced weight of fodder obtained with each successive cut.

Lastly, let us examine the third cutting.

The years with an abundant harvest are found to occur with a frequency of 43% (4·3 times in 10 years), and for these rainfall in July had a mean value of 64 mm.   When the harvest proved to be scarce, which happens with a frequency of 57% (5·7 times in 10 years), the number of mm. registered in July was only 16.

The equivalent for drought is found to be 35 mm.

Both the mean values and the equivalents therefore continue to diminish proportionately to the decrease in the weight of hay obtained, which is related to the progressive fall in the quantity of water at the disposal of the plant, and to the decrease in its capacity to resume growth.

COTTON

We present below the results of some experiments carried out by Roganović to determine the critical periods for cotton with respect to rain and temperature.   These researches undertaken at Skoplje (Macedonia) in relation to the development and yield of the cotton plant have shown that there exist three well-defined critical periods : two for rainfall and one for temperature.

Roganović, following the method outlined in this book, divided the vegetative cycle of cotton into the following five sub-periods :

(1) from sowing to sprouting ;
(2) from sprouting to the appearance of the floral buds ;
(3) from the appearance of the floral buds to blooming ;
(4) from blooming to the dehiscence of the first capsules ;
(5) from the dehiscence of the first capsules to the end of the harvest.

Below are given the yields, in kilograms of raw fibre per hectare, for those years for which it was possible to have exact figures.

Year.	Yield, kg.	Year.	Yield, kg.	Year.	Yield, kg.
1934	543	1937	883	1946	834
1935	860	1939	508	1947	1,220
1936	183	1940	294	1948	399

Critical Periods with Respect to Rainfall

In order to single out the time within which the critical period falls, the years were divided into two groups, according to whether the yield was good or poor through drought. The sum of precipitations for intervals of 30 days (period which could more or less correspond to the duration of the critical period) was then calculated for each group and at different times. Then the interval during which the difference between mean precipitations in abundant years and those for the poor years had reached a maximum was determined. This period may, with good approximation, be taken as the critical period of cotton with respect to rainfall.

The following combinations, each having a duration of 30 days, were considered :

    (1) first, second and third 10-day periods of May;

    (2) second and third of May, and first of June;

    (3) third of May, and first and second of June;

    (4) first, second and third of June;

    (5) second and third of June, and first of July;

    (6) third of June, and first and second of July;

    (7) first, second and third of July;

    (8) second and third of July, and first of August;

    (9) third of July, and first and second of August;

    (10) first, second and third of August.

The following tables give the pluviometric figures in mm. at the station of Skoplje for the ten combinations, while the yields are divided into two groups : above normal and below normal.

Years with yield above normal.	Intervals.									
	1.	2.	3.	4.	5.	6.	7.	8.	9.	10.
1935	39·0	0·5	32·1	61·0	73·3	71·8	43·0	34·6	24·5	11·0
1937	112·0	71·2	116·3	87·0	103·5	61·1	48·0	30·7	33·6	29·0
1946	47·8	51·8	42·4	50·4	33·6	32·0	0·0	0·0	0·0	2·6
1947	81·5	88·5	69·9	29·0	40·0	40·6	25·1	16·2	15·1	28·9
Mean	70·0	53·0	65·3	56·8	62·7	51·3	29·0	20·7	18·3	17·9

Years with yield below normal.	Intervals.									
	1.	2.	3.	4.	5.	6.	7.	8.	9.	10.
1934	58·0	31·0	36·7	50·0	42·1	32·6	34·0	39·1	45·7	31·0
1936	89·0	61·7	66·0	49·0	45·3	26·5	8·0	37·5	46·8	39·0
1939	21·0	27·4	24·3	21·0	11·4	11·2	10·0	6·7	0·3	18·0
1940	69·0	83·2	101·0	105·0	69·8	39·9	33·0	16·9	34·6	33·0
1948	71·6	98·5	80·1	82·7	34·1	24·0	31·0	38·6	38·7	13·9
Mean	61·7	60·3	61·6	61·5	40·5	26·8	28·0	27·7	35·2	26·9

Below are reported the mean differences in mm. between the two groups of years in their various combinations (intervals of time).

Groups.	1.	2.	3.	4.	5.	6.	7.	8.	9.	10.
I	70·0	53·0	65·3	56·8	62·7	51·3	29·0	20·7	18·3	17·9
II	61·7	60·3	61·6	61·5	40·5	26·8	28·0	27·7	35·2	26·9
Difference	8·3	− 7·3	3·7	− 4·7	22·2	24·5	1·0	− 7·0	− 16·9	− 9·0

The greatest differences are found for the fifth and sixth intervals, from the 11th June to 20th July, over a period of 40 days. On the other hand, from phenological data at hand, we find 18th July as the mean date for the beginning of flowering; it therefore becomes evident that the critical period is to be referred to the flowering phase.

Even though rains can be considered useful after flowering has set-in, the critical period may, without further ado, be limited to the 30 days preceding flowering. At this time the processes of development increase in intensity from day to day, when the fruit-bearing branches rapidly develop, and the processes of flowering and fructification result in a high absorption of water. Therefore the plant becomes particularly susceptible to water deficiencies at this time.

Although we have not a mass of data, the figures are clearly defined, and it has been possible to calculate, in a first approximation, the equivalent for drought during the critical period of the cotton plant. This is 38 mm.

We must now point out the decidedly negative action of the rains from 21st July to the end of August, having a maximum effect at the ninth interval, when the mean precipitation during the period of 21st July to 20th August is 18·3 mm. in the years when the yield is above normal and 35·2 mm. in the year when the yield is below normal, the difference being 16·9 mm.

During this interval the very delicate processes of pollination, fertilisation and of setting occur, and, as we can say in general

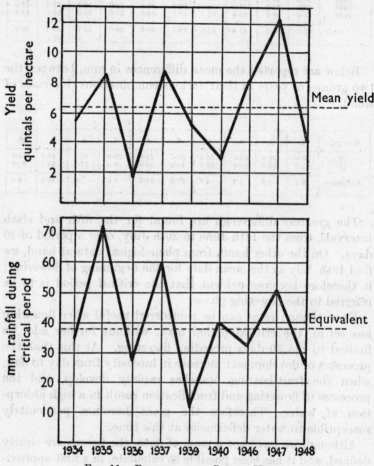

FIG. 11. RAINFALL AND COTTON YIELD.

for all crops, they take place in the most favourable conditions when the sky is clear and luminous.

Except for the year 1939, when the yield was evidently low owing to drought throughout the whole vegetative period, it becomes possible (with some reservation in consideration of the not very numerous figures available) to fix the equivalent for excess in approximately 34 mm.

The two critical periods having opposite characteristics, drought and excess thus follow one another, the first in the interval from 21st June to 20th July and the second from 21st July to 20th August (see Fig. 11).

Critical Period with Respect to Temperature

Since mean temperatures never reach such values as to be harmful through excess, we limit our research to the study of an eventual negative action due to deficient temperature, examining the period May–June.

Temperatures are split up in groups corresponding to the following eleven intervals :

(1) first, second and third 10-day periods of May;
(2) second and third of May;
(3) second and third of May, and first of June;
(4) third of May and first of June;
(5) third of May, and first and second of June;
(6) first, second and third of June;
(7) second and third of June;
(8) second and third of June, and first of July;
(9) third of June and first of July;
(10) third of June, and first and second of July;
(11) first, second and third of July.

In the following tables are given the mean temperatures at the station of Skoplje for the eleven combinations, while the years are divided into two groups : above and below normal yield.

Years with yield above normal.	Intervals.										
	1.	2.	3.	4.	5.	6.	7.	8.	9.	10.	11.
	° C.	° C.	° C.	° C.	° C.	° C.	° C.	° C.	° C.	° C.	° C.
1935	16·8	18·8	20·3	21·9	22·8	23·0	22·9	23·0	22·2	22·9	23·7
1937	17·6	19·2	20·1	20·6	21·3	22·3	22·5	23·3	22·1	22·1	23·0
1946	18·0	18·7	19·6	20·1	20·7	22·1	22·4	25·5	24·6	24·6	25·9
1947	17·4	17·8	19·0	20·2	19·9	20·7	20·3	21·7	22·9	22·9	23·3
Mean	17·4	18·6	19·7	20·7	21·2	22·0	22·0	23·4	22·9	23·1	23·9

Years with yield below normal.	Intervals.										
	1.	2.	3.	4.	5.	6.	7.	8.	9.	10.	11.
	° C.	° C.	° C.	° C.	° C.	° C.	° C.	° C.	° C.	° C.	° C.
1934	18·0	18·8	19·6	19·7	22·7	20·6	24·7	24·6	24·7	22·2	23·4
1936	16·6	16·6	17·7	17·7	18·5	20·1	21·3	22·4	23·6	24·6	25·8
1939	17·5	17·9	18·3	18·3	19·3	19·8	23·3	23·9	25·1	25·6	25·8
1940	15·5	16·3	16·5	17·5	18·9	21·9	21·3	21·6	21·4	22·4	23·9
1948	17·8	18·4	17·6	17·4	18·8	18·9	20·2	20·7	20·2	21·3	22·8
Mean	17·0	17·6	17·9	18·1	19·6	20·2	22·1	22·6	23·0	23·2	24·3

Below are reported the mean differences between the two groups of years in their different combinations (intervals of time).

Groups.	1.	2.	3.	4.	5.	6.	7.	8.	9.	10.	11.
	° C.	° C.	° C.	° C.	° C.	° C.	° C.	° C.	° C.	° C.	° C.
I	17·4	18·6	19·7	20·7	21·2	22·0	22·0	23·4	22·9	23·1	23·9
II	17·0	17·6	17·9	18·1	19·6	20·2	22·1	22·6	23·0	23·2	24·3
Differences	0·4	1·0	1·6	2·6	1·6	1·8	−0·1	0·8	−0·1	−0·1	−0·4

The greatest difference, which is 2·6°, corresponds to the fourth combination, i.e. for the interval between 21st May and 10th June, with the mean temperature of 20·7° in the years having the yield above normal, and 18·1° in those with yields below normal. The yield in fibre is therefore in direct relation to temperature and the coefficient of correlation is very high : 0·809. We can thus speak of a true critical period with respect to cold in the 20 days preceding the appearance of the floral buds : this generally takes place around the 11th June.

In this critical interval, and from the very first stages of development of the plant, the high and continually increasing temperature favours the preparatory processes for the sound formation of floral buds, which generally make their appearance after the fourth to sixth leaves have been formed. Low temperatures, which slow up these processes, would, from the very beginning, render the normal development of the floral ramifications difficult. The equivalent for thermic deficiency is very high, 19·7° C. and gives a measure of the thermic requirements of this plant (see Fig. 12).

The researches have therefore enabled us to establish, for cotton, three critical periods : two for rain and one for temperature.

(1) In the 30 days preceding blooming, cotton is particularly

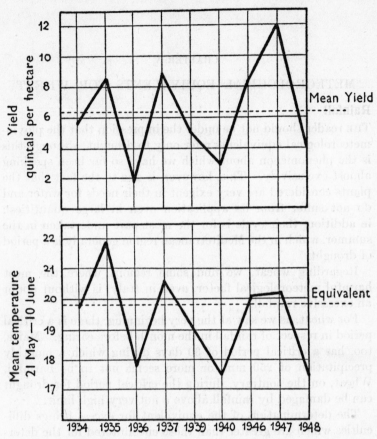

FIG. 12. TEMPERATURE AND COTTON YIELD.

sensitive to water deficiency, the phenomenon acting strongly on the entity of the yield. The equivalent for drought in this critical period is 38 mm.

(2) During the impollination, fertilisation and setting phases, the plant requires dry and clear weather, and is highly susceptible to excess of rainfall. The equivalent for excess is therefore very low, being 34 mm.

(3) In the 20 days preceding the appearance of floral buds, low temperatures can notably lower the yield. The corresponding equivalent for thermic deficiency is 19·7° C. (mean temperature).

G

CHAPTER V

METEOROLOGICAL EQUIVALENTS FOR WHEAT

Rainfall

THE reader should not be under the impression that the pluvio-meteorological equivalents refer only to drought, although this is the phenomenon about which we have so far been speaking almost exclusively. This, however, is due to the fact that the plants considered are very exigent in their needs for water and do not suffer from its application even in large quantities : in addition, their cycle is for the most part undertaken in the summer, which in the Mediterranean region generally is a period of drought.

Regarding wheat, we find some regions where the most harmful meteorological factor, even in Italy, is without doubt an excessive rainfall.

For wheat, as we saw at the very beginning, there is a critical period in respect of rainfall in the month before earing. Maize, too, has a critical period of 30 days during which a monthly precipitation of 250 mm. or more seems not to be harmful. Wheat, on the contrary, during the critical period for drought can be damaged by rainfall above a not very high limit.

The determination of the equivalent for excess brings difficulties which are greater than those encountered for the determination of the equivalent for drought. Drought, although in different measure, behaves in such a way that its action is always negative. Excess rainfall, however, even if on the one hand it damages the plant,[1] does on the other hand assure a sufficient quantity of water to satisfy all the plant's needs. It therefore becomes understandable that a good harvest is not compatible with a regime of drought, while with rainfall, even though excessive, a good harvest is obtainable, in that the losses through excess are compensated, at least in part, by the advantages which abundant water supplies afford.

[1] One of the most harmful consequences of excessive rains is certainly represented by the elimination of nitrogenous compounds which are lost in depth, or can be washed away by streaming waters.

The equivalent for excess rainfall, in the month before earing, is equal to 116 mm.

The determination of this same equivalent in the month after earing is rendered ever more difficult.

In this, as in the interval before earing, rainfall is undoubtedly advantageous in being still able to exercise a beneficial action on the intrinsic productivity of the plant until the yellowing of the leaves and culms.

On the other hand, these rains can prove very harmful and give rise to lodging and to the spread of rust, the entity and intensity of which are not proportional to the quantity of rainfall. In fact, a downpour of 5–6 mm. accompanied by strong wind may cause total lodging for wheats, while 20–25 mm. of no particular intensity more evenly distributed in time and with no wind, leaves the plants erect. As for rust, it is well known that a slight fog or drizzle can be sufficient to cause violent attacks of this disease under favourable thermic conditions.

On the other hand, it is evident that, on the whole, an increase in total precipitations in the month after earing will increase the probability of conditions which bring attacks of rust and lodging.

Beyond certain limits, therefore, the negative action of rainfall will undoubtedly clearly emerge, making possible the determination of the equivalent for excess in spite of wide interference and the mixing of positive and negative results. This equivalent is, in fact, 92 mm. (see Fig. 13).

In the graph the black circlets (poor harvest through excess) are naturally massed together in the higher portion, the white ones (abundant harvest) in the lower, while the mixed zone, for the above-mentioned reasons, is enclosed within a broader band than that found when determining the equivalents for drought.

Fig. 13 clearly illustrates the situation.

In the month before earing, the water requirements of the plant gradually increase, more so the nearer one gets to the phase of maximum weight. At this point the plant's water requirements gradually diminish until the time comes when the organism can no longer utilise further applications of water, and the plant has turned yellow.

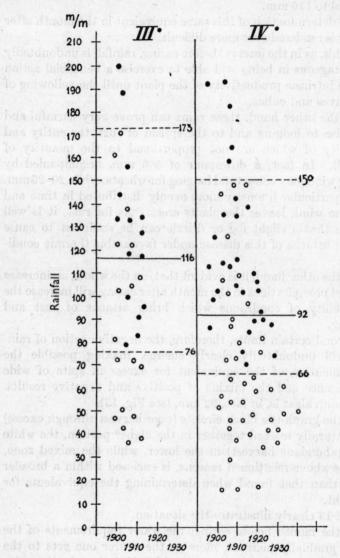

FIG. 13. EQUIVALENT OF EXCESSIVE RAIN FOR WHEAT IN THE THIRD AND FOUTH SUB-PERIOD.

Hence the existence of two different equivalents for excess in the month before (116 mm.) and in the month after earing (92 mm.). The plant in its fourth sub-period uses less and less water, and it is evident that the negative action of rain will show itself sooner than in other sub-periods, and the total precipitation will be less than that causing excess in the preceding sub-period.

.   .   .   .   .

Similar situations are found for the equivalent for deficiency, which in the month before earing, is 40 mm., but in the month after earing falls to 15 mm.

In perfect analogy the equivalent for drought for maize during the critical period reaches 46 mm., while in the month immediately after it is a mere 18 mm., as is clearly seen in the graph (see Fig. 14).

It is during the third and fourth sub-periods that rainfall displays its more intense action on the yield, both in the positive and in the negative sense.

Certain fields of wheat at the beginning of the spring may appear in a poor state as a consequence of drought and winter adversities, but in spite of this, they are able to recover and produce abundant yields, provided that the rain and temperature regimes are favourable from the resumption of growth until harvest.

.   .   .   .   .

The equivalent for excess during the second sub-period (winter rest) has been established at 60 mm., and this figure refers to the month of February in particular, even though not very abundant rainfall causes the development of roots close to the surface of the soil, thus exposing the plant in greater measure to the eventual negative influence of spring–summer drought and, at the same time, making the crop more inclined to lodging.

Drought in winter is not too dangerous, since in that season neither transpiration nor evaporation is intensive. On the other hand, a relative water deficiency in the most superficial layer of the earth has an undoubted positive action, in that it

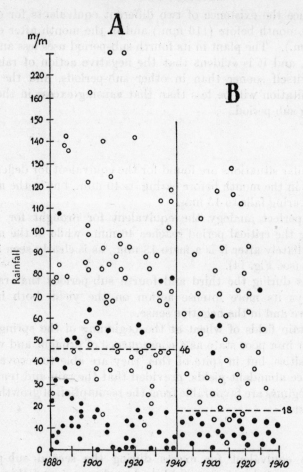

FIG. 14. EQUIVALENTS OF DROUGHT FOR MAIZE IN THE CRITICAL PERIOD (SECOND SUB-PERIOD) AND DURING THE MATURING OF THE GRAIN.

causes a development of the root apparatus in depth, thus rendering the plant more resistant to drought. It is not so strange, therefore, that the equivalent for drought in the second sub-period has been fixed at the low figure of 20 mm.

Rainfall and the Water Balance in Winter

The existence of such a low equivalent is understandable if it is borne in mind that during the winter the relationship between the amount of rain and moisture reserves in the soil is quite different from this relationship in summer, when higher rates of evaporation and transpiration cause rapid dispersal of water.

The four months January–April in 1949 proved to be particularly poor in rainfall in the territory of Perugia. In this case we therefore have favourable conditions for the study of the water balance in the soil in a regime of scanty precipitation in winter.

Below is given the rainfall per 10-day period for 1949, together with the average for the 25 years period 1901–25. The mean temperatures are also given, as it is well known that they are directly related to the losses of water through evaporation.

Rainfall and Mean Temperature—Perugia

	Average rainfall, mm.		Mean temperature, 0° C.	
	1901–25.	1949.	1901–25.	1949.
January :				
1st ten-day period .	20·3	30·10	4·2	8·77
2nd ,, ,, .	12·9	5·50	4·2	5·67
3rd ,, ,, .	17·7	0·00	4·0	5·47
February :				
1st ten-day period .	24·9	15·55	4·4	2·36
2nd ,, ,, .	25·8	2·45	4·7	6·10
3rd ,, ,, .	19·1	3·85	5·4	9·68
March :				
1st ten-day period .	32·0	0·90	6·9	11·53
2nd ,, ,, .	24·2	0·00	7·6	15·24
3rd ,, ,, .	25·0	19·00	9·3	16·63
April :				
1st ten-day period .	32·0	0·90	10·1	11·53
2nd ,, ,, .	24·2	0·00	10·8	15·24
3rd ,, ,, .	25·0	19·00	12·2	16·63

Precipitation was evidently very scarce, while temperatures, due to the inverse correlation between precipitations and temperature, were, on the whole, above normal : in consequence the negative effect caused by drought was accentuated still further. The division between the dry and the wet layers of the soil may be taken at 14·25% (the mean of numerous determinations). Below are given the percentages of humidity at different depths :

Percentage Humidity in the Soil

Date of observation.	Depth, cm.			
	0–10.	20–30.	45–55.	90–100.
22nd December, 1948 . .	18·3	18·5	18·7	18·8
5th January, 1949 . .	21·8	22·5	18·8	18·1
13th January . . .	21·8	21·1	18·5	18·9
21st January . . .	22·2	18·6	18·2	18·5
22nd February . . .	19·4	17·6	16·4	15·3
4th March	19·6	18·5	—	17·6
15th March . . .	21·4	19·9	17·4	17·8
13th April . . .	14·3	15·2	16·0	17·0

In spite of an obvious deficiency of rainfall, the humidity in the soil never drops below the limit for drought, not even at a depth of 10 cm.

It may be of interest to compare situations in cold and warm seasons respectively.

The following table refers to the rainless period from 15th March to 15th April (cold season) and to the practically dry period between 22nd June and 7th July (warm season), and gives a good picture of the effect of temperature on soil humidity.

Percentage Humidity in Soil

	Depth in cm.				Mean air temperature, ° C.
	0–10.	20–30.	45–55.	90–100.	
Cold season .	14·3	15·2	16·4	17·0	8·83
Hot season .	7·2	9·3	13·5	15·1	22·77

While with total lack of rainfall during the cold season the dry limit is never reached, in the hot season we pass below this point, up to the 44–55-cm. layer, and it is only at a depth of 90–100 cm. that we find 15·1, a value which is just inside the limit for the humid zone (namely, 14·25%).

The above clearly illustrates why it is that the drought equivalent becomes so low in winter—20 mm. per month.

This manifestly is so not only because the plant grows very slowly in this interval which limits its losses through transpiration, but also because water is retained in the soil for a longer period owing to the big reduction in evaporation caused by low temperatures.

.   .   .   .   .   .

In the first sub-period, which practically includes the interval from a month before sowing to a month after sowing, we find 205 and 50 mm., respectively, as equivalents for excess and deficiency.

Naturally here it is not only a question of rainfall acting directly on the germination and initial development of the plant, but precipitation is also essential in a region with a dry summer in order to work the soil and prepare the seed-bed.

In the Mediterranean region, where conditions in winter are never too hard, excess rainfall or drought at the time of sowing is not liable to cause great damage.

With the exclusion of highly clayey soils, all others can be sown even in rain, while a state of drought can only help to delay the period of sowing; in both cases, provided that both winter and spring conditions are favourable, excellent yields may be obtained.

In northern regions, however, and in general in countries with an accentuated continental climate where winter adversities repeat themselves frequently and intensely, those conditions which have acted negatively on the initial growth of the plant manifest themselves in the successive phases of development with a decidedly negative effect on the yield.

At the station of Mariinsk (Saratov), as may be seen from Fig. 15, a direct relationship is found between the precipitation in August–September in the year preceding the harvest and the yield in grain of winter rye.

The summer–autumnal rains are in this case useful because they make early sowing possible, resulting in a development of the young plants before the autumnal frosts.

Development becomes poor when sowing is delayed, especially for the root, thus rendering the plant less able to resist winter adversities, and especially sudden drops in temperature, and the alternate occurrences of frosts and thawing.

The Voronex meteoro-agricultural report for the years 1908-9 records the following : in the middle of November—i.e. when the first autumnal frosts appear—the plants sown early (between 1st and 16th August) were already well developed and tillered and

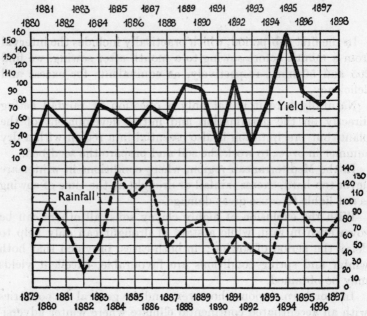

Fig. 15.   Yield of Winter Rye and the Rains of the Preceding Summer.

suffered no damage.   The second sowing, however (first 10-day period of September), was somewhat damaged, while the last (end of September to beginning of October) was practically destroyed by drought and frost.

The diagram (Fig. 16) gives a clear picture of the water balance for wheat in the different sub-periods from the sowing up to the harvest.

Temperature

We have until now spoken of rainfall as if temperature presented no contrasting action either in the sense of deficiency or of excess.

In fact, in the Mediterranean region the thermic factor is, on the whole, less important than the water factor.

If, however, the whole area of distribution of wheat is considered, from the Scandinavian peninsula, where the limiting factor is just thermic deficiency, to the pre-Saharian zone,

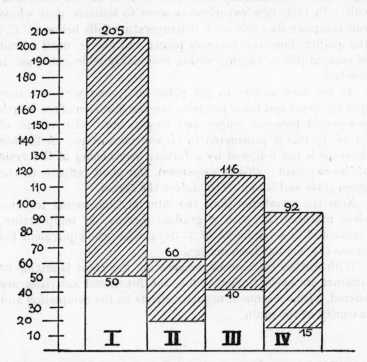

FIG. 16. THE PLUVIOMETRIC EQUIVALENTS OF WHEAT IN THE FOUR
SUB-PERIODS.

The shaded part is the normal for each sub-period, that is the precipitation lying between the equivalents for excess and deficiency.

where the limiting factor is excess temperature (even for irrigated crops), the dominating action of the thermic factor near the equatorial and polar limits clearly emerges, and has enabled us to establish the equivalents for excess and deficiency.

These are of 24° C. and 14° C., respectively, with reference to the mean temperature in the sub-period comprised between the earing phase and complete maturity. Their negative action, however, especially for low temperatures (i.e. deficiency), makes itself particularly felt on the quality rather than on the quantity of the product.

This circumstance renders an exact determination of the equivalent for deficiency in respect of yield all the more difficult. In fact, new experiments seem to indicate that wheat can complete its cycle even if temperature falls below 14° C. : the quality, however, becomes poorer and poorer, until a limit of compatibility, varying within reasonably wide extremes, is reached.

As we draw nearer to the polar limit, and with a consequently lower and lower temperature, the duration of the fourth sub-period becomes longer and longer, until with means of 13–14° C. this is protracted to 70 and more days. A further decrease is not followed by a further lengthening of the cycle of development; this is suspended, the plant remains in the green state and is unable to mature the kernel.

Near the equatorial limit the interval from earing to complete maturity is, with a gradual increase in temperature, contracted to a minimum of 30 days, when the equivalent for excess (24° C.) has been reached.

With further increase in temperature the plant is unable to contract its cycle further, while the functional activities are altered, with consequent negative effects on the completion and maturity of the grain.

Still referring to temperature, the peculiar behaviour of winter and spring forms of wheat in relation to the intensity of tillering is worthy of note.

The factor which dominates in regard to tillering is without doubt temperature, as it becomes quite evident from the results of geographical trials organised by me and to which I shall refer later.

The situation, however, is quite different, according to whether we consider winter or spring forms. For the latter, dividing the reporting stations into three groups according to the intensity of tillering, we have :

	Tillering per plant.	Mean temperature, ° C.
Great intensity . .	6·50	15·8
Intermediate . . .	4·08	12·3
Scarce	2·50	10·8

The positive influence of temperature cannot be questioned : the higher it is, the more intense is tillering. By calculating the coefficient of correlation we obtain a decidedly positive value of 0·626. Although the coefficient of correlation is clear proof of temperature's dominating action, there is no doubt that rainfall also has a bearing on tillering.

In the reports from some stations the rains evenly distributed over the tillering period are very often looked upon as the most favourable meteorological phenomena for tillering.

But the effects of moisture are most clearly seen at the stations of Algiers and Rabat, where, at equal temperatures, we find widely differing situations as to water availability in two series of plots—one irrigated, and one dry.

	Dry.	Irrigated.
Algiers . . .	6·25	7·88 tillers per plant
Rabat . . .	3·92	4·63 „ „ „

In any case, it remains clear that, at least within the limits of variation of the meteorological values obtained from a great number of stations, the dominant action is to be attributed to temperature.

The following table gives the figures relative to tillering in respect of temperature, for winter wheats :

Station.	Year.	Mean tillering per plant.	Mean temperature, ° C.
Waltdorf . . .	1931	6·28	−2·30
Rastatt . . .	1932	4·98	−1·85
Voll . . .	1931	4·56	−1·40
Szeged . . .	1932	4·52	0·20
Forus . . .	1931	4·20	0·50
Forus . . .	1932	3·77	0·50
Rastatt . . .	1931	3·29	7·86
Halle . . .	1931	2·55	12·10

Contrary to what happens for spring forms, tillering would here be inversely proportional to temperature, it being more intense the lower the mean temperature.

The maximum mean of 6·28 tillers per plant is obtained at −2·3° C.

We will reconsider the peculiar behaviour of winter and spring forms when dealing with the process of vernalisation.

Hot Spells

Up to the present we have considered only the mean temperature. However, in the regions where thermic excesses are a common occurrence, the most important negative phenomenon for wheat is undoubtedly represented by hot spells, which are a function of thermic maxima, and not of mean temperatures.

In fact, in the large majority of cases thermic excesses are identifiable with maximum temperatures, in that they are the direct cause of the shrivelling of the grain, the most apparent symptom of a hot spell.

The formation of the kernel is suddenly interrupted, and the almost empty grain is reduced to a mass of cellulose with a very scanty gluten and starch content.

Hot spells are found in hot, dry climates with particular frequency and intensity. They can, however, also affect irrigated cultures, proving that lack of water is not always the essential factor determining the appearance of the phenomenon. When those factors accentuating transpiration reach an intensity such that the roots, although pumping water fully from the soil, are unable to compensate the mass lost through transpiration, heat-stroke occurs even in soils saturated with water.

In the three hundred and thirty-eight cases which I examined and in which a hot spell acted as the principal negative factor on the yield, the temperature was in no case inferior to 28° C.

In the province of Alicante (Spain) the heat-stroke caused by the lowest high temperature of all the three hundred and thirty-eight cases examined was recorded, namely :

Maximum temperature = 28·6° C.
Direction and intensity of wind = south-west violent.

The report says : " After a long and intense period of drought which lasted from winter until the first decade of March, there were abundant rains which bettered the situation in wheat fields whose appearance at the end of May was very promising. The harvest, however, was very poor owing to a hot spell brought on by high temperature (28·6° C.) with strong winds in the month of June."

With maximum temperatures below 28° C. the shrivelling of the grain does not take place irrespective of the intensity of the other factors which can affect the appearance of the phenomena, such as wind, low relative humidity, etc.

In these cases the environmental adverse factors, and more particularly drought, do not impede the process of maturity, but only diminish the size of the grain, which is much smaller, but is still compact and well formed.

In 1913 in the province of Coruña (Spain) the formation and maturity of the kernel took place regularly in spite of the hot, dry regime, the very low relative humidity and the violence of the wind, and this thanks to the fact that temperature did not rise above the limit of 28° C. We find :

Maximum temperature	= 27·7° C.
Rainfall during the formation and maturing of the grain	= 0·3 mm.
Direction and intensity of the wind	= south-west violent.

The maximum temperature—28° C.—would therefore represent the threshold for hot spell. (Compare Alicante 28·6° C. and La Coruña 27·7° C.)

On the other hand, in several stations of central Europe very high temperatures were observed—up to 39° C.—without in any way altering the normal evolution and maturing of the grain.

Peak temperatures in themselves are not therefore sufficient to bring on heat-stroke—we must also have wind as an indispensable integrating factor.

When temperature has risen above 28° C. a violent wind and an atmospheric condition favourable to transpiration and evaporation are necessary to cause the shrivelling of the grain.

When temperatures, however, are well above the thermic threshold a hot spell can make itself apparent with relatively moderate winds and in a regime of quite high relative humidity.

In conclusion, we have mapped out the meteorological framework of hot spells and have isolated the different atmospheric factors involved, separating them from those which until now have been partially confused with heat-stroke.

It is well known that hot spells are especially harmful throughout the whole Mediterranean region and south-eastern Russia, where a heat-wave accompanied by dry winds in the third and fourth quadrant can in a few hours render vain all hope of an abundant harvest.

The thermic threshold for hot-spells stroke (28° C.) must not be confused with thermic equivalent of these in the Euro-African region, which would appear to be around 32° C. This implies that in these regions the atmospheric complex (wind, rainfall and relative humidity in general) appear with such values and in such combinations that they cause hot spells only when temperature reaches a maximum of 32° C.

Here, too, as always, the equivalent cannot be used to verify situations in particular cases, but only to value their frequency. It is in fact evident that above and below the line corresponding to 32° C. we have several abnormal cases of heat-stroke with lower maxima, and an equal number without hot spell, although having maxima above 32° C.

Geslin would appear to have determined a critical period for wheat in relation to hot spell, which shows itself by the shrivelling of the grain. On a graph (Fig. 17) we plot on the abscissæ the values for the factor K, which is the product of mean daily temperatures by the square root of the corresponding global radiation and on the ordinate the quantity of water contained in 1,000 grains.

The curve which shows the variation of this value may be divided into three segments :

(1) *Rapid Increase of the Aqueous Value.*—This corresponds to the phase of cell multiplication up to the moment of the grain reaching its complete form.

(2) *Horizontal.*—The quantity of water is constant; in this phase the active condensation of proteic and amilaceous substances takes place.

(3) *Rapid Decrease.*—This corresponds to the purely physical phase of the drying of the grain.

Excessive temperatures may cause injury at the time of setting and during the cell multiplication phase, but shrinkage of grain can, of course, be observed only when the kernel has reached a certain size and its complete form.

In the third stage—i.e. when drying of the kernel is already under way—damage through hot spells is not to be expected.

Geslin has therefore come to the conclusion that we can take as a critical period for hot spells that 10-day interval which runs from the formation of the grain to the initial stages of

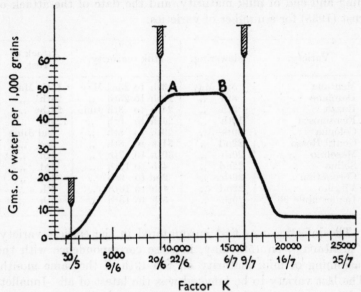

FIG. 17. WATER CONTENT IN 1,000 WHEAT GRAINS.

maturity, during which the absolute water content in 1,000 kernels would remain constant.   From the beginning until the end of the said period the effects of hot spells gradually lessen, and according to calculations made by the said Geslin, the loss attributable to the adverse phenomenon is of 50% in the first part of the horizontal segment of the curve, while at the centre of the same this has already been reduced to 20%.

Critical Period for Rust

In order to make the representation and the evaluation of bio-ambiental relationships of grain yield more complete, I want to refer to the experimental results obtained by Rocchi for the critical period of wheat in relation to rust.

H

This period clearly makes itself apparent a little time before the beginning of milk maturity. The existence of such a critical period is proved by the fact that the attack does not take place in all varieties at the same time, but at different moments, according to the degree of earliness, and always coincides with the beginning of milk maturity.

The following table shows the dates of blooming, the beginning and end of milk maturity, and the date of the attack of rust (1935) for a number of varieties.

Variety.	Flowering.	Milk maturity.	Attack of rust.
Mentana . .	5th May	13th to 23rd May	15th May
Damiano . .	8th ,,	18th to 25th ,,	24th ,,
Razza . .	9th ,,	24th to 8th June	24th ,,
Fieramosca .	10th ,,	24th to 6th ,,	24th ,,
Cologna . .	20th ,,	29th to 8th ,,	2nd June
Gentil Rosso .	22nd ,,	31st to 8th ,,	2nd ,,
Masolino . .	20th ,,	30th to 7th ,,	4th ,,
Solina . .	22nd ,,	4th to 13th ,,	3rd ,,
Coronation . .	26th ,,	2nd to 9th ,,	3rd ,,
Virgilio . .	22nd ,,	4th to 10th ,,	4th ,,
Inallettabile 96 .	26th ,,	5th to 15th ,,	6th ,,

The infection was first encountered in the earliest variety, " Mentana ", on 15th May, in close correspondence with the beginning of milk maturity on the 13th of the same month. The last variety to be infected was the latest of all—Innallettabile 96—on the 6th June, and therefore 22 days after " Mentana ", and in this case also in close agreement with phase of milk maturity, which started on the 5th June.

Other varieties occupy an intermediate position, and the date on which rust first appears always corresponds to the milk-maturity phase.

We may affirm that :

(1) The critical period in relation to rust coincides with the milk maturity for which temperatures superior to the threshold for rust development are required. Thus during the critical period temperature is generally sufficient to permit an outburst of the infection.

(2) Once the thermic threshold is reached, the relative humidity becomes the most important factor involved.

Referring to the 2-month period May to June 1935, the earliest variety—

(a) *Mentana* entered the milk maturity phase on 13th May. On that same day the humidity from preceding lower values rose to 89%. Two days after, on 15th May, rust appeared, although humidity was already declining rapidly.

(b) *Damiano Chiesa Variety*. This began milk maturity on 18th May : humidity on the 18th, 19th, 20th and 21st was very low—40%, 32%, 38% and 45% respectively. On the 22nd it suddenly increased, reaching 67%, and 93% on the 23rd, while rust appeared on 24th May.

(c) *Gentil Rosso*. This began milk maturity on 31st May, on which day the relative humidity was of 46%. On the following day—1st June—this touched on 71%, and on the 2nd June rust appeared.

(d) *Inallettabile* 96. This began milk maturity on 5th June; on this and on the following day humidity remained high (73–74%) and rust appeared on 6th June.

The positive effects brought about by a not abundant but widely distributed rainfall is noticeable in the majority of cases. Situations are found, however, in which the attack took place in total absence of rainfall, thanks to the high degree of humidity. In 1934, "Mentana" began milk maturity on 20th May, and rust made its appearance on the 27th, after humidity had risen to 70% and 83%, respectively, on the 25th and 26th. From 18th May there had been no precipitation.

Data for 1933 and 1934 confirm what has been said for 1935 and permit us to draw the following conclusions :

(1) Rust appears whenever in a favourable thermic regime a degree of humidity above 70% (hygroscopic threshold for attacks from *Puccinia*) is registered.

(2) Attack is observed not more than 2 days after the said humidity has been reached.

(3) At the milky stage the plant is most vulnerable to rust.

(4) The positive action of small quantities of rain is quite evident. However, in certain cases infection occurs with total lack of rainfall.

Similarly, Prof. H. Silveira Grillo (Brazil), observed that *Phytomonas linearis*, a bacterium producing the pathological condition in sugar-cane known as " red stripe " is particularly virulent only when relative humidity reaches 85% and the plant is about 2 or 3 months old. When humidity is below this limit the infection is of no particular economic importance, and the symptoms consist solely in the appearance of a red stripe close to the vascular bundles in the leaf.

The discovery of the critical period eliminates many causes of confusion and allows us to understand the behaviour of the plant on the one hand (degree of resistance or of receptivity) and of the environment on the other with regard to the intensity of the infection. The consequences of the infection can be quite different in view of the following four combinations :

(1) ambiental conditions favourable to the development of rust in the period of maximum sensitivity of the plant (strong virulent attack);
(2) favourable ambiental conditions for rust, but the plant is at a point of less susceptibility to the attack (light attack);
(3) ambiental conditions contrary to the development of rust, plant highly receptive (light attack);
(4) unfavourable ambiental condition for rust during the intervals of minor sensibility of the plant (practically no attack).

A very resistant variety, attacked by rust during the critical period, will suffer much more than a variety susceptible to the disease but which, at the moment of infection, is not in its critical period.

From the above it will come as no surprise to find that in a given year highly susceptible plants may remain immune to rust while resistant varieties can be considerably damaged.

In Florence in 1931 the " Mentana " variety, very early and usually resistant to rust, was sorely hit by the parasite, while

" Inallettabile 96 ", well known for its susceptibility suffered only from a light attack because, thanks to its tardiness, the critical phase fell in a dry moment : for " Mentana " this came a month earlier, at a time when high temperature, fogs and frequent drizzles prevailed.

In 1932, on the contrary, early varieties suffered no harm, even the most sensitive, such as " Ardito " and " Villa Glori ", and this thanks to the dry season during the period of greatest susceptibility.   There followed a hot wet period favourable to the infection, which sorely tried even the most resistant late varieties such as " Cologna " and more especially " Rieti ", whose critical period coincided with a meteorological situation favourable to the development of rust.

CHAPTER VI

DETERMINATION OF THE EQUIVALENTS FOR CERTAIN WOODY PLANTS

PART of the water from the atmosphere penetrates into the soil and there forms the water reserves which the plant utilises during its development. Rainfall can be a source of direct and immediate supply of these reserves. However, the plant can also make use of rains fallen previously, provided that in the interval from the falling of rain and its utilisation by the plant the humidity in the soil has not fallen below certain limits.

This period naturally varies, and can be longer or shorter, according to the nature of the soils and the amount of preceding rain. It cannot, however, be extended beyond certain restricted limits.

We shall see in greater detail later on, that after abundant rains have saturated the soil, a fortnight is sufficient to reach the point at which the exhaustion of moisture reserves is indicated by the wilting of maize (30 days in the most resistant soils, and 8 days in those most susceptible to drought).

So much for herbaceous plants. Woody plants present a different picture. From experimental research carried out by Briccoli in Perugia it emerges that after a dry and clear 3-month period ending in October, drought was apparent only up to 1 metre in depth in the soil, and at this time the first autumnal drizzles were already falling. The passage from dry to moist soil is marked, in that over a vertical distance of 7–8 cm. an increase of the humidity from 6% to 14% is observed.

Woody plants, which always have deep penetrating roots (a metre into the soil) can therefore obtain their water from the reserves in the humid layer during the dry spring–summer period and so utilise the rains which have fallen a considerable time before—i.e. in the autumnal–winter period.

VINE

For the vine, as already stated, the vegetative period is divided into the following sub-periods :

(1) from the end of the vintage to budding;
(2) from budding to the beginning of flowering;
(3) from the beginning of flowering to the completed set;
(4) from the completed set to the onset of ripening (first stages of maturity : grapes take colour);
(5) from the onset of ripening to complete maturity;
(6) from the beginning to the end of the harvest.

It is during the fourth and fifth sub-periods, from setting to maturity, that drought can negatively affect the yield both from a quantitative and qualitative point of view.

The requirements of the plant, however, in relation to rains are very modest during summer, the equivalent for drought being a mere 12 mm., and cases can be quoted in which a very good harvest was obtained with total lack of rainfall in this interval (from the completed set to full maturity).

If we think now of the rapid increase in the mass of fruits during the summer—an increase in weight which necessarily implies the expenditure of large quantities of water—it becomes clear that it cannot be the odd summer precipitations which satisfy the plant's needs.

In reality it is the copious winter–spring precipitation which assures the necessary water for the normal processes of transpiration and assimilation of the vine even when the small amount of water in the topmost soil menaces the development of herbaceous plants.

At Mineo the following is reported for 1906–7 :

(1) precipitations from the end of the harvest to fructification the following year (winter–spring period) : 471 mm.;
(2) precipitations from fructification to complete maturity (summer period) : 4·1 mm.

In spite of the summer drought, 4·1 mm. (practically no rain at all) and the partial withering of leaves as a consequence, the harvest proved to be three times above normal.

When, however, rain is also deficient in the winter–spring

period, drought makes itself felt, exercising its damaging action in full even though the other ambiental factors be favourable.

In Termini Imerese (Sicily) for the years 1907–8 we have :

(1) precipitations from the end of the harvest until fructification (winter–spring period) : 251·9 mm. ;
(2) precipitations from fructification to complete maturity (summer period) : 2·5 mm.

The harvest was very poor.

De Gasperi has calculated that 300 mm. is the minimum precipitation for the winter–spring period up to the flowering phase, in order to have sufficient water reserves in the soil to assure the normal development of the plant during the long rainless summer (300 : 6 = 50 mm. monthly).

Now, even in the driest regions of Italy, it very rarely happens that precipitation falls below this limit, and is the reason why Sicily produces such magnificent grapes and superb wines in spite of the almost constant summer droughts.

In fact, water deficiencies would very rarely make themselves felt were it not for the intervention, from time to time, of strong winds which accentuate transpiration and upset the equilibrium : this is when the roots, although "pumping" water to the aerial portions of the plant at full speed, cannot match the great demand from the foliar transpiring surface, and it is just at such a time that these downpours of a few millimetres of rain may occur : they generally fall after these strong winds have stopped, and are very beneficial, as by lowering the temperature and increasing the humidity of the air they increase turgidity and re-establish the momentarily disturbed water balance.

FIG

The functions of summer rains is yet more clearly shown up by an examination of the data relating to the fig tree.

For the winter interval A–B (November–April) see Table on p. 105.

As may be seen in the graph (Fig. 18), the mixed zone is found between 315 and 540 mm. The line separating an equal number of asymmetric cases corresponds to 367, which,

November–April Rainfall

Abundant harvest.		Poor harvest.	
Year.	Rainfall, mm.	Year.	Rainfall, mm.
Pomarico.		Pomarico.	
1884–85	603	1887–88	215
1893–94	420	1888–89	383
1906–07	536	1892–93	202
		1902–03	185
Cittanova.		1907–08	181
1902–03	366		
1909–10	756		
Reggio Calabria.		Reggio Calabria.	
1880–81	319	1881–82	304
1884–85	417	1886–87	362
Picerno.		Tropea.	
1915–16	420	1913–14	250
Lecce.		Lecce.	
1880–81	340	1904–05	344
1885–86	556	1911–12	306
1888–89	486		
1890–91	416		
1902–03	510		
1903–04	436		
1905–06	431		
Alessano.		Alessano.	
1914–15	635	1909–10	540
		1910–11	437
Catanzaro.		1913–14	237
1880–81	1,060		
Cosenza.			
1880–81	935		

divided by 6 (number of months), gives us 61 mm. as the equivalent for drought in winter.

In order to supply evidence of the effects of summer rains (C–D), we give on p. 107 the figures for several well-situated stations for the interval 11th July to 10th August, which comprises the critical period for the fig tree.

If the rains during the winter have been such that water reserves for the rest of the vegetative period are assured, it is

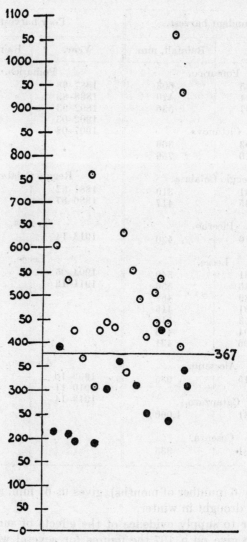

FIG. 18. DROUGHT EQUIVALENT FOR THE FIG IN THE WINTER INTERVAL
(INTERVAL A–B).

Rainfall : 11th July to 10th August

Abundant harvest.		Poor harvest.	
Year.	Rainfall, mm.	Year.	Rainfall, mm.
Pomarico.		Pomarico.	
1885	42·0	1888	3·2
1907	28·0	1889	4·8
1894	15·5	1893	41·0
		1903	6·0
Cittanova.		1908	2·0
1903	4·5		
1910	2·0		
Reggio Calabria.		Reggio Calabria.	
1881	0·0	1882	2·4
1885	15·0	1887	2·0
1893	4·0	1888	0·0
Picerno.		Tropea.	
1916	53·4	1914	3·0
Alessano.		Alessano.	
1915	10·5	1910	0·0
		1911	18·5
		1914	3·0
Lecce.		Lecce.	
1881	6·2	1905	8·0
1886	20·2	1914	0·0
1889	4·6		
1891	14·0		
1903	2·5		
1904	3·5		
1906	16·4		
Catanzaro.			
1881	53·0		
Cosenza.			
1881	67·0		

possible to obtain an abundant harvest even with total absence
of rainfall in summer. This was so in 1903 at Lecce, with
436 mm. in the interval *A–B* and 2·5 mm. only during the
critical period *C–D*.

On the other hand, the precipitation during the critical period
in the two groups of years which presented, respectively, a poor

harvest and a good one is equal to a mean of 6·7 and 19·0 mm., thus demonstrating the positive action of the casual summer rains.   The equivalent for drought would be 9 mm.

The positive action of so slight a quantity of rain finds an explanation when considering certain characteristics of the summer Mediterranean climate.

In this season, as I have said before, dry and very violent winds may blow from Africa, intensifying evaporation to a maximum and also tending to accentuate transpiration, so that the roots, even though absorbing water continually, are not able to supply the exigencies of the intense transpiration, and the leaves become less turgid and present symptoms of withering.   These heat-waves often end with storms and downpours of a few mm., sufficient, however, to freshen up the atmosphere and to dampen the leaf-surfaces, which then resume their turgidity, and the equilibrium between absorption and transpiration is re-established.

This is the function of the small summer rains which give the modest equivalents of 12 mm. for the vine and 9 mm. for the fig.

OLIVE

The bio-hydric problem in the area of distribution of the olive has a different aspect in the southern section and in the northern section of its zone.

In South Italy the thermic situation is so favourable that the plants show continuous growth without an apparent winter rest, and reach such dimensions that they are comparable to the great oaks of the north.

In the Cilento region, plants are able to produce 9–10 quintals of olives, and consequently the imposing figure of 2 qnts. of olive oil are not uncommon.

The powerful trunks and the mass of branches are healthy and whole, and the roots, as we have seen for the vine, penetrate deeply into the soil, and there obtain the necessary water for the normal development of the fruits.   Under such conditions the winter rains are sufficient to assure a good harvest even when the summer is hit by drought.

But nevertheless if summer drought is in many cases compatible with abundant harvest, there is no doubt that in absence of the olive-fly (of which we shall speak later) the rains in summer are generally advantageous to the development of the fruits.

At Lecce, situated in the region where ambiental conditions are particularly favourable to the olive, we have the following values for the sum of precipitations from the completed setting to maturity (July–September) in the two groups of years in which the harvest was, respectively, abundant and poor through drought.

Rainfall in Lecce : July–September

Abundant harvest.		Poor harvest.	
Year.	Rainfall, mm.	Year.	Rainfall, mm.
1880	97	1897	28
1882	70	1903	18
1887	101	1905	46
1888	93	1908	55
1889	88	1910	64
1890	70	1913	65
1891	72	1916	51
1898	123	1917	56
1906	126		
1911	90		
1912	141		
1914	189		
Mean	105	Mean	48

We observe, therefore, two means which are markedly different, and the relationship between them—1 : 2—is clear proof that in the regions under examination, summer droughts have a decidedly negative effect on the final production, and that rainfall in this season, when there are no attacks of fly, acts, on the whole, all the more favourably the more plentiful it is.

During the sub-period of the development of the fruits (from the completed set to the beginning of maturity) the drought equivalent in the province of Lecce is 22 mm. per month.

During the sub-period from the first stages of flowering to fructification, which exactly falls in the months of May and June, an almost identical value is obtained (following the usual method) for the equivalent for drought—namely, 23 mm.

On the other hand, during blooming and fructification, rains may be decisively harmful, there being a very low equivalent for excess—36 mm.

Favourable or normal zones are therefore highly restricted, in having for drought and excess equivalents of 23 and 36 mm., proving that in this interval the plant is particularly sensitive to oscillations of the pluviometric regime both above and below the optimum, which can be fixed round 60 mm. for the 2 months considered (30 mm. monthly).

Near the limit for latitude and altitude of the olive the long winter reduces the possibilities of growth, and moreover, the intensely cold regimes which occur two or three times a century give the plant a vigorous natural pruning which can sometimes extend to primary branches. The result is irregular and poor development of the trees, which present contorted trunks, deeply attacked by " heart rot " and cut into strips longitudinally.

In consequence the root apparatus is reduced and cannot develop the depth it does in South Italy. Moreover, the stagnating water brought about by the abundant winter rains and the fog which forms in the plains and along the valleys, oblige farmers to plant the olive almost exclusively on gravel and the loose sandy soils on slopes facing south-west, with naturally grave consequences in cases of drought.

Hence the existence of a very high positive coefficient of correlation between rainfall in the four months June–September and the yield in olives for the zone of Perugia, situated near the cultural limit for this plant, which reaches a value of no less than 0·86.

It will readily be seen that the equivalent for drought in central Italy, where the culture of the olive is limited to the most permeable soils, will be higher than in South Italy, where the plant is cultivated also in the best soils of the plains.

The following table gives for the period 1881–1940 in Perugia the sums of rains June–September for the two groups of years— those with good harvest and those with very low yields as a consequence of drought.

Rainfall in Perugia : June–September

Abundant harvest.		Poor harvest.	
Year.	Rainfall, mm.	Year.	Rainfall, mm.
1881	236	1890	111
1884	395	1897	142
1888	178	1912	165
1905	260	1917	113
1910	387	1925	156
1915	293	1927	167
1926	261	1931	121
1930	353	1935	188
1933	249		
1934	271		
1937	377		
1938	241		
1940	288		
Mean	291	Mean	145

With these figures as a basis, the partial equivalent for Umbria, determined by the usual process, is 45 mm. monthly (against 22 mm. in South Italy), a measure of the negative influence exercised by the dry, stony soils on the slopes, where it is necessary to put the olive-groves in order to combat the negative action of waterlogging in the winter period.

Under these particular agrogeological environmental conditions not even the excesses of rainfall during the blooming phase are observed : on the contrary, abundant and violent precipitations at this time are useful because by their mechanical action they liberate the inflorescences from the waxy involucre of *Euphyllura olivina*, Costa, which tends to suffocate them.

The Atmospheric Environment and the Diffusion of Dacus oleae

Let us now consider a different aspect of the problem of bio-atmospheric relationships for the olive, when rainfall can at the same time be both beneficial and damaging. This is the case of summer rains and their effects on the diffusion of the olive-fly.

Although the deep-water reserves in good soils are generally sufficient to meet the olive's requirements during the summer drought, there is no doubt that rains in this season are decidedly favourable to the development of fruits, as already seen for Lecce, but this is only when a serious setback does not appear—namely, the fly, whose advent is favoured by rains and abundant moisture.

Vollono has determined the coefficient of correlation between summer rains and yield of olives in the province of Naples, and it appears that this coefficient is practically nil, as if rainfall had nothing whatever to do, either positively or negatively, with the fructification and yield of the plant.

The apparent paradox is explained by the action of rain, which, although directly positive in its effects on the fruits, is indirectly negative, in that it favours the attack of *Dacus*. The two actions tend to balance one another.

Separating the years into two groups—the first group of those years in which there was fly and the second of those in which there was no particular damage from the insect—and calculating the coefficient of correlation between the yield in olives and the sum of rains, we get a negative value for the infested years of $r = -0.63$, and a very high positive value for the years in which the fly did not appear of $r = +0.81$: the undoubtedly favourable action of rainfall on the harvest is demonstrated, but only when, for one reason or another, the attacks from *Dacus* are not of importance.

The most important factor having a direct bearing on the number of generations of the insect and on the intensity of attack is without doubt represented by temperature (Fig. 19).

At the extreme south of the distributional area, in the pre-Saharian regions of Africa, the very high maxima restrain the infestation of *Dacus oleae*, not only through the directly unfavourable action of excess heat on the adults, but also because high temperatures favour the development and rapid multiplication of ectophagous insects which attack and destroy the larvæ of the fly.

In the north, near the polar thermic deficiency limit of diffusion of the insect, only the zero of development had until now been considered, that is to say, the temperature at which the insect should theoretically remain for an indetermined period in the same state of evolution in which it found itself when the temperature fell to this limit.

The zero of development for the olive-fly is, according to Rossi, of 9·2° C.

From a practical point of view, the cold limit or threshold of reproduction calculated by Rocchi assumes particular importance : this constitutes the true thermic limit of diffusion

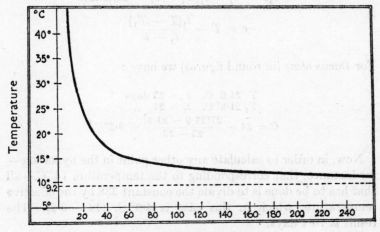

Fig. 19.   Duration of the Life-cycle of *Dacus oleae* (Olive-fly) in Relation to Temperature.

of the fly both in latitude and altitude. This temperature is approximately 13·5° C.

At mean temperatures between 9·2° C. and 13·5° C. the insect can develop, complete its cycle and reach the perfect form, but is not in a position to reproduce : the fly then flutters innocuously through the groves without causing any damage.

The relationship between rapidity of development and temperature is represented by an equilateral hyperbole situated between the zero of development (c) and a theoretical optimal temperature above which further applications of heat have a negative influence by lengthening the cycles.

I

On the other hand, the product of the length of cycle in days (t) by the effective temperature (difference between mean temperature T and the zero of development c) is a constant, which in this case is 338.

Once two points have been determined (experimentally or by direct research in an open field) it becomes possible to calculate the zero of development and construct the whole hyperbole :

$$t(T - c) = t_1(T_1 - c) = \text{constant}$$

$$c = T - \frac{t_1(T - T_1)}{t_1 - t}$$

For *Dacus oleae* (in round figures) we have :

$$T\ 24 \cdot 0° \text{ C.}\quad t = 23 \text{ days}$$
$$T_1\ 21 \cdot 8° \text{ C.}\quad t_1 = 27\quad,,$$
$$C = 24 - \frac{27(24 \cdot 0 - 21 \cdot 8)}{27 - 23} = 9 \cdot 2°$$

Now, in order to calculate any other point in the hyperbole—for instance, that corresponding to the temperature 14° C.—all that has to be done is to divide the constant 338 by the effective temperature, which in this case is 4·8° C. (14 − 9·2). The result is 70·4 days.

With these points of reference, we can investigate the possibilities of development, and therefore the probable intensity of damage caused by the fly. This is seen along an axis which runs from the cold limit to the most favourable situations for the development of the pest.

In the table on p. 115 are given the mean temperatures for the 10-day periods running from the beginning of July to the second 10-day period in December in the following localities : Reggio Calabria, Sassari (Sardegna), Savona (Liguria) and Salò (Garda).

The line *A* shows the moment of the first attack, while the line *B* indicates the date when the temperature falls below the threshold of reproduction of the insect (13·5°).

For the first attack it is necessary that the fruits should have reached a sufficient development and the exocarp such a thickness that the female may be enabled to lay the eggs into a mass of tissue soft and sufficient for the nourishment of the newly hatched larvæ.

The moment when the attack becomes possible is reached very early in the south—in the middle of July—while in the region of the Lake of Garda the fruits reach the required size about 20th August.

Mean Temperatures, ° C.

Station.	July. 1st. 2nd. 3rd. 10-day periods.			August. 1st. 2nd. 3rd. 10-day periods.			September. 1st. 2nd. 3rd. 10-day periods.		
	A								
Reggio C. (0) .	23·7	24·4	25·1	25·2	25·1	24·5	23·7	22·6	21·6
Sassari (5) . .	23·5	24·1	24·3	24·2	24·2	23·6	23·1	24·1	19·3
Savona (9) . .	23·6	24·2	24·4	24·4	24·5	23·4	22·5	20·8	19·4
Salò (13) . .	22·9	23·5	23·6	23·5	23·1	21·0	21·1	19·0	17·7

Station.	October. 1st. 2nd. 3rd. 10-day periods.			November. 1st. 2nd. 3rd. 10-day periods.			December. 1st. 2nd. 3rd. 10-day periods.		
						B			
Reggio C. (0) .	20·0	19·0	17·6	16·1	15·0	14·0	13·2	12·2	—
Sassari (5) . .	18·3	16·5	15·6	14·3	13·3	11·4	10·0	9·6	—
Savona (9) . .	18·0	15·8	14·2	12·6	10·9	9·6	8·4	7·8	—
Salò (13) . .	16·5	13·7	12·0	10·8	8·6	6·2	5·3	4·3	—

The available period for the development of the parasite lengthens to 140 days in Reggio Calabria, 110 in Sassari, 90 in Savona and finally to 50 days in Salò.

Let us now calculate for a single locality the number of possible successive generations.

To do this the fractions of the length of the cycle of development corresponding to each day are successively noted, from the beginning of every cycle, using the mean daily temperature. Thus to a mean temperature of 24° C. there corresponds a length of 23 days : therefore one day at a mean temperature of 24° C. represents $\frac{1}{23}$ of the period of development of the life cycle of the fly.

These daily fractions are summed together until unity has been reached : the cycle is then ended.

Example :

$$\text{At } 24° \text{ C. the cycle is 23 days}$$
$$\text{,, } 21° \text{ C. ,, ,, 27 ,,}$$
$$\text{,, } 14° \text{ C. ,, ,, 70·4 days}$$
$$\text{,, } 25° \text{ C. ,, ,, 21·4 ,,}$$

$$\frac{1}{23} + \frac{1}{27} + \frac{1}{70} \cdots + \frac{1}{21} = 1$$

The same result, avoiding the simple but laborious summing of fractions, may be obtained by noting for each day the percentage of the period of development. Thus if at 24° C. the duration is of 23 days, the daily quota is 4·35%; at 14° C., with a 70·4-day period for the cycle, the figure is 1·42%. Adding up the daily temperatures expressed as a percentage of the duration of the cycle, the complete cycle for one generation is ended when 100 has been reached. In the case under consideration we naturally limit the addition to the period from the laying of the eggs to the cold limit for reproduction, and we find that there are four possible successive generations for Reggio Calabria, three for Sassari, two for Savona and only one effective generation for Salò.

Heat gradually decreases from south to north, and from the plains upwards to the mountains, as does, consequently, both the number of generations possible and the virulence of the infection.

. . . . .

Temperature is the dominating factor : there is, however, no doubt that atmospheric humidity also notably influences the development of the insect : in fact, the fly abounds on coastal regions due, in particular, to the high humidity which becomes more and more reduced as we approach the interior of the continent. When the air is very dry, the insect, after completing its development, is not able to force an exit and dies enclosed within the pupal involucre, which becomes harder and more rigid as a consequence of the dryness of the atmosphere.

It is therefore evident that even in optimal temperatures the conditions for survival become more and more difficult with the progressive decrease in relative humidity. The graph of these thermo-hygroscopic relationships has been brilliantly constructed for *Anthonomus grandis* by Dwight Pearce. The temperature axis and the humidity axis show one perpendicular

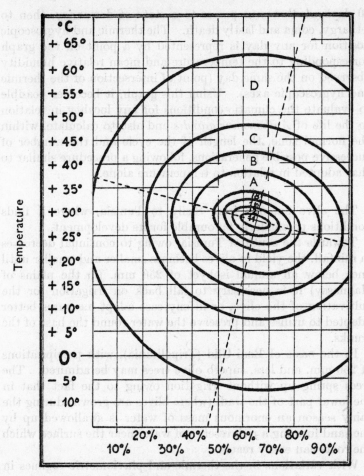

FIG. 20. DIAGRAM OF THE DEVELOPMENT OF *ANTHONOMUS GRANDIS* (COTTON
BOLL WEEVIL) IN RELATION TO TEMPERATURE AND HUMIDITY. (*After Dwight Pearce.*)

A = Dormancy; B = Lethargy; C = Coma; D = Instantaneous death.

crossing the other at a point corresponding to the thermic and hygroscopic optima.   At this point the cycle lasts a mere 11 days (Fig. 20).

Moving away from this point in any direction, the situation gradually worsens, and after reaching a maximum duration of

20 days, *Anthonomus* passes to a state of dormancy, then to lethargy, coma and lastly death.   The thermic and hygroscopic position for any day is represented by a point on the graph corresponding to the temperature and mean relative humidity observed on the same day (point of intersection of the thermic and hygroscopic axes).   Using this graph, it becomes possible to evaluate the climatic conditions for any locality in relation to the life of *Anthonomus grandis* and also to calculate, within the normal zone, the length of the cycle and the number of successive possible generations, following a procedure similar to that adopted in relation to temperature alone.

. . . . .

The olive extends from Sicily to Tunisia, where it finds conditions particularly favourable for its development.

Towards the south of Tunisia, owing to continual decreases in rainfall, the yield in olives becomes smaller and smaller until once below an annual isohyet of 250 mm. (in the plains of Mahnassy) it is necessary to fall back on irrigation for the cultivation of the olive, or in any case adopt measures better adapted to utilise and preserve the water round the base of the trunks.

In the oasis of Beni-Ulid (Tripolitania), with precipitations of 250 mm. and less, superb olive trees may be admired.   The trees spring up without irrigation owing to the fact that in the lower part of the wadi (where olives are grown) during the rainy season an enormous mass of water is swallowed up by the sand forming a rich reserve of water near the surface which the roots can easily reach.

With variations in the thermic and pluviometric regimes in different latitudes, three zones may therefore be distinguished :

(1) South (irrigated or dry in the Uidian).
(2) Central (arid).
(3) North (arid–cold).

In this last zone the danger of infection from fly disappears, while the harshness of the winter, and from time to time the exceptional cold spells occurring at long intervals, sorely try the olive, sometimes destroying the whole foliar surface, and even killing the poorer and weaker specimens in the low and humid basins.

CHESTNUT

While the chestnut has need of large quantities of water to nourish the large mass of fruits produced, it is very often found in the mountains, where the layer of earth is generally very thin and the slopes steep, for which reasons the reserves of water are rapidly exhausted unless plentiful and frequent rains supply the quantities necessary to keep the soil moist.

The vegetative period of the chestnut may be subdivided into the following five sub-periods :

(1) leafing : from the awakening in spring to the beginning of flowering ;

(2) flowering : from the beginning of flowering to setting ;

(3) formation and development of fruits : from the completed set to the beginning of maturity ;

(4) maturity : from the beginning of maturity to the end of the harvest ;

(5) fall of the leaves and winter rest : from the end of the harvest to the resumption of life in spring.

Even if excess rainfall can undoubtedly prove harmful in the very delicate phases of flowering and setting (Vigiani has calculated the equivalent for excess in the second sub-period as 80 mm.), there is no doubt that the most harmful phenomenon for the chestnut is represented by drought in the sub-period from the completed setting to the beginning of maturity.

For the three months July–September (in which the said sub-period is to be found), and using the data from twenty-four stations and over 15 years, Briccoli has determined the equivalent for drought as approximately 30 mm., demonstrating the dominant action of rainfall in August, which appears to be a true critical period. Vigiani, in researches carried out in the Casentino region, confirms the prevailing action of rain in August.

Using these pluviometric data and the yields obtained between 1921 and 1940 quoted in Vigiani's work, we can provisionally fix 37 mm. as the equivalent for drought during the critical period of the chestnut (month of August for central and northern Italy).

This equivalent, although much higher than that registered

for the olive and vine in South Italy, draws much closer to the local drought equivalent for the olive in Umbria during the development of the fruits. Both the chestnut and olive, for reasons mentioned above, grow on very droughty soils, a fact naturally implying that larger quantities of water are necessary to avoid drought in those sectors of central Italy where these plants are cultivated on the mountain slopes.

ARBUTUS UNEDO L. (*Ericaceae*)

The framework of bio-ambiental relationships for this shrub, which forms part of the undergrowth of the forests of the Mediterranean region, presents peculiar characteristics, especially in relation to the photo-period, of which we shall speak later (see page 125), and in relation to temperature on the growth of fruits.

Since *Arbutus* is a short day plant, flowering takes place only when the season is well advanced, from the middle of October to the middle of November. The development of the fruits is protracted from November to the first 10 days of December of the next year, so covering on the whole an interval of nearly 13 months in which there is a partial overlapping of the cycles.

The curve for the weight of fruits (see Fig. 21), may be divided into four parts :

(1) of very slow growth ;
(2) of moderate growth ;
(3) of fast growth ;
(4) of rapid decrease in weight (from the moment the maximum weight is reached until the end of the cycle of development).

The study of temperature in relation to the growth of fruits gives us the possibility of defining (with a first approximation) the equivalents for excess and for deficiency for the development of fruits.

The most favourable conditions for growth are, without doubt, those falling in the period between the middle of September and the 20th November. In summer, high temperatures act in a manifestly negative sense; this is quite explicable when one considers that this is a plant which thrives in the fresh and shaded environment of the forest. From the middle of April until the middle of September, in fact, growth is only moderate, owing to the high temperatures, even in a regime of abundant rainfall.

The equivalent for excess can, with good approximation, be taken as 21° C.

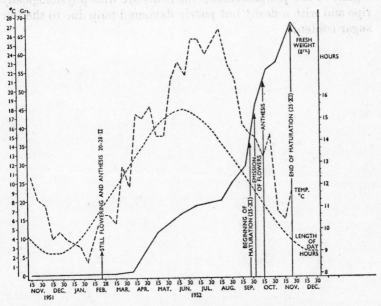

FIG. 21. CURVE OF WEIGHT OF FRUITS OF *ARBUTUS UNEDO*.

From the moment setting has begun—that is, from the middle of November until the 19th April—growth is very slow, and the equivalent for deficiency of temperature, with regard to the development of the fruits, may be fixed in approximately 12° C. We have, therefore, 21° C. and 12° C. as equivalents for excess and deficiency of temperature, respectively.

I will call the reader's attention to the fact that notwithstanding its natural habitat (Mediterranean region), the fruits of *Arbutus unedo* show a high resistance to low temperatures, overcoming the coldest interval of the year.

Given below are the minimum temperatures in ° C. obtained in January and February for a period of 10 years.

	1901.	1902.	1903.	1904.	1905.	1906.	1907.	1908.	1909.	1910.
January .	−7·5	−2·8	−4·5	−0·6	−9·5	−4·4	−6·2	−2·1	−4·6	−5·4
February .	−7·0	−1·0	−0·3	−1·4	−5·6	−2·7	−2·4	−2·7	−5·0	−1·4

The intrinsic, genotypical characteristics of the plant and the environmental conditions determine a late maturation in a regime of low temperatures; the fruits are thus physiologically ripe and with a fleshy but poorly flavoured pulp due to the low sugar content.

CHAPTER VII

FIXED FACTORS

Phenomena of Photoperiodism

It sometimes happens that a plant in optimal climatic conditions (rain, temperature and soil), does not manage to develop normally, and this without any apparent reason. For instance, the varieties of potato from the Equatorial-Andine region in practically identical conditions of soil, temperature and rainfall to those in the country of origin, cannot develop their tubers in Europe. The cause is of course the length of day.

The interval of time between the rising and setting of the sun at an intermediate latitude, Rome, for instance, varies from a minimum of 9 hours 4 minutes in December to a maximum of 15 hours 9 minutes in June. Farther south, and in proximity of the equator, these variations diminish until, once on the equator itself, day and night have the same length of 12 hours through all the year.

Towards the pole, however, the contrast between extreme situations is naturally more marked; at 60° N. the minimum length of day is 6 hours 8 minutes in winter, and the maximum 18 hours 17 minutes in summer.

The variation of length of day and night, as Allard and Garner demonstrated, can have a decided bearing on the development of the plant, consisting in anticipating, delaying or sometimes excluding the formation of the organs of reproduction (flowers).

Agricultural plants may be divided into two categories :

(1) plants favoured by a short day : where a relatively short day encourages and hurries flowering;

(2) plants favoured by a long day : where a relatively long day encourages and hurries flowering.

Between these two extreme groups, varieties or even species are to be found which are practically " indifferent ", in that they react very feebly to variations in length of day. It is so, as is well known, for certain plants of equatorial countries where the length of day and night balance, or tend to balance each other almost completely.

Plants Favoured by a Short Day

The behaviour of the Indian Chrysanthemum is particularly interesting with regard to photoperiodism. This plant, as is well known, blooms very late in the season—towards the end of October, when temperature has fallen to a level entailing the almost total suspension of growth in the vegetable world. At first sight, the long cycle could be attributed to the high thermic requirements of the plants, which would then make use of the heat supplied throughout the whole summer, reckoning from the time of transplanting in spring. However, artificially reducing the length of day to 8 hours (from transplanting), the flowering phase is reached in 55 days only, and the plant blossoms in July with a total sum of temperatures of 1,036° C., as against the 172 days taken by the control plant with a sum of mean daily temperatures amounting to 3,916° C.

The delay in blooming under normal conditions in summer is consequently not due to any particular requirement of temperature, but purely to the fact that the Chrysanthemum belongs to the group of plants requiring a short day : the appearance of the reproductive organs is put off until the autumn, when the natural shortening in the length of day provides the photoperiodic conditions necessary for flowering. The Chrysanthemum is thus a typical short-day plant.

In Indo-China in the Governor-General's park at Hanoi there exist *in situ* specimens of *Euphorbia splendens*, an evergreen and thorny plant which blooms every year for a few months. Part of this group of plants was subjected at night to the light from a large chandelier fitted with 25-candle-power lamps at a height of 2·50 metres. It was observed that while flowering had been abundant in other plants, those which had been constantly exposed to light showed only a few blooms : *Euphorbia splendens* would thus appear to be a short-day plant.

Originally maize, also, was a short-day plant. Even though it manages to complete its cycle at the height of summer in Europe, in a long-day regime, this is in all probability to be attributed to the effects of natural selection and to the fact that the varieties which thrive well in Europe originated from American countries situated very far from the equator, where the day in summer is rather long.

If, as was done at Perugia in 1933, a variety from the equatorial zone of Brazil (where it normally reaches heights of 2–3 metres at the most) be sown, the plant continues to develop throughout the summer in a purely vegetative sense, without producing an inflorescence : it was only in autumn, and after having reached a height of 7 metres, that the male inflorescences appeared ; at the same time two cobs developed and managed to produce grain, without, however, reaching maturity, because of deficiency of temperature.

This typically short-day variety of maize behaved exactly like the Indian Chrysanthemum. It had to await the autumn, when the length of day had shortened the necessary photoperiod for flowering.

Arbutus unedo is a typical short-day plant : blooming in Perugia is delayed till the middle of October. In Central Italy, in the interval which precedes the appearance of the inflorescences and during which the floral buds develop, the day's duration falls to approximately 12 hours 15 minutes, which we may take as the limiting photoperiod for this plant.

The short photoperiod which renders possible the formation of the reproductive organs is reached very late in autumn and consequently the inflorescences appear at the beginning of October (the first newly formed fruits are only to be seen early in November).

On the other hand, the high summer temperatures delay the development of the fruits (derived from the flowers of the preceding year) so that maturation is reached very late, (just at the time when the first inflorescences of the new cycle are appearing). Ripening of the fruits is achieved at the end of November.

So it is that in October–November we have an overlapping of the two cycles and we can then find, on the same branch, inflorescences, blooms and fruits in all stages of development from setting to complete maturity.

It could, theoretically, be admitted that in the equatorial region, between 2,000 and 3,000 metres, with constant temperatures between 15° C. and 16° C., and where, as is known, the duration of day is 12 hours, the interference of the cycle should be unlimited, since the two braking actions—the thermic and the photoperiodic—are lacking. It should thus be possible to find at any moment all the stages of development on any plant, from the emission of the inflorescences to the complete maturation of the fruits, as is precisely what is found for coffee in the equatorial regions of the Amazon.

Plants Favoured by a Long Day

During my stay in Venezuela (1946–7), the Government of the Republic asked me to import a considerable number (10,000) of young olive plants from Italy in order to try out the cultivation of this tree in their country : the request resulted from the information that good results had been obtained in Colombia.

Although in many regions of Venezuela the soil conditions, precipitation and temperature appeared to be highly favourable for the development of the olive, I decided to make a preliminary inquiry before committing the Department of Agriculture to considerable expense.

From my inquiries I found that what was being said of olive cultivation in Colombia did not at all correspond to the facts. I was also able to note during a trip in Peru really magnificent olive trees of great size that produced insignificant quantities of fruit, which, moreover, were not suitable for making oil. These olives were, in fact, suitable only for pickling. The plants produced very large, handsome fruits which were very poor in oil and dispersed in small numbers among the abundant foliage. The reason for this was of course the fact that the olive is a long-day plant, so that in tropical countries the relatively brief duration of day renders the development of the sex organ difficult.

The most outstanding example of a long-day plant is wheat. Wheat-plants kept in a green-house during the winter, when the day is very short, remain in the herbaceous state—that is, at the tillering phase—producing a large mass of leaves and tillers which do not continue to develop further and do not, therefore, reach the earing phase. The same result is obtained by reducing the extent of the illumination, with appropriate shields, to 8 hours per day during the summer. On the other hand, by artificially lengthening the duration of the day by means of electric light, the long-day plants can further contract their cycle to a minimum which had not been considered possible. The spring wheat from Pengalengan (Java), sown at the normal time, in normal conditions, ears 60 days after sprouting. Kept in a regime of continual illumination the interval from sprouting to earing is reduced to 30 days. Hence wheat represents a typical long-day plant.

*   *   *   *

Two factors—temperature and length of day—have a decided influence on the length of the interval from sprouting to earing.

The northern limit for wheat in the Scandinavian peninsula is around 63° latitude N. Nearer the pole, the culture of this cereal becomes impossible, because the first frosts at the end of summer, which can occur from the third 10-day period of August, and the last frosts in spring, which can continue up to early summer, curtail the utilisable period to a brief space of time which can be neither increased nor altered. Near to the polar limit of wheat culture the sum of temperatures in the interval between earing and the harvest is barely sufficient for the kernels to reach maturity.

The actual limit of culture, owing to the gradual and progressive decrease in temperature from south to north, could certainly not be reached were it not for the length of day factor, which in summer increases near the pole and causes, at equal temperatures, an anticipation in the formation and subsequent appearance of inflorescences, thus compensating for the progressive decrease of available temperature.[1]

An important example is to be found in the work of Salvatori, which gives us an idea, even though approximate, of the entity of the retreat of the polar front of expansion for wheat were the photoperiodic stimulus lacking.

For this determination we use the results derived from geographical trials with spring wheats undertaken from the polar to the equatorial limits for wheat. The polar limit is marked

[1] In this connection it is interesting to note that in mountainous regions in the equatorial zone the altimetric limit cannot be compared to the latitude limit; this is because while temperature obviously decreases with increase in altitude, the relative length of day remains unaltered.

by a mean temperature of 13–14° C., and the equatorial limit by a mean temperature of 24° C. (in the sub-period from earing to maturity).

Around the 15th Parallel the length of day during the cycle of development of the wheat-plant reaches a minimum value of approximately 11 hours; this is due to the fact that, since temperatures are very high, the cultivation of wheat must be undertaken in the four coldest months of the year, and therefore in winter, when the day is shortest. In these conditions the sum total of mean daily temperatures from sprouting to earing is 1,470° C. In moving northwards the day (during the summer) becomes longer while the sum of temperatures decreases to a minimum of 750° C. at the polar limit of earing (65° N.) with a mean length of day reaching 20 hours 45 minutes, from sprouting to earing.

Latitude N.	Sum total of mean temperatures, ° C.	Length of day.	
		hrs.	mins.
65°	750	20	45
60°	815	18	55
55°	900	17	30
50°	980	15	50
45°	1,055	14	45
40°	1,135	13	45
35°	1,210	12	50
30°	1,300	12	00
25°	1,410	11	10
20°	1,450	11	00
15°	1,470	10	55

If the photoperiodic stimulus were lacking, the mean daily temperature in ° C., multiplied by the duration of the interval in days from sprouting to earing would be a constant, and we have agreed to take that obtained where the minimum duration of day prevails—that is, 1,470° C.

Once the earing phase is reached, and so that the cultivation of wheat may be possible, it becomes necessary for the available temperature to be on the one hand sufficient to guarantee maturity (polar limit) and, on the other, not so high as to cause shrivelling of the grain by hot spells (equatorial limit).

The product of the mean daily temperature in ° C. multiplied by the duration of the fourth sub-period (earing–maturity) in days is 900° C., which at the polar limit agrees with a duration of 70–75 days (interval from earing to maturity) and a mean temperature of 12–14° C., while at the equatorial limit we have 30 days and 24° C., respectively.

Adding, therefore, 900° C. to the sum of temperatures from germination to earing, we have the total temperature for the whole biological cycle of the wheat plant, as follows :

15th Parallel	.	.	.	2,370° C. (1,470° C. + 900° C.)
30th ,,	.	.	.	2,200° C. (1,300° C. + 900° C.)
45th ,,	.	.	.	1,955° C. (1,055° C. + 900° C.)
60th ,,	.	.	.	1,750° C. (815° C. + 900° C.)

In order to see which are the available temperatures utilisable for the development of wheat in any point of the area of distribution of this plant, we must begin to sum up, from sprouting onwards, the mean daily temperatures, until the point is reached where the mean daily temperature falls permanently below 12° C.

Thus in Perugia the wheat harvest takes place at the end of June, while temperatures of the July–October period would still be available for the plant.

Proceeding north, the sum of utilisable temperatures gradually decreases, until at last the total available temperature is only just sufficient to assure completion of the cycle. Beyond this limit the cultivation of wheat is no longer possible owing to thermic deficiencies. We give below the series of temperatures utilisable at the various latitudes :

Latitude N.	Sum of utilisable temperatures, ° C.	Latitude N.	Sum of utilisable temperatures, ° C.
65°	800	35°	6,590
60°	1,800	30°	8,000
55°	1,900	25°	9,100
50°	2,430	20°	9,790
45°	3,330	15°	10,140
40°	5,960		

We are now in a position to establish how much the present polar front of wheat would retreat if the photoperiodic stimulus were to disappear.

K

The sum of necessary temperatures, being the result of two constants, will itself be a constant : it is 2,370° C. (1,470 + 900). It now becomes very easy to establish the geographical point to which the cultivation of wheat would reach were it not for the photoperiodic factor. It would evidently extend to a point at which the sum of utilisable temperatures does not fall below 2,370° C., and this would appear to be between the 50th and 51st Parallels. We should thus get a retrocession of more than 560 miles from the present actual limit of 60° N. in Sweden, beyond which the cultivation of wheat, although to a certain extent possible, yields its place almost completely to rye and barley.

.   .   .   .

The inter-action of temperature and length of day on the time of earing must evidently be taken into consideration when ascertaining the earliness of certain varieties of wheat. The degree of earliness in earing cannot be absolute, but only relative, as it is under the complementary action of two ambiental factors which vary independently one from the other.

There are certain varieties which are early because they are highly susceptible to the accelerating action of the long day (AAbb) : while others are equally early because they are very sensitive to the accelerating action of temperature (aaBB), as a presumable consequence of natural selection.

Canadian varieties, considered very early in their home soils, are late in North Africa (as was clearly seen in the geographical trials), and all because the degree of earliness is a consequence of the plant's sensitivity to the accelerating action exercised by the long day in the period from sprouting to earing. In North Africa, where for the corresponding period of the cycle the day is much shorter, the date of earing is delayed, so that the variety becomes late, as the stimulus to which the plant specifically responds is lacking.

On the other hand, wheats of the Mediterranean region which are sensitive to the action of temperature become very late when sown in the north, where the stimulus to which they particularly react is missing (i.e. thermic stimulus).

In our opinion, a cross between the two varieties AAbb and aaBB should give interesting results. The hybrid AaBb, given the dominance of the characteristic " earliness ", according to Lysenko's theory, should behave as an early plant in any region, and therefore be successful either with a long day and low temperatures, or with a short day and relatively high temperatures.

Photoperiodic Optima and Limits

Not all long-day plants respond to the prolonged application of light, beyond certain limits, by a progressive increase in earliness of flowering. *Solanum melongena, L.*, "Black Beauty" variety, sown on 9th May, bloomed in the open and under normal conditions (length of day 14–15 hours) on 26th July— namely, 75 days after the sowing.

By diminishing the day's duration to 12 hours with appropriate screening, flowering is delayed a little, which delay becomes more highly accentuated when illumination is reduced to 8 hours daily. A typical long-day plant, therefore : but if daylight is prolonged to 24 hours daily by artificial means (continuous illumination), the plant blooms with the same delay as that observed when daylight is reduced to 8 hours. In both cases flowering took place on 3rd August.

An optimal photoperiod of 14–15 hours would therefore best suit the plant's requirements.

Photoperiodism of the Potato and Development of the Tubers

In evaluating the effects of length of day in the practical problems of adapting plants to environment we want to know if the product finally to be utilised by man is the result of the development in the reproductive sense (flowers, fruits, seeds), or of growth in the vegetative sense (leaves and stems, bulbs, tubers, etc.).

Thus for the typically long-day varieties of potato of the equatorial region (Andine regions of Ecuador), it is quite clear that in order to have well-developed tubers, a short-day regime will have to be sought which will curtail the development of the reproductive organs and, at least in part, suppress the useless flowers and fruits, for the benefit of tuber development. This is why in Europe, where the summer days are very long, these potato varieties cannot be grown. *Solanum tuberosum, L.*, on the other hand, derived from the centre and south of Chile, where the length of day in summer is the same as that found in Europe, develops regularly.

Research carried out by Rasumov on numerous wild species of *Solanum* is worthy of notice, and has formed a basis by which Soviet geneticists have obtained, by means of cross-breeding, new types having a sufficient productivity and at the same time specific resistance to diseases (*Phytophthora infestans*, De Bary) and to meteorological adversities (low temperature).

The experiments were made in order to determine the effect of a long-day regime (17 hours) at the latitude of Moscow and of a day artificially shortened (by using shields) to 10 hours.

In order to calculate the relative yield of the various plants, indices were employed, taking as 100 the weight of tubers from the plants kept in a short-day regime.

For the evaluation of the total mass of leaves, stems and stolons, the weight of the green mass of the plant in a long-day regime is made equal to 100.

The species employed for the experiment may be divided into three groups, according to the results :

First Group. This group is typically represented by a variety of *Solanum tuberosum* from the isle of Chiloe (Chile). The plant in a long-day regime—from sprouting to the end of the cycle—began to form its tubers 30 days after sprouting. In a short-day regime the plants began to form tubers 24 days after sprouting, and therefore was 7 days early.

The weight of tubers was practically the same in the two cases. It must be recognised, however, that the short-day regime is the most favourable for tuber formation. In a long-day regime the yield in tubers is, it is true, a little higher, but one must observe that the aerial parts of plants in a short-day regime are only a third of those found on long-day plants : in spite of this and the consequently reduced photosynthetic action, the yield in tubers is still high.[1]

---

[1] In order better to interpret the results of this research it is to be noted that in connection with the formation of tubers the best results were obtained by keeping the plants in a long-day regime during the first part of the vegetative period : a considerable mass of leaves is so obtained. In the second part of the plant's life, and therefore from the beginning of tuber formation up to the harvest, the plants were kept in a short-day regime thus favouring the development of the tubers. These profited in their turn from the intense photosynthesis of the large foliar mass produced in the first part of the vegetative period.

For *Solanum tuberosum* we have :

Length of day.	Beginning of tuber forma- tion, days.	Weight of plant with- out tubers, index number.	Weight of tubers, index number.
Long . . .	31	100	109
Short . .	24	30	100

These species therefore remain practically indifferent to the day's duration, being able to develop tubers regularly even with a relatively long-day regime. The plant's capacity for development in central and north Europe, where the days during the vegetative period are very long, is thus explained.

Solanum rybinii behaves in a similar fashion.

Second Group. This includes those species which manage to form tubers, though with considerable delay, in spite of a relatively long photoperiod. The results obtained with *Solanum andigenum* present a quite different picture from those of *Solanum tuberosum.* The greater development of the aerial portions is a natural consequence of the long-day regime, while the production in tubers is, in this case, one-eighth of that obtainable with short-day conditions, while in the first group the yield was practically the same in the two cases (as above indicated).

The formation of tubers in *Solanum andigenum* with a short-day regime, commences 33 days after sprouting, while under long-day conditions it is delayed for 78 days, thus reducing the duration of the period available for the formation and growth of the tubers.

The following figures are for *Solanum andigenum* :

Length of day.	Beginning of tuber forma- tion, days.	Weight of plant with- out tubers, index number.	Weight of tubers, index number.
Long . . .	78	100	8
Short . .	33	28	100

Similar behaviour may be observed in *S. goniocalyx* and *S. ahanhuiri.*

Third Group. This includes the species which do not produce a single tuber in a long photoperiod.

The typical representative of this group is *S. demissum.* Here is the relative table :

Length of day.	Beginning of tuber formation, days.	Weight of plant without tubers, index number.	Weight of tubers, index number.
Long . . .	0	100	0
Short . .	50	8	100

With a long-day regime, the plants have a vigorous development of the aerial portion with stems 30–35 cm. long and with larger although not numerous leaves. The flowering phase, which was well manifest with a large number of blooms, began in the middle of the biological cycle and was protracted until the end of the vegetative period, producing a considerable number of fruits. There was no sign of tuber formation while the stolons were richly developed.

In a short-day regime the plant's behaviour is quite the opposite. The greatly reduced aerial portion presents a prostrate habit of growth and has few leaves densely overlaid one above the other and closely adherent to the soil; there is no ramification and no flowering. In spite of the extreme contraction of the green parts, the production in tubers, begun from the fiftieth day after sprouting, was very abundant.

It is quite clear that tuber formation in *S. demissum* is decidedly influenced by length of day, and this explains why cultivation of it is impossible in Europe, where the day is of a minimum of 14–15 hours long in the summer period. *S. demissum* represents a typical species of the equatorial regions, where the length of day is always of approximately 12 hours.

WINTER AND SUMMER LETTUCE

The common lettuce is a long-day plant, so that if the length of day be prolonged, the plant is seen rapidly to go to seed, becoming very tall and producing few and widespread leaves. To obtain a well-developed foliar mass and a compact and juicy head a short day is necessary.

The different behaviour of the two types of lettuce known

as " winter lettuce " and " summer lettuce " is interesting.
In an artificially shortened regime, from 8 to 9 hours (which is
the mean duration of a winter's day), both types show considerable delay in blooming, 5–6 months, and can therefore develop
their heads well.

With the lengthening of the day, blooming is brought forward at the expense of the good formation of the head. In
this case, however, the behaviour of the two varieties is very
different. The " *Bionda dell'ortolano* "—a summer type—takes
about $3\frac{1}{2}$ months to flower, with 14–15 hours length of day
(normal length at the end of spring and beginning of summer) :
it thus gives the plant the time to develop a mass of succulent
leaves. This type of lettuce can therefore be used until the
beginning of summer. The " *Pallottina* " however—a winter
type and more susceptible to the accelerating action of a long
day, goes to seed in only 2 to 3 months, and thus cannot form
a good head : it must be used exclusively for the winter sowing, being a typical " winter lettuce ".

From the above it will be understandably clear, and no
longer seem so strange, that certain species of plant sown outside their zone are unable to flower (and produce fruits),
although growing in favourable conditions of moisture and
temperature : the cause is to be sought in the negative action
exercised by an unfavourable photoperiod. The length-of-day
factor can now take its place with temperature and humidity
as an important environmental characteristic, and open the
way for a series of experiments with the object of obtaining a
better adaptation of cultures to this ambiental factor. In
addition, the photoperiod as opposed to rainfall and temperature, which are extremely variable at different places and
times, has the advantage of remaining unaltered from one year
to the next, and varies only from one point to another of the
globe in relation to the geographical co-ordinate, and according
to the rigid rules of astronomy.

For every plant we must admit the existence of an optimal
photoperiod and of two photoperiodic limits, one for excess
(too long length of day), and one for deficiency (too short length
of day).

In the evaluation of what we may well call the excess or deficiency equivalents for the photoperiod, it becomes of the utmost importance to consider if the parts utilised by man are the result of a development in the reproductive sense (fruit and seed), or of a development in a vegetative sense (stems and leaves), as has been mentioned above.

In the latter case the most favourable photoperiod will be the one that, being contrary to blooming, will push development in a vegetative sense, and so increase the stem, or foliar, or root masses.

Influence of the Moon on the Development of Plants

In the series of experiments mentioned above, luminous sources of low intensity (25 candle-power) were often used, and these frequently had an undoubted positive action : the artificial extension of length of day.

In these cases the action of light cannot be considered to have an effect on photosynthesis, while on the other hand the artificial lengthening of the day's duration so obtained is sufficient to bring forward the flowering of a long-day plant.

The observation that a source of light insufficient for photosynthesis can have an influence on other important functions opens up a possible field of research which could enlighten us on many problems at present unsolved.

I allude to the supposed action exercised by lunar phases on the development and growth of plants.

Here are two examples taken from practical observations on long-day plants :

(1) According to experienced farmers, lettuce sown when the moon is waning is well developed vegetatively, producing a voluminous and juicy head : if sown with a rising moon, the plants rapidly go to seed without forming a good head.

(2) Radishes sown with a rising moon blossom in 50–60 days when temperatures are reasonably high : sown with a waning moon, the interval between sprouting and blooming is much longer, so permitting the plant to develop regularly the meaty root mass utilised by man.

In these cases, as in many others which are empirically admitted but not yet scientifically proven, it could be affirmed that the period of time between new and full moon is a favourable one for reproduction, while the period between the full and new moons would be favourable to vegetative growth.

We cannot but notice an evident analogy between the results which are presumably obtained when sowing with a rising moon (or artificially prolonging the day), and the results which would be obtained when sowing with a waning moon (or artificially shortening the day)—always with reference to long-day plants.

Research carried out over the last few years, although it has drawn attention to the possible relationship between lunar phases, growth and development of plants, has not yet furnished sufficient evidence for even a preliminary positive conclusion in this direction.

Recently some experiments were carried out on the onion which, though not resolving this attractive and complex problem, seem to show some undoubted relationship between lunar phases and the subsequent development and growth of cultivated plants.

In 1936 different sowings were made at different lunar phases. The figures relative to dates of sowing and sprouting are given in the following table :

Experiments with Onion-sowing at Different Moon Phases

  (1) *Sowing :* 9th May (3 days after full moon).
      Sprouting : 21st May (1 day after new moon).

From sowing to sprouting took 12 days, and the whole sub-period took place with a waning moon.

  (2) *Sowing :* 16th May (2 days after the last quarter).
      Sprouting : 28th May (in the first quarter).

As in the first case, the interval was 12 days, partly including the waning moon and partly in the rising moon.

  (3) *Sowing :* 23rd May (3 days after new moon).
      Sprouting : 3rd June (3 days before full moon).

With increase in temperature, the interval between sowing and sprouting was shorter (11 days), and took place during the rising moon.

(4) *Sowing* : 30th May (2 days after the first quarter).

　　　Sprouting : 10th June (2 days before the last quarter).

Interval 11 days long : partly in waxing and partly in waning moon but always with strong lunar illumination.

(5) *Sowing* : 13th June (1 day after last quarter).

　　　Sprouting : 21st June (1 day after new moon).

Owing to the high temperature, the interval is reduced to 8 days, with the moon on the wane.

In 1937 notable and significant differences in the behaviour of the various lots sown at different times were observed with particular reference to the formation and appearance of inflorescences (reproductive development).

We find the following :

First sowing : normal growth : no trace of inflorescences in the middle of April.

Second sowing : the plant branches a little : no trace of inflorescences.

With reference to these two sowings, the period from sowing to sprouting had coincided with a waning moon in the first case, while the second took place in the phase between a waning and a waxing moon : in both cases the illumination was scanty.

Third sowing : the plant is abundantly branched : inflorescences appeared on 24th March.

Fourth sowing : the plant has ample ramifications, while the appearance of inflorescences is brought forward to 23rd March, in spite of the 7 days' delay in sowing in comparison with the preceding case (the true anticipation is therefore of 9 days).

In the third case the sub-period from sowing to sprouting took place with a rising moon, the fourth began with a rising moon and finished with a waning moon; in both cases therefore there was abundant lunar illumination.

Fifth sowing : the plant made normal growth without branching : in the middle of April there was no trace of inflorescence (regime of waning moon in the preceding year).

Fig. 22. Influence of the Moon on the Development of the Onion.

I. Sowing to sprouting 9 May–21 May.   Waning moon.
II.   ,,   ,,   16 May–28 May.   Waning then waxing moon.
III.   ,,   ,,   23 May–3 June.   Waxing moon.
IV.   ,,   ,,   30 May–10 June. Waxing then waning moon.

It seems unnecessary to recall that in 1937 the various plants grown in 1936 were transplanted at the same date.

The positive effect of abundant lunar illumination now becomes evident in relation to development of reproductive organs : anticipation in the appearance of inflorescences is correlated with a tendency to tiller amply (Fig. 22). With equal quantities of light, however, the best results would appear to be obtained with a rising moon.

The onion is a long-day plant. We can thus see that the light from the moon, although not intense, assures the continuity of the stimulus inducing reproductive development. Under certain conditions, the lunar glow would assure a connecting link between two successive days, and eliminate the abrupt interruption of vital processes brought about by darkness.

Night creates an interruption in development, obliging the plant to resume life every morning, with a consequent delay and loss of energy.

Sowing with a waning moon, and thus acting in such a way that the interval from sowing to germination approximately coincides with a new moon, the formation of the reproductive organs is consequently retarded or put off, while the bulbs tend to reach a considerable size.

A certain analogy between the phenomena of photoperiodism and the effects of the moon seems to exist.

From these results we could assume the existence of a stage (or phase) of particular sensitivity to the action of the moon's rays, a phase which would coincide with the very first stages of the development of the plant, as we shall see later when considering the " Stadial " theory.

CHAPTER VIII

RÉSUMÉ OF METEOROLOGICAL EQUIVALENTS

I now consider it opportune to give a résumé of the equivalents of the most important cultivated plants, bearing in mind that in the determination of these equivalents we have particularly considered the critical periods and those bio-meteorological situations which are of the greatest importance in their dominating influence on yield.

WHEAT

In the month before earing, the precipitation equivalents for excess and deficiency are 116 mm. and 40 mm., respectively.

From earing to the harvest, and with the progressive decrease of the plant's needs for water, the equivalents also assume lower values : 92 mm. for excess and 15 mm. for deficient rainfall.

For the autumnal period (first sub-period), in which we find sowing and the initial development of the young plants, the equivalents are 205 and 50 mm. During the period of winter rest (second sub-period), the equivalents for excess and for deficiency are of 60 and 20 mm., respectively.

During the fourth sub-period—from earing to the harvest—the thermic equivalents were determined from the figures supplied by Russian and Scandinavian stations (for deficiency) and from those of North Africa (for excess). The equivalent for excess is represented by a mean temperature of 24° C. when the length of the interval between earing and maturity is reduced to a mean of 30 days and cannot, by further increases in temperature, be reduced still further without resulting in decidedly abnormal situations. The equivalent for deficiency is, on the other hand, of 13–14° C., and the fourth sub-period is prolonged to a mean of 70–75 days. Any further decrease in temperature makes the completion of the cycle an impossibility : the plant remains in the green state, and the kernels are unable to mature.

With regard to thermic excesses in the Mediterranean region, it is not the mean temperature which plays a decisive role, but the very high maximum temperatures accompanied by strong winds. The thermic equivalent for hot spells is represented by a maximum of 32° C. for this region.

MAIZE

The equivalent for drought—undoubtedly the most harmful adversity—is given as 46 mm. in the interval from 15 days before to 15 days after the appearance of male inflorescences and as 18 mm. in the interval between the maximum weight reached by the cobs up to maturity.

Maize can be damaged by thermic excesses independently of the presence or absence of drought. The phenomenon is, however, rare, but it was observed in certain sectors of Jugoslavia, when at the time of pollination the maximum temperatures reached 42–43° C., the pollen was literally " burnt ", so that fertilisation was greatly handicapped.

POTATO

From the beginning of tuber formation to flowering (third sub-period) the equivalent for drought is 35 mm., while 90 mm. represents the excess humidity which favours, and is the cause of the infection by *Phytophthora* in the second and third sub-periods, from sprouting to flowering.

In the month preceding the harvest, when the aerial portions have in great part ceased to function, total monthly precipitation of 102 mm. (or more) causes the rotting of the tubers.

BROAD BEAN

The equivalent for drought from flowering to the maximum weight of the pod (third and fourth sub-periods) is 21 mm.

SUGAR-BEET

The equivalent for drought in the June–August quarter (third sub-period : principally development of the root) is of 35 mm. per month.

HEMP

The drought equivalent from the beginning of rapid growth of the stems up to flowering is practically the same as that found for beet and for potato—34 mm.—while from sprouting to the beginning of rapid growth the equivalent is lowered to 20 mm.

ALFALFA

The equivalent for drought, with the progressive decrease in weight, gradually decreases, and is 54 mm. for the first cutting, 48 mm. for the second and 35 mm. per month as drought equivalent for the third cutting.

OLIVE

Throughout flowering the olive is very susceptible to both deficiency and excess rainfall and the two equivalents are very close—23 mm. and 36 mm., respectively.

In the sub-period from the completed fruit set to the beginning of maturity (July–September) the drought equivalent is 22 mm. In the regions of central Italy, where, for reasons which have already been explained in detail, planting of the olive is limited to mountain or hilly slopes with extremely permeable soils, the partial equivalent for drought is naturally very high, 45 mm.

VINE

In the quarter July–September (development of fruits and maturity) the drought equivalent is very low—12 mm.—because the plant generally absorbs the necessary water from the deep layers of soil, making use of rains, fallen in the winter–spring period. During this interval (winter–spring) we have a drought equivalent of 50 mm. per month.

From flowering to fructification (third sub-period) the plant is highly susceptible to excesses, so that 35 mm. represents the equivalent for pluviometric excess. These excesses are harmful indirectly rather than directly, inasmuch as they facilitate the diffusion of *Peronospora*.

From 21st September to 10th October in central-southern Italy, at the last phases of maturity of the grapes, the equivalent for thermic deficiency is represented by mean temperatures of 14–15° C.

As for the negative effects of thermic minima, we limit ourselves to a reminder that the shoots of the vine can resist up to 8 hours at a temperature of $-15°$ C. without damage, while at $-17°$ C. the shoots succumb after a very brief period of time.

Thermic excesses can cause damage during both the development of fruits and at the time of maturity, and the relative equivalent is represented by a maximum of $39·0°$ C.

CHESTNUT

Total precipitations above 80 mm. per month are decidedly harmful during the flowering phase (second sub-period), while the development of fruits from the completed setting up to the beginning of maturity (third sub-period) is often damaged by drought.   The relative equivalent is of 30 mm. per month for the quarter July–September, but this rises to 37 mm. for the month of August, which thus assumes the characteristics of a critical period.

A mean temperature of $11·5°$ C. may be considered deficient for maturity in the fourth sub-period.

FIG

The equivalents for drought are 61 mm. in the winter–spring interval (November–April) and 9 mm. only during the period of maximum growth of fruits from 11th July to 10th August, i.e. at the first stages of maturity (in the Salentine Peninsula).

COFFEE

The drought equivalent for coffee in the 3 months preceding blooming (first sub-period) is 40 mm. (13 mm. monthly).

EGG-PLANT

With reference to the development of the generative sense (formation of blooms), the optimal photoperiod of *Melongena* is 14–15 hours, and to this corresponds an interval between sowing and flowering of 78 days.

Both the artificial lengthening of day to 24 hours (with continuous illumination) and its reduction to 8 hours by means of screens cause an equal delay in the appearance of the blooms : the interval is prolonged to 86 days.

ARBUTUS UNEDO

With reference to photoperiodism, *Arbutus unedo* is a short-day plant, and the limit may be fixed in 12 hours. In relation to the development of fruits the mean temperature 21° and 12° C. may be taken as equivalent for excess and deficiency respectively.

CHAPTER IX

CLIMOSCOPE AND CLIMATIC FORMULÆ

Definition. The equivalents are much like the letters of the alphabet : they represent, we might say, the key which gives us the possibility of deciphering and resolving the riddle of the relationships between the atmospheric environment and the development of cultivated plants in terms of the yield. In order to accomplish this, all that is necessary is to construct climoscopes. By a climoscope is meant a framework in which the meteorological values are sub-divided not by calendar months, but by groups corresponding to the sub-periods into which the vegetative cycle of the plant is divided.

The following conditions have to be observed in the construction of climoscopes :

Temperature. For each sub-period the sum of mean daily temperatures is calculated, and this total is divided by the number of days which constitute the said sub-period.

Rainfall. The sum total of rains for each sub-period is divided by the duration of same in days, and the quotient is multiplied by 30 : in this way comparable monthly values are obtained, however long the sub-period might be.

Here is a theoretical climoscope for the wheat-plant in which we find many extreme negative situations present :

Rainfall and Temperature. Wheat

| | Sub-periods, rainfall in mm. | | | | Mean temperature, in ° C. 4th sub-period. |
	I.	II.	III.	IV.	
1931	251	74	102	94	28
1932	48	58	124	55	18
1933	67	15	85	63	21
1934	102	56	68	81	22
1935	94	19	74	9	13
1936	36	46	61	14	25
1937	263	38	56	67	19
1938	44	41	14	102	21
1939	73	53	43	84	20
1940	14	11	12	121	12

Taking this table as a basis, and with reference to the equivalents for wheat which are already determined, the frequency of favourable as well as of unfavourable situations through excess and deficiency may immediately be calculated. In the case in hand we have :

First sub-period (autumnal) : sowing and initial development of the young plants :

> Excess rainfall : twice (more than 205 mm.).
> Deficient rainfall : four times (under 50 mm.).
> Favourable conditions : four times (between 50 and 205 mm.).

Second sub-period (winter rest) :

> Excess rainfall : once (over 60 mm.).
> Deficient rainfall : three times (under 20 mm.).
> Favourable conditions : six times (between 20 and 60 mm.).

Third sub-period (from resumption of growth to earing) :

> Excess rainfall : once (over 116 mm.).
> Deficient rainfall : twice (under 40 mm.).
> Favourable conditions : seven times (between 40 and 116 mm.).

Fourth sub-period (from earing to maturity) :

> Excess rainfall : three times (over 92 mm.).
> Deficient rainfall : twice (under 15 mm.).
> Favourable conditions : five times (between 15 and 92 mm.).
> Thermic excesses : twice (over 24° C.).
> Thermic deficiency : twice (under 14° C.).
> Normal thermic situation : six times (between 14° and 24° C.).

Thermic and pluviometric excesses and deficiencies are represented by the following symbols :

> EP : excess precipitations.
> DP : deficient precipitations.
> ET : excess temperature.
> DT : deficient temperature.

The climatic situation for wheat in the theoretical locality considered here may be assembled in the following manner (after each symbol the frequency of the phenomenon for 10 years is noted in superior Arabic figures and the sub-period in inferior Roman figures :

$$EP_I^2 \quad EP_{II}^1 \quad EP_{III}^1 \quad EP_{IV}^3 \quad DP_I^4 \quad DP_{II}^3 \quad DP_{III}^2 \quad DP_{IV}^2 \quad ET_{IV}^2 \quad DT_{IV}^2$$

In this scheme the favourable conditions are omitted, as they naturally are obtained by subtraction. The case considered is purely theoretical, owing to the impossibility of finding so many negative combinations in any one single locality. It is, for instance, impossible to have for the same place the equivalents for excess and for deficiency of temperature in two successive years in the interval between earing and maturity.

In any case, negative phenomena which cause only slight losses may be left aside, and in the representation of climate we should consider only those phenomena which induce notable decreases in yield.

To take a concrete example, here is the formula for Umbria relative to wheat :

$$(EP_{III}\, EP_{IV})^4 - DP_{III}^2 - ET_{IV}^3$$

This schematic formula gives us an immediate idea of climatic conditions in Perugia in regard to wheat. It must, however, be completed, because I would recall that an adverse phenomenon for which the equivalent has not been exactly determined is found in Perugia with a frequency of 2 years in 10. I refer to frosts and sudden drops in temperature at flowering time. By integrating the climoscope with a table of losses, the representation becomes of greater value.

Adversity.	Frequency per 10 years.	Loss in quintals, ha.	
		Year.	10 years.
Drought	2	11	22
Excess rainfall . . .	4	9	36
Thermic excesses . .	3	6	18
Spring frosts . . .	2	7	14

We have therefore a mixed negative regime in which damage is caused through excess and deficiency of both rain and temperature.

For maize the only meteorological adversity is represented by drought during the critical period so that the climoscopic formula is reduced to :

$$DP_{II}^{5\cdot8}$$

With reference to a mean yield of 18 qnts. in favourable years, and to a mean of 7·2 in drought years (difference of 10·8 qnts.), we will thus have a loss of 62·6 qnts. (10·8 × 5·8) in a 10-year period.

For the vine we have the following formula :

$$(EP_{III} - EP_{IV})^{5.4} \quad DP_{IV}^{1.5} \quad DT_{II}^{2.3} \quad DT_{V}^{2.3}$$

Here, too, if we integrate the formula with a table of losses, the representation of climate in relation to grape production is quite conclusive (we refer to specialised cultures) :

Adversity.	Frequency per 10 years.	Loss in quintals, ha.	
		Year.	10 years.
Drought	1·5	36	54
Excess rainfall (*peronospora*, scarse lodging) . .	5·4	51	275
Frosts and spring colds .	2·3	53	122

Excess rains and thermic deficiency cause a total loss of 400 quintals in 10 years, as against the 54 quintals imputable to drought. The loss from lack of rain, on the other hand, is largely compensated by the improvement in quality of the product. The effect of thermic deficiencies during maturity (fourth sub-period), which without diminishing the crop noticeably worsens its quality (at least three times in 10 years), accentuates the damage derived from excess rainfall and thermic deficiency, which constitute the dominating group of adverse phenomena.

For the olive, still referring to Perugia, we find :

$$DP_{III}^{5} \quad DT_{III}^{3.3}$$

Rains and cold spells at harvest time affect the quality rather than the quantity of the product. For specialised cultures the quantitative losses are :

Adversity.	Frequency per 10 years.	Loss in quintals, ha.	
		Year.	10 years.
Drought	5	6·1	30·5
Fog and cold spells at flowering time . . .	3·3	8·0	26·4

Drought and cold spells undoubtedly constitute the most harmful group of phenomena.

The physical climate cannot in itself give us any idea as to the effect it has on plants if we have not determined, for every cultivated species and with reference to each single sub-period, what are the normal thermic and pluviometric situations and what the abnormal through excess or deficiency.   There is no need to point out that a temperature which is excessive for one species can be deficient for another and, similarly, the same amount of rainfall can be deficient for certain species and excessive for others.

Climatic conditions must therefore be studied in relation to the various cultivated species taken singly, so that the expressions which we have introduced—" climate of wheat ", " climate of the vine ", " climate of the olive ", etc.—assume a definite and precise significance.

The climate of Perugia, with its well-defined meteorological characteristics, gives rise to four different agricultural climates in relation to the four most important cultivated plants :

(1) mixed for wheat,
(2) dry for maize,
(3) wet–cold for the vine,
(4) dry–cold for the olive.

After what has been said, it seems unnecessary to add that only now, for the first time, has the true relationship between climate and the development and yield of the different cultivated species been clearly defined.

CHAPTER X

THE IMPORTANCE OF MICRO-CLIMATIC STUDIES IN ECOLOGICAL RESEARCH

WHEN it is required to establish the relationship between the yield of a certain plant and meteorological factors, we rely for the yield on the statistical figures from a more or less large territory, while the meteorological values correspond to the small area in which the observatory happens to be situated.

The consequence of this lack of comparability and the causes of error deriving from such a situation become particularly evident in hilly and mountainous tracts where thermic and hygroscopic conditions can differ greatly from one locality to another (even in places which lie in close proximity to one another). This is due principally to the effects produced by altitude and the orientation of the slopes.

Altitude

To give a good idea of the effect which altitude can have, it is sufficient to recall that between the equatorial and polar limits for wheat there is a distance of over 3,829 km. on the horizontal plane (corrected to eliminate the effects produced by the factor " length of day "), while at the equator, between the lowest and highest limits, respectively 900 and 3,900 metres above sea level, there is a difference of 3 km. on the vertical plane. This phenomenon is due to the rapid fall in temperature with increase in height, so that 1 km. on the vertical scale corresponds to more than 1,276 km. in latitude on the horizontal scale.

Going up the mountain-sides stretching above the Sicilian and Ionian seas, one passes in rapid succession from the altimetric limit for the orange to that of the olive, then to the vine, to wheat and, finally, on the high plains of the Aspromonte we find climatic and agricultural conditions similar to those in central-northern Sweden, where spring rye is the only cereal crop.

The effects are in great part determined by temperature, which progressively decreases with the altitude.

By thermic gradient is meant the difference in temperature (increase or decrease) for every 100 metres in altitude. This is approximately 0·5° C., but the figure varies from one place to another and should be determined separately for each region. Moreover, and as is well known, the gradient is not constant even for a given locality, but can vary between large limits according to the season. The evaluation of the effect of altitude on the thermic regime is also often complicated by the inversion of temperature. This phenomenon appears most markedly in the winter, when the masses of colder, and so heavier, air slide down along the slopes and accumulate at the bottom of the depressions in the valley. For this reason an increase of minimum temperature is observed as we gradually pass from the bottom of the valley up the slopes, until the point is reached at which altitude again prevails, leading to a progressive decrease in temperature with height.

There will therefore be a certain level of the highest minimum above which (as an effect of the altitude) and below which (as an effect of the inversion of the temperature) the minimum drops lower and lower.

In the hills around Perugia the quota for the highest minima coincides, more or less, with the hypsometric curve for 375 metres. The lowering of temperature for every 100 metres above and below this quota varies according to the season— i.e. the six hot months, or the six cold months.

Here are the decreases in ° C. for the thermic minimum for every 100 metres :

	Downwards, ° C.	Upwards, ° C.
In the cold season . .	2·0	0·8
In the hot season . .	1·6	1·8

With these measurements it becomes possible, through the readings of the central observatory only, to calculate the thermic variations with fair approximation from one spot of the region to another, according to altitude. If, for instance, the observatory at Perugia, situated at a height of 460 metres, gives a reading of 0·3° C. for the minimum temperature in the cold season, in order to calculate the approximate minimum at a point situated at 610 metres we have only to subtract 1·2° C., and so obtain −0·9° C. The figure 1·2° c. represents the product of the difference in height (150 metres) between the observatory and the quota under consideration, multiplied by 0·8° C., which is the difference in temperature found for every increase of 100 metres in altitude.

For another locality at, say, 215 metres, we will first have to correct the figure by taking into consideration the difference between 460 metres (position of the observatory) and 375 metres (inversion point).

To do this, we multiply the difference between the two positions (85 metres) by 0·8, and the product so obtained, added to the reading of the observatory, gives an approximate minimum of 0·98° C. for quota 375.

Finally, between 375 and 215 there exists a difference of 160 metres, which multiplied by 2 (for every 100 metres in the direction of the valley there is a decrease of roughly 2°, owing to the inversion of temperature) gives 3·2.

Subtracting 3·2 from 0·98 we obtain −2·2, which approximately represents the minimum at a height of 215 metres when the central observatory registers 0·3° C.

·   ·   ·   ·   ·

Exposure of the Slopes

Meteorological conditions, especially in relation to the thermic factor, are apt to vary considerably on slopes which, although at the same quota for height, are differently exposed.

Experience shows that slopes facing south are in a privileged position compared with those facing north, and this is easily understood when we recall that in the Apennines it is possible to have the olive on one side of the watershed and the chestnut on the other, both at the same altitude. The olive, as is well known, has particularly high temperature requirements, while the chestnut adapts itself quite well to a cold regime on the mountains.

By research it has been possible to establish the variations of temperature on the different slopes compared to the horizontal plane for the territory around Perugia. These are :

Slope facing south	. . . .	$+1\cdot0°$ C.
,, ,, west	. . . .	$-0\cdot6°$ C.
,, ,, east	. . . .	$-0\cdot7°$ C.
,, ,, north	. . . .	$-4\cdot0°$ C.

The contrast between the two slopes (north and south) is such that in the same zone it is possible to have hot spells for wheat on the slope facing south and the thermometer below the thermic limit for hot spells on the slope facing north.

In the same manner, the plant may be damaged by thermic deficiency on the slopes facing north and still have a favourable situation on those facing south.

. . . . .

The equivalent of thermic deficiency for the sub-period for the development of the fruits of the chestnut, from setting to the maximum weight, was calculated by Briccoli at $11\cdot5°$ C.

In the summer of 1938 on the mountains around Bologna temperatures were very low in the second half of August and the first half of September. The observatory of Loiano, 800 metres altitude, close to the altimetric limit for the chestnut, registered a mean of $15\cdot5°$ C. for the period 21st August to 10th September against the general mean of $19\cdot5°$ C. This observatory is situated on a slope facing south-west, so that taking the $15\cdot5°$ C. recorded, there would have been a temperature of $11\cdot3°$ C. on the slope facing north (making the necessary correction), and so deficient for the development of the chestnut. Given the fact that the observatory of Loiano is situated on the south-west slope, the deviation of this from the figure of the horizontal plane will be $+0\cdot2°$ C., or a difference of $4\cdot2°$ C. when compared with the slope facing north ($15\cdot5 - 4\cdot2 = 11\cdot3°$ C.).

Rocchi observed that on the north slope fruit was incomplete and badly formed, while on the other slopes, although a little late, the chestnuts reached normal form and dimensions.

. . . . .

Further to the above facts, the determination of the Iodine Index for olive oil in connection with the orientation of the slopes is of particular interest.

All fats are glycerids of stearic, palmitic, oleic and other acids. The stearic and palmitic compounds at ordinary temperature are solids, while the oleic compound is liquid; the larger, therefore, the quantity of oleic acid in a fat, the more will it tend towards the liquid state, and the higher the content of stearic and palmitic acids, the more will the fat (in this case the oil) tend towards the solid condition.

Neither the palmitic nor the stearic acids absorb iodine, as their molecules do not present double bonds and there are no free carbon valencies which could be saturated by iodine. This is not so for oleic acid, which has free valencies which can become saturated. The higher, therefore, the Iodine Index (i.e. the quantity of iodine expressed in milligrammes absorbed by one gramme of oil), the higher the quantities of liquid fatty acids present.

In general, for olive oil the Iodine Index varies according to the latitude—between 79° on the equatorial limit and 88° on the polar limit of distribution of the plant.

I draw the reader's attention to the iodine number for olive oil of the " Agogia " variety on slopes differently orientated (in the Perugian territory), and of the " Imperiale " variety found on the slopes facing north and south of the Aspromonte (Reggio Calabria).

Slope facing south locality.	Iodine number.
La Rimessa	80·7
Palazzetto di Riccione .	82·5
Fontana	81·2
San Pasquale di Compresso .	82·5
Tiro a Segno (Perugia) . .	81·8
Southern slope in Aspromonte	80·9
Mean	81·6

Slope facing north locality.	Iodine number.
Palazzetto di Agello . . .	87·2
Comurlo	86·6
Cura di S. Antonio . . .	84·3
Montepecoraro	87·0
Fonte Acquaviva . . .	85·7
Monte del Lago	83·8
Morello di Compresso . .	86·5
Northern slope in Aspromonte .	87·1
Mean . . .	86·0

In research carried out on flax in Soviet territory between the 41° parallel and the 60th north, Ivanov observed that with decrease in temperature, as he moved closer to the pole, the Iodine Index increased, and this because with the lowering of temperature the percentage of liquid (fluid) fatty acids increased.

In perfect analogy, we have found a decisively higher Iodine Index on the slopes facing north, which have an average temperature of 5° C. lower than those found on the slopes facing south. On the latter slopes the percentage of oleic acid decreases, while the content in palmitic and stearic acids increases : these, as we have seen, are solid fatty acids.

The difference between the two groups of figures is so remarkable that no doubt is left as to the precision of the determinations.

In perfect harmony, the analytical data for the slopes facing west and east present the following results : 83·3 for the west slope, and 83·7 for the east slope, and we recall that the difference in temperature in respect of the horizontal plane is, in perfect accordance with the quoted figures, −0·6° C. for the slope facing west and −0·7° C. for that facing east.

． ． ． ． ．

We must not, however, believe that the effects (relative to the orientation of the slopes) will always correspond to the N.–E.–W.–S. sequence for increasing temperature and to S.–W.–E.–N. for decreasing temperature.

It may well be, in fact, that with regard to a given biological phenomenon, the temperature on the west slope (in relation to the specific exigencies of a given plant) might be closer to the optimum than it is on any of the other slopes.

As an example we give the recorded percentage of fats in the olives of the Umbrian territory.

Slope.	Percentage of oil.	Variation from the mean normal.
West	22·79	0·88
South	22·42	0·51
East	22·24	0·33
North	20·21	−1·70

The largest yield in oil is thus found on the west slope : this is followed respectively by those facing south and east : lastly, with a notable difference, the slope facing north.

The intensity of the damage brought about by thermic deficiency (frosts and waves of cold) changes in relation to the micro-climatic situation occasioned by the different topographical conditions. It is therefore possible to have widespread damage and slight losses, respectively, on two positions lying in close proximity to one another.

The exceptional cold wave which struck Italy in February 1929 did enormous damage to the olive, and by the intensity of its action made it possible to determine the negative effect of ambiental factors in relation to the complex micro-climatic conditions.

In estimating the damage we adopted the following grading (indicating the parts that were destroyed) :

1st-grade Damage.		Part of the year-old branches destroyed.
2nd ,,	,,	All the year-old branches destroyed.
3rd ,,	,,	One-third of secondary branches destroyed.
4th ,,	,,	One-half of secondary branches destroyed.
5th ,,	,,	All the secondary branches destroyed.
6th ,,	,,	Part of the primary branches destroyed.
7th ,,	,,	All the primary branches (which were to be cut) destroyed.
8th ,,	,,	Part of the trunk destroyed.
9th ,,	,,	The whole trunk destroyed, so that the plants had to be cut at the base.
10th ,,	,,	Destruction of the radical apparatus followed by death of the plant.

Here, too, the extent of the damage varies within wide limits according to altitude and the position of the slopes, but with different modality from that previously described. Stagnating fog and the thawing processes of the tissues in the rapid passage from cold night to sunrise come into play and have a marked effect.

In fact, it may be observed that in relation to altitude, above a certain quota losses are insignificant, while below it, and for distances which may be of only 20–30 metres in the vertical direction, we find extensive damage.

At Castiglione del Lago, in an olive-grove facing east, the plants were badly hit and seventh- to ninth-grade damage was encountered up to a height of 270 metres. As we climbed higher, the damage observed decreased, and at 300 metres the loss was limited to the complete defoliation of the branches (damage below that of first grade).

In another olive-grove at Umbertide, on a slope facing south, the contrast is again quite evident. Sixth- and seventh-grade damage up to a height of 400 metres was found, while above this quota there was a sudden drop to 0·5 grade of damage and the loss was limited to leaves and a few young branches.

The same phenomena may be observed all over the Umbrian region, though not always with such marked effect. Now, the point above which the damage decreases so rapidly coincides with the highest level reached by the stagnating nocturnal fog, a level which approximately coincides with the point of the highest minima, as already stated when we discussed temperature inversions.

What has been seen above is congruent with the observations made that the humid–cold regime is particularly harmful to living organisms, while in a dry–cold regime the plant is able to withstand considerable falls in temperature. I would like to recall the case of an apricot plantation in California (already referred to elsewhere) which in full bloom withstood an extraordinary fall in temperature without great damage, thanks to the dryness of the atmosphere.

.   .   .   .   .

The following are the figures relative to mean intensity of damage corresponding to the four exposures (see scale) in Umbria, taken from the examination of a great number of olive-groves situated over the most varied topographical conditions :

Slope facing south	.	.	.	.	5·3
,, ,, east	.	.	.	.	5·2
,, ,, west	.	.	.	.	3·5
,, ,, north	.	.	.	.	2·9

We find the greatest damage on the slopes facing east and south.

When the nocturnal minimum is reached temperature begins to rise rapidly. The thawing process of the tissues on the east and south slopes, directly hit by the sun's rays from the earliest dawn, takes place rapidly and destructively : the tissues and the cells composing them are, as it were, thrown into a state of collapse, and as a consequence we find the bark detached, peeling of the wood and consequent rot; the phenomena of necrosis in the various parts of the plant have been observed in many cases.

On the slope facing north, however, which in winter remains longer in the shade, the thawing processes took place regularly and slowly and the resulting lesions were much smaller.

In this manner the statements of Gaetani and Vizzotto that the slopes facing north are less affected by frost in spite of the lower sum of temperatures and the more accentuated thermic drop, are confirmed.

Valley Unit

The effect of a particular orientation of the slope on temperature can be quite different from one region to another, according to the general conditions of the relief. It is for this reason that we insist in practice on the study of the local character of micro-climate—that is, the adjustment of the data from a given observatory in order to determine the corresponding values of the temperature for the various points in the surrounding territory.

A slope with a certain exposure—facing south, for instance—may present different conditions of temperature according to whether it is situated in a valley stretching to the north, or in one opening to the south.

It is opportune to mention here the meaning of Valley Unit.

From a climatological point of view, we call a " Valley Unit " that complex of geo-morphological values (dimensions, form and orientation) of a valley, or of the whole basin of a river, which gives particular characteristics to the enclosed air masses, distinguishing them from the masses of air of the surrounding atmosphere.

Each " Valley Unit " in this way limits a more or less defined mass of air, whose meteorological characteristics are decisively influenced by the general orientation of the valley and by its transversal and longitudinal profiles.

I will just mention that in the mountain groups of central Italy fruit cultures can, under equal conditions of latitude and altitude, prosper in the valleys open towards the south-west, while this is found impossible in those facing north-east and, consequently, more exposed to thermic deficiencies and sudden variations in temperature. In spring, at flowering time, the wind from the south-west may cause sudden and favourable increases of temperature, while the north-eastern wind may cause sudden and harmful falls in temperature.

The Valley Unit organically links micro-climatic values with surrounding climate.

The thermic contrast existing between the slopes facing north and those facing south is particularly noticeable, considering the total sum of available temperatures, near the polar and equatorial limits for cultivated plants.   Towards the north, where the distribution limit for the various crops is determined by thermic deficiency, the area of distribution will gradually be reduced to a number of areas—that is, topographical islets—corresponding to the slopes facing south.

The equivalent for deficiency is, in fact, first reached on the slope facing north, then on those facing east and west successively.   The cultivation of any particular plant will therefore, when moving in the direction of the pole, first disappear on the slopes orientated towards the north and, eventually, it will be only on those facing south that we shall encounter favourable thermic conditions.   Consequently we find that extreme topographical islets occur on the southern slopes near the polar limit for culture (cold limit).   Moving in the direction of the Equator, on the other hand, we shall find quite the opposite. The equivalent for excess will first be reached on the slopes facing south, then on those orientated towards west and east, and the culture will gradually disappear until, at last, only the cold slope—that facing north—will have topographical islets corresponding to the northern slopes on the equatorial limit of culture (hot limit).

From what has been said above, the existence of particular effects of altitude and slope orientation having repercussions on temperature is undoubted. It is essential therefore, in regions with a varied topography, to make the necessary micro-climatic calculations in order to utilise the meteorological data of the observatory for evaluating, with a sufficient approximation, the temperature figures at different points of the surrounding territory.

CHAPTER XI

AXES OF FREQUENCY, WEATHER CARTOGRAMS, CLIMATIC AXES AND PHYSIOGRAPHIC ZONES

WE have until now considered each point in itself, regardless of what the bio-meteorological situation in other points might be. We now pass to a comparative examination of the situations at the different points spread over a given area and to their general co-ordination in the geographical plane.

There is no doubt that the representation of such a complex matter is of particular value, in that it enables us to unite into a single group all those places where a given phenomenon, of favourable or unfavourable nature through excess or deficiency, appears with the same characteristics; and, conversely, to have a measure of the difference between two places situated in different zones.

For this schematisation we use :

(1) the axes of frequency and the weather cartograms ;
(2) the climatic axes and physiographic zones.

Axes of Frequency and Weather Cartograms

Moving from a point with optimal rainfall conditions for a given crop and proceeding towards the distributional limit for the said crop, the frequency of the adverse phenomenon " rain deficiency ", for instance, gradually increases.

The segment along which, departing from the zero mark, the frequency gradually increases to one, two, three times in a 10-year period up to a maximum of ten (namely, when rain deficiency occurs every year), is called the " axis of frequency for drought ".

These frequencies are expressed as percentages. If, therefore, drought is found twice in a 10-year period in a certain station, we say that this station has a drought frequency of 20%.

Here is the axis of frequency for drought during the critical

period of the maize-plant in the Mediterranean region, with the
corresponding mean yields per hectare :

Frequency, %.	Yields, quintals per ha.	Frequency, %.	Yields, quintals per ha.
0	35·5	60	16·4
10	32·0	70	13·0
20	28·7	80	10·1
30	26·0	90	7·0
40	22·8	100	3·8
50	19·5		

The frequency has naturally been valued on the basis of the
equivalents for drought, constructing the relative climoscope
for each station, and then counting how many times in a 20-year
period (at least) the sum of precipitations during the critical
period was below 46 mm.

The same method can be applied for excess rainfall, just as it
can be for deficient and excess temperature in the successive
sub-periods of development of the plant.

To give an idea of the intensity of the frequency in a 10-year
period, the following scale may be adopted :

Very frequent	6·0 and more
Frequent	6·0–3·0
Intermediate	3·0–1·5
Rare	1·5–0·5
Very rare	0·5 and less

Weather Cartograms

Research carried out by Brounov on the distribution of
drought in Russia is worthy of particular attention as regards
the method of representation of meteorological phenomena
related to agriculture. Brounov considers dry a 10-day period
in which there were 5 mm. or less of rainfall, and on this basis
calculates drought frequency in the various provinces of the
U.S.S.R., period by period, from the first one in April to the
third in October. The process is simple. Wishing, for instance, to determine, at any particular spot supplied with a
meteorological observatory, the drought frequency for, say,
the first decade in June, he calculated the number of times
over a 20-year period in which the sum of precipitations in that

M

particular decade was equal to or less than 5 mm. Supposing
that this minimum limit had been surpassed eight times in the
negative sense, we would then say that the drought frequency
in the first 10 days of June for that station is 40% (four times
over a 10-year period).

By this system Brounov gives us one single and constant
equivalent for drought of 5 mm. per 10-day period for all
crops at any phase of development. In view of what we have
said on the equivalents, it is not difficult to appreciate that such
a representation, even if it might have some meteorological
significance, is of no use for our purposes.

It is sufficient to recall that the drought equivalent for maize
during the critical period preceding earing is 46 mm. The
corresponding 10-day periods must therefore be considered dry
whenever the total precipitation is equal to or below 15·3 mm.
(46 ÷ 3).

All those points in which a negative phenomenon repeats itself with the same frequency are united by a curve known as
the frequency curve. These curves drawn on a map give us
the " weather cartograms " and a clear idea of the geographical
distribution of the phenomenon considered. The area between
two successive curves may be defined as a " frequency zone ".

In the evaluation of the frequency of summer drought for
maize we shall naturally have to take as a basis the 30 days
corresponding to the critical period (Fig. 23).

This 30-day interval is found at different times, according
to the locality and the distribution of the temperature, which
decreases gradually with altitude and latitude, giving rise to
a more and more accentuated delay for the dates at which the
different phases of development take place.

Moreover, owing to the irregular distribution of land and
sea, the position, height and orientation of the mountain
ranges, temperature varies considerably, naturally influencing
the development of isophanes and the isoclimatic curves
which are bent and undulating, a situation which is also reflected
in the contours of the zones of frequency.

The frequency of drought relative to maize at the critical
period varies within wide limits in Italy (Fig. 24).

From the Alpine region, with a regime of summer rains in which drought hardly ever occurs, one reaches certain sectors

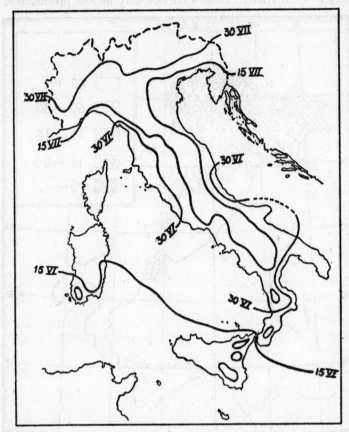

FIG. 23. ISOPHANES FOR THE END OF THE CRITICAL PERIOD OF MAIZE IN ITALY.

of South Italy where this negative factor repeats itself practically every year, and so renders the cultivation of maize impossible unless one resorts to irrigation.

We distinguish five frequency zones :

1st zone	.	.	.	.	0·5 and less
2nd ,,	.	.	.	.	0·5–1·5
3rd ,,	.	.	.	.	1·5–3·0
4th ,,	.	.	.	.	3·0–6·0
5th ,,	.	.	.	.	6·0 and more

With the gradual increase in frequency, it evidently becomes more and more necessary to choose hardy varieties resistant to drought, even though these varieties may be less productive.

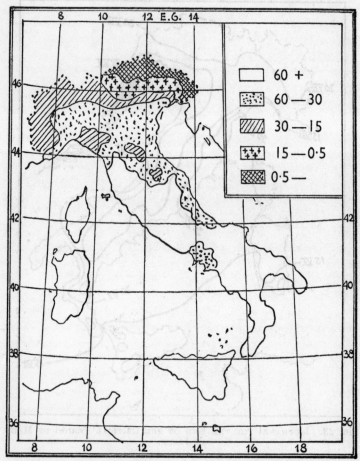

FIG. 24. DROUGHT FREQUENCY ZONES FOR MAIZE IN ITALY.

When one adversity alone (such as drought for maize) is harmful, the zones of frequency coincide with the physiographic zones mentioned below.

Climatic Axes and Physiographic Zones

By a physiographic zone is meant the localities which present the same climatic and meteorological characteristics with regard to a given plant. The soils and topographical conditions cannot, it is evident, be utilised to divide the area of distribution of a plant into physiographic zones. To do this it becomes necessary, in fact, to base oneself on factors which act in such a way as to define the contours of the said area, clearly separating the locality in which the plant under consideration is cultivated (or might be cultivated), from those in which it is not cultivated (or in which it could not be cultivated).

The environmental factors which act in this way are meteorological, principally temperature and rainfall.

The different combinations of the climatic axes give us a rational basis on which we can theoretically project the physiographic zones.

By a climatic axis is meant the linear segment which joins the point in which deficiency reaches its maximum frequency to that in which, after having passed through zero (of frequency), we reach the maximum frequency for excess.

We will thus have a pluviometric climatic axis and a thermic climatic axis : these two axes are brought perpendicular to one another on the same plane, so that at the point of intersection the frequency for the respective adversities is zero (this is the optimal condition), which gives us a rational system of geographical representation of the phenomenon and a theoretical basis for the determination of physiographic zones.

As we move along the frequency axis for a particular adverse phenomenon (say thermic excess), passing from the zero to the maximum—namely, to a frequency of 100% (ten times in a 10-year period)—the yield progressively decreases as this frequency increases until, at the maximum, the yield has decreased to a minimum through excess of heat ; this in spite of optimal conditions in respect of the pluviometric factor. In a purely conventional manner, we make the value for the yield at this point coincide with the limit of practical cultivation (beyond this point cultivation is economically unsound).

Moving either to left or right of the extreme thermic point, the yield will naturally go below the limit of practicability, in that the conditions relative to the factor rainfall worsen through deficiency or excess.

In order to remain inside the limit for yield, we have to diminish the frequency for the adverse phenomenon " thermic excess ", and the same may be said for the extreme points of the other three axes of frequency relative to thermic deficiency and to deficient and excess rainfall, so that the complete series of limiting yields will theoretically be integrated by a circle which joins those points in which a maximum frequency for the negative situations (compatible with the minimum convenient yield) is reached. The other circles inscribed within the outer one successively unite the points at which the sum of frequencies progressively diminish, and therefore in which the yields progressively increase (Fig. 25).

The horizontal lines parallel to the pluviometric climatic axis join together, above the same axis, the points in which thermic excess repeats itself with successively increasing frequency from 1 to 10 (frequency of 1 on the first line, of 2 on the second, etc.).

The horizontal lines below the said axis join together the points of equal frequency for thermic deficiency (and here too we have a successive scale from 1 to 10).

The vertical lines parallel to the climatic axis for temperature join together the points of equal frequency for drought on the left, and on the right the points of equal frequency for excess rainfall. The diagram joins together and co-ordinates all the possible pluviometric and thermic situations under which wheat is, or can be, cultivated.

This diagram, which may be divided in four sectors— (1) humid–hot, (2) humid–cold, (3) dry–hot, (4) dry–cold— quite fairly represents the " climate for wheat ", for instance, co-ordinating all the bio-atmospheric combinations in a single organic system. At the same time it enables us to represent schematically the climatic conditions of any place in relation to wheat, so as to facilitate the comparison of different points scattered in the area of distribution of this cereal.

For example, four typical situations are :

Alicante (Spain)	.	.	. Dry–hot
Viatka (U.S.S.R.)	.	.	. Dry–cold
Bergen (Norway)	.	.	. Humid–cold
Burgos (Spain).	.	.	. Humid–hot

Alicante. This is a typical station for the hot–dry zone. The effects of a hot spell are serious six times in a 10-year period (both as regards the quality and the quantity of the product), while drought exercises a deleterious influence with equal frequency—i.e. 6 years in 10—and can harm the crops not only in spring but also in the autumn and winter.

Cold is reported only once in a 10-year period, and its action is not considered particularly harmful. Only once is a hot–wet condition found, and therefore there is no serious harm from rust.

Rains are always looked upon as favourable, as are the summers in which temperature is well below normal, a situation which, without reaching the equivalent for deficiency, removes the possibility of damage from a hot spell.

The polygon for Alicante, therefore, gives us a well-defined example for a station in the hot–dry zone.

Viatka is situated in the cold–dry zone. Drought in spring is present with a frequency of 7 years in 10. Cold is harmful to spring wheats five times in a 10-year period, creating difficulties during the development and sometimes rendering maturation impossible.

The cultivation of winter wheats becomes a problem owing to the adverse conditions encountered in winter. Great drops in temperature on open ground, frosts and thaw, asphyxia under the snow, etc., damage the crop.

Harm from excess humidity in spring occurs only with a frequency of 1 to 2 years in 10 and has no particularly damaging effect, at least, in well-drained soils.

Viatka can well represent, therefore, a typical cold–dry station.

Bergen. For the cold–wet combination we take the station of Bergen, on the west coast of Norway, where winter adversities and thermic deficiencies, at maturation, are found with a frequency of at least 6·5 years in 10; while practically every year excess rains produce harmful results in the south. For this reason, the cultivation of wheat, even though restricted within certain boundaries owing to particularly favourable microclimatic situations, is notably reduced, and is in any case damaged by excess rainfall and humidity with a mean of 7 years in 10.

Under such general conditions, near the polar limit of wheat distribution, the yield is not only low but is also poor in quality, often through imperfect maturation.

This typical cold–wet station may be represented by thermic deficiencies and excess rainfall only. Drought or thermic excesses are never encountered.

Burgos. Finally for the hot–wet zone, we refer to a complex which can, in effect, present quite different characteristics. In the inter-tropical zones the dominating cereal is rice, which does wonderfully in a hot–wet environment. In those zones wheat is also found, though in greatly reduced quantities. In such cases, besides abundant downpours (which lead to lodging and development of weeds), are also found constantly high temperatures, causing widespread attacks by cryptogamic pests, especially rust. This, however, does not reach the equivalent for excess in the sub-period from earing to maturation (mean temperature of 24° C.). On the other hand, the phenomenon of hot spell, brought on by high temperatures (maximum temperature 32° C.) accompanied by winds, is never found.

In such regions we can well speak of a decisively negative hot–wet condition. But this situation would not be comparable with that already described for the other three sectors, where the equivalents for deficiency and excess of rainfall and temperature are, with greater or lesser frequency, reached and surpassed. It was therefore necessary to find an example in which the most harmful adversity was represented by excess rainfall plus hot spell and where drought did not make itself particularly felt.

This situation of humidity plus hot spell (without or with only slight effects from drought) is not very frequent; but I eventually found it possible to single out a clear example, documented by official meteoro-agricultural bulletins, in the province of Burgos (Spain).

Hot spell is encountered with a frequency of 5·4 years in 10, while damage from excess rainfall and humidity has a frequency of six times in a 10-year period; the negative effects on the yield are quite evident.

Drought is a rare occurrence—1·5 times in 10 years—and nearly always manifests itself in autumn or in winter, so that the negative effects derived therefrom are practically nil. The presence of cold has been reported, but the effect is only a delay in maturation, without in any way damaging the plants. This delay renders the crop more susceptible to possible and more frequent attacks of hot spell later on.

Only once in a 10-year period is the return of cold found to be harmful at flowering time.

The dominating action of the "excess rainfall–hot spell" combination becomes quite clear, and the polygon for Burgos may well be taken as a typical example of a hot–wet station.

The varied relationship between land and sea, the alternation of plains, mountain ranges and high plateaux, the widespread

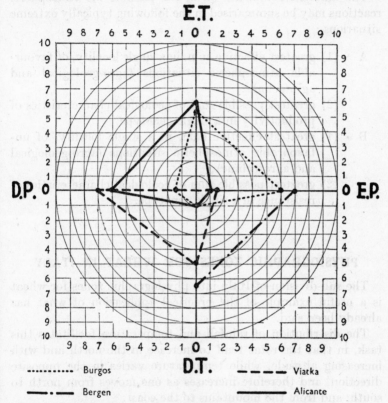

FIG. 25. THERMO-PLUVIOMETRIC DIAGRAM FOR WHEAT.

E.T. = Excess Temperature; D.T. = Deficient temperature; E.P. = Excess Precipitation; D.P. = Deficient Precipitation.

forests and the great deserts, renders the distribution of temperature and rainfall values rather confused, and as a natural consequence the physiography of wheat becomes extremely complicated.

The diagram, however—an abstract representation based on absolute values—enables us to single out and co-ordinate the different components of the geographical framework of wheat in a very satisfactory manner (Fig. 25).

The different complexes of all the possible bio-atmospheric reactions may be summarised in the following typically extreme situations :

A = (1) greatest effective sum, in a single locality, of favourable atmospheric situations (agro-geological and agrotechnic);

    (2) greatest possible sum of ecological characteristics of productivity in a single genotype.

B = (1) greatest effective sum, in a single locality, of unfavourable atmospheric situations (agro-geological and agrotechnic);

    (2) greatest possible sum of ecological characteristics of resistance in a single genotype.

PHYSIOGRAPHIC ZONES FOR WHEAT IN ITALY

The sub-division of Italy into physiographic zones for wheat is a useful example of the practical application of what has already been said.

The distribution of rainfall and temperature facilitates this task, in that the rains tend to increase in the north and with increasing altitude, while temperature varies in the opposite direction, and therefore increases as one moves from north to south, and from the mountains to the coast.

We can therefore visualise a dry–hot zone in the south and along the coastline, and a humid–cold one in the north and in the mountains : between these two extremes we find an intermediate zone in which the two groups of adverse phenomena tend to balance one another.

On page 171 is shown the climoscope for rainfall (relative to the third and fourth sub-periods) at three stations, the first of

which is situated in the arid region, the second in the intermediate region and the third in the wet zone—Agrigento, Ancona
and Cuneo :

Climascope for Rainfall—10-*year Period*
Wheat.
Rain, mm.

Agrigento :									
Earing .	10	76	33	24	23	27	41	47	7	37
Maturity .	16	3	0	14	10	25	6	7	6	2
Ancona :									
Earing .	47	88	95	78	54	22	64	16	21	117
Maturity .	41	10	19	53	144	25	54	119	11	128
Cuneo :									
Earing .	74	83	78	32	139	241	78	91	162	235
Maturity .	171	33	103	26	88	82	118	39	63	129

In Agrigento, as may readily be seen, where rain is never
excessive, we find fifteen cases in which drought occurred :
seven in the month before earing (equivalent for drought
40 mm.), and eight in the month after earing (equivalent for
drought 15 mm.).   In Cuneo, by contrast, there is but a single
case of deficiency, while there are eight cases of excess—four in
the month before earing (equivalent for excess 116 mm.), and
four in the month after earing (equivalent for excess 92 mm.).
Lastly, for Ancona, situated in the intermediate zone, there
are five cases for drought (three before earing and two at
maturity) and four of excess (one before earing and three during
maturity).

Co-ordinating the sum of the frequencies with the losses
imputable to meteorological adversities in the two extreme
situations, the representative value of the physiographical zones
emerges all the more clearly.

In order to bring out the positions and contrasts between the
two regions, I will now deal with the provinces of Foggia and
Reggio Emilia.

Foggia is situated in the hot–dry sector where the meteorological, soil and agrotechnic conditions are not very favourable :
the yield of wheat has a mean of 13 quintals, while yields
of 18 quintals or more represent the maxima obtainable
in years in which there are no accentuated meteorological
adversities.

The following table is a classification of mean yields in quintals :

Abundant	18 quintals
Good	15 ,,
Medium	13 ,,
Mediocre	10 ,,
Scarce	6 ,,

I now quote for each of the adverse phenomena :

A = the frequency, $i.e.$ the number of times the phenomenon occurs in 10 years;

B = the yearly loss, imputable to the adverse phenomenon;

C = the loss due to the adverse phenomenon for a 10-year period (AB).

The determinations were carried out from a considerable body of meteoro-agricultural data for the period 1880–1942.

Foggia. Losses of Wheat and Frequency of Loss

Adverse phenomenon.	A. Frequency per 10 years.	B. Loss, quintals. per ha.	C. Loss for 10 years. ($A \times B$)
Drought	3·7	4·4	16·3
Hot spell	1·7	5·2	8·8
Rust	0·4	6·5	2·6
Lodging	1·7	2·0	3·4
Cold spells during flowering.	1·4	1·4	2·0

Drought and hot spells are the two dominant adverse phenomena, these being the cause of a loss of 25 quintals in 10 years.

Considering that we are in a typically hot–dry zone, the effects of spring frosts are remarkable. Though it is rare, frost takes the plant by surprise during the delicate phases of flowering and setting, with a consequent thinning out of the ears. The causes are certainly to be sought in the notable earliness of the date of earing due to a mild winter, a precociousness which exposes the plant, already in an advanced state of development, to the insidious action of frost.

Twice, in 1914 and in 1930, rust had the effect of lowering the yield well below normal. This adversity is, however, rare owing to the general lack of humidity, but when, either because of scattered downpours or dew and thick fogs, a favourable hydric and hygroscopic situation is created, the high temperatures common in southern Italy make the attack of the fungus particularly harmful.

In the territory of Reggio Emilia, in spite of the frequency and intensity of several adverse meteorological conditions, the undoubtedly more favourable soil and agrotechnic conditions lead to decidedly higher yields.

For the various classes of yield we have the following series :

Abundant	30	quintals
Good	26	,,
Medium	23	,,
Mediocre	17	,,
Scarce	14	,,

For each of the principal groups of adverse phenomena we now give the frequency and losses, singly and as a whole for a 10-year period.

Reggio Emilia.   Losses of Wheat and Frequency of Loss

Adverse phenomenon.	A. Frequency per 10 years.	B. Loss, quintals per ha.	C. Loss for 10 years. $(A \times B)$
Drought	1·0	2·8	2·8
Hot spell	0·7	9·1	6·4
Rust	2·5	2·5	6·2
Lodging	5·1	4·7	24·0
Cold spells during flowering	1·8	2·1	3·8

Excess rainfall (causing lodging, rust and weeds) and thermic deficiency are responsible for the loss of 33·8 quintals ; a figure 3·7 times greater than the 9·1 imputable to drought and thermic excesses.

It must furthermore be noted that the introduction of early wheat such as " Ardito ", " Mentana ", etc., has considerably reduced the frequency, and consequently the amount, of the damage caused by hot spells, thus accentuating still more the difference between the negative actions of the two groups of phenomena.

To give a comparative idea of the situation in the provinces under consideration, I draw the attention of the reader to the following table of the losses imputable to drought and hot spells on one hand, and to lodging, rust and cold on the other, for the two provinces :

	Foggia.	Reggio Emilia.
Drought and hot spells .	25·0	9·1
Lodging, rust and cold spells .	7·9	33·8

In Foggia, situated in the hot–dry zone, the loss over 10 years through drought and hot spells is 3·2 times greater than that imputable to the opposite phenomena, while in the region of Reggio Emilia, found in the humid–cold belt, the damage due to excessive rains, rust and sudden colds is 3·7 times greater than that caused by hot spell and drought.

The entity of the loss is therefore a confirmation of the frequency values of the different adversities.

The humid–cold region in its turn can be sub-divided into two zones, cold and humid, according to whether the greater damage is caused by excess humidity (lodging, rust and weeds) or thermic deficiency, which in a few places is said to be the worst adversity for wheat during the winter.

Cold Zone.   Damage due to winter adversities constitutes the dominant phenomenon, followed by excess humidity. This zone includes certain sectors of the province of Cuneo and certain, more or less extensive, stretches of the Alpine region and high plains of the Apennines (see Fig. 26, Zone D).

Although it is true to say that the phenomenon (damage in winter) can in certain cases be the most harmful for wheat, it is, however, far from reaching the intensity found in Scandinavian countries, Central Europe and U.S.S.R., where, in proximity to the limit of winter wheat, it is often necessary to re-sow on a large scale in spring (with spring wheats) to make up for the losses caused to the crop by winter adversities.

Humid Zone.   The valley of the Po is typical. In the greater part also of central Italy excess rainfall and humidity constitute the dominant adverse phenomena, thus favouring lodging, rust and the development of weeds. Thermic deficiencies in this zone (Zone C) do not generally occur.

Intermediate Zone.   The damage caused by the two groups

of adverse phenomena tend to balance each other. This zone includes the coastal and sub-coastal regions of central Italy, the hilly sectors of Campania and Lucania, and more particularly, the Maremma of Lazio and Tuscany (Zone B).

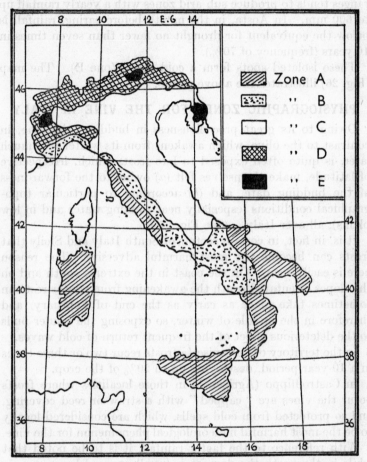

FIG. 26. PHYSIOGRAPHIC ZONES OF WHEAT IN ITALY.

Hot–Dry Zone. Drought and hot spells undoubtedly constitute the dominant meteorological adversities (Zone A).

Dry–Cold Zone. In Val Venosta and some parts of Trentino it is the structure of the sandy, gravelly soils, incapable of preserving water for long rather than rain deficiency, that obliges local farmers to turn to irrigation, even for wheat culture.

Moreover, on the high valleys of Piedmont, facing west, and particularly in Val d'Aosta, the orientation of the mountain ranges tends to produce sub-arid zones with a yearly rainfall up to 600 mm. In Aosta, in the month before earing, rainfall is below the equivalent for drought no fewer than seven times in 10 years (frequency of 70%).

These isolated spots form a cold zone (Zone E). The map (Fig. 26) illustrates the above points.

PHYSIOGRAPHIC ZONES FOR THE VINE IN ITALY

Owing to its great precociousness in budding, the vine, in contrast to the olive, which awakens from its winter rest much later, is quite often exposed to late frosts which, irrespective of latitude, make themselves felt (a) owing to the forwardness of the budding date, and (b) according to particular topographical conditions (especially near running water and in low plains), all over Italy. (See Fig. 27.)

It is, in fact, in certain sectors of South Italy and Sicily that frosts can become the most harmful adversity. The reason here is easily seen. On the coast in the extreme south and on the slopes orientated south the awakening from winter rest can sometimes take place as early as the end of February, and therefore in the middle of winter, so exposing the tender buds to the deleterious effect of the frequent return of cold waves.

In the territory of Caltanisetta frosts recur two or three times in a 10-year period, destroying up to 20% of the crop.

In Castrofilippo (Agrigento) in those localities where frosts occur the vines are " capped " with a straw or reed covering, and so protected from cold spells, which are considered locally to be the most harmful meteorological phenomenon for the vine.

With reference to the factor rainfall, it is to be noted that while in the north the damage is usually caused by excess, in South Italy and on the islands round the mainland it is drought which damages the vine both quantitatively and qualitatively.

To bring out the contrast between the two extreme situations yet more, I will give the contrasting examples of Foggia (where there is a regime of scarce precipitation) and Reggio Emilia (a wet region).

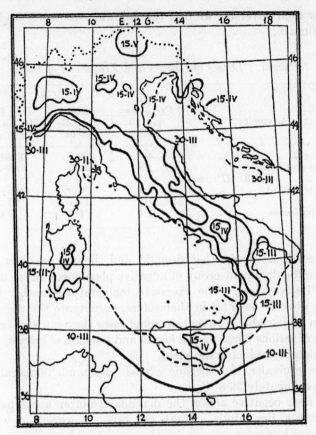

FIG. 27. ISOPHANES OF VINE BUDDING IN ITALY.

For Foggia I give the mean values in quintals per hectare for the vine.

Yield of Grapes. Foggia

Classes of yield.	Quintals of grapes per ha.
Abundant	102
Good and satisfactory	75
Medium	50
Mediocre	35
Low	21

N

For each adversity we find the following frequency and loss in quintals :

Foggia.   Losses of Grapes and Frequency of Loss

Adversity.	A. Frequency per 10 years.	B. Loss, quintals per ha.	C. Loss for 10 years. $(A \times B)$
Drought	4·0	29·5	118·0
Excessive heat . . .	2·8	32·3	90·4
„ rainfall (*Peronospora*, etc.) . .	2·8	36·0	100·8
Hail	1·3	17·1	22·2
Spring frosts . . .	1·1	6·4	7·0

There is no doubt that drought and thermic excesses constitute the dominant group of negative phenomena in regard to quantitative yield. The excessive temperatures, rather than being directly harmful in themselves, accentuate the negative action of drought. However, in some cases they can also be the cause of serious burns on the leaves and bunches of grapes, thus considerably reducing the yield.

The equivalent for thermic excess (maximum temperature) is approximately 39·8° C.

In their negative action the maxima are often accompanied by strong, dry winds. There are cases, however, in which excessive temperatures can by themselves be harmful, even in total absence of wind. For instance, in Algiers on the 25th June 1934, in a regime of perfect calm, the temperature remained steady at 44° C. for the whole afternoon, caused havoc through burns to leaves and bunches of grapes and destroyed 80% of the total harvest.[1]

Damage from excess rainfall is a rare occurrence. The considerable losses from *Peronospora* in this particular case are (in addition to the direct action of precipitation) also caused by the hot–wet regime. In some years a simple fog or abundant dew with a high temperature is sufficient to produce widespread and virulent attacks of the fungus. The damage is on the

---

[1] Verbal communication from Prof. Vivet.

whole, however, considerably less than that found in the wetter
zones of central and North Italy, as we shall see later.

Both drought and high temperature, especially the latter,
cause the shrinkage of the practically ripe bunches, and so
are a negative influence, too, on the quality of the product.
The high concentration in sugars renders the fermentation of
musts imperfect, and the result is that we obtain those bitter-
sweet wines which the French call " Scirocotés ".

Below are the figures as given to me by Prof. Paulsen (grams
per litre) :

	Normal wine.	Bitter-sweet wine.
Sugars	4	18
Acids	5	10
Extracts	28	25

When drought persists up to the autumn, the grape cannot
reach maturity, and we again have poor wines, which, however,
present different characteristics—viz. high grade of acidity (as
in the preceding case) accompanied by low concentration in
sugars.

Foggia has the fundamental characteristics of the dry–hot
zone, where the summer maxima can often reach and surpass
the equivalent for excess (39·8° C.). It is found that in many
regions in the south and in the islands, especially in the hilly
districts, such high temperatures are never reached, so that the
only dominant negative meteorological factor is drought : we
can thus distinguish a dry–hot zone from a dry one.

For Reggio Emilia we have :

Yield of Grapes.   Reggio Emilia

Classes of yield.	Quintals of grapes per ha.
Abundant	95
Good and satisfactory . .	72
Medium.	54
Mediocre	41
Low	30

For each adversity we find the following frequency and loss in quintals :

Reggio Emilia. Losses of Grapes and Frequency of Loss

Adversity.	A. Frequency per 10 years.	B. Loss, quintals per ha.	C. Loss for 10 years. (A × B)
Drought	1·5	5·6	8·4
Excessive heat . . .	—	—	—
,, rainfall *(perono-spora*, etc.) . . .	4·9	33·0	161·7
Hail	1·2	16·3	19·5
Frosts and winter cold spells	2·1	23·2	48·7

Thermic excesses no longer appear, while drought, besides being very infrequent (less than twice in 10 years), is also of relatively brief duration, so that only exceptionally can it have any extensive effect on the yield.

On the other hand, the harm it might eventually cause is largely compensated, as has been said elsewhere, by the absence or reduced action of *Peronospora*, which latter undoubtedly constitutes the most damaging phenomenon.

In fact, rainfall, in that it favours *Peronospora*, disturbs the phenomena of pollination and fertilisation and can, in an advanced or complete stage of maturity, cause rotting, and so lead to the loss of a considerable part of the crop; it is without doubt the dominant negative phenomenon.

The late spring frosts, though rare, can also cause damage but it in no way surpasses that found in many parts of Sicily, where, as we have seen, frosts are often the most harmful element.

With regard to the quality of the product, drought and high temperatures, contrary to the condition found in the dry–hot sectors, are undoubtedly favourable for the attainment of a good must; unlike rainfall and humidity, which are in this sense always decidedly negative.

Making spring frosts the common denominator for the whole of Italy, we may well affirm that Reggio Emilia has the character of a typically wet zone, where the greatest losses are without doubt to be attributed to excess rainfall and humidity.

These two factors favour the development of *Peronospora* (with particularly serious consequences during flowering and setting), as do the September rains, which act negatively on the quality of grapes and must.

The following is a brief and interesting comparison between Foggia and Reggio Emilia :

Yield of Grapes per Hectare

	Excessive rains and cold spells.	Drought and severe heat spells.
Reggio Emilia . . .	210·4 quintals	8·4 quintals
Foggia	107·8 ,,	208·4 ,,

Two or three times in a century in the wet region there are waves of cold, and these can, in winter, kill the plants, or large parts of their aerial portions.

This phenomenon, on the other hand, is found with considerable frequency in the cold Alpine regions, and obliges vine-growers to take special precautions against frost.   In the zones of Salorno and of Lavis the phenomenon named as the most dangerous is, in fact, winter frost.   The following is from a report by the Agricultural Inspectorate of Trento : " Every eight to ten years in the month of January when the temperature remains for several nights at or below −10° C., the mortality of vine shoots at the bottom of the valley is considerable and can reach from 40% to 50%.   In the zones where we find very wet soil, and where damage would be even greater and more frequent, the vine growers protect the shoots and branches by covering them up after pruning with a layer of earth 20–25 cm. thick."

During the period of winter rest the vine is highly resistant to thermic depressions.   The resistance varies during the interval of rest, reaching its maximum value in the depths of the winter, as may be seen from the research of Baltadori, who carried out a series of trials in which he took up shoots at different times from December (after the complete fall of the leaves) until the beginning of April, just before the resumption of plant life.

Here are the percentages of dead and live shoots in relation to the various times of lifting :

	Dead.	Alive.
11th December . . .	59·39	40·61
27th January . . .	19·72	80·28
20th February . . .	36·92	63·08
2nd April . . .	88·68	11·32

The highest resistance is found in January and February, as can be judged from the lower number of shoots dead through low temperatures, while as we approach the moment of resumption of plant life the sensitivity of the plant rapidly increases.

A certain number of shoots, however, is lost independently, from the effect of temperature, and this loss is, in general, of the order of 30%, so that when 70% of the plants have taken root one may speak of a normal situation, and consider that there has been no loss through frost.

It is evident that with equal temperatures the effect will vary with the duration of the experiment. In the table below are given, with reference to the second trial (where the resistance is higher), the figures relative to temperatures of $-15°$ C., $-17°$ C. and $-20°$ C. by different lengths (durations) of cold treatment. We give the percentage of shoots which have taken root.)

Vine-shoot Experiments (Baltadori)
Percentage of shoots rooting after exposure.

Length of treatment.	Temperature, ° C.		
	−15.	−17.	−20.
½ hour . . .	98	76	24
1 ,, . . .	73	40	2
2 hours . . .	60	22	0
4 ,, . . .	74	0	0
6 ,, . . .	68	0	0
8 ,, . . .	65	0	0

Up to a temperature of $-15°$ C. the European vine can well resist cold spells. Two degrees lower a rather abrupt change is noted. While, in fact, half an hour at this temperature does not cause any noticable damage to the plant, if the treatment is continued for 1 hour the negative action becomes quite clear : a figure of 76% rooting is reduced to one of 40%.

.   .   .   .   .

Experimental data which would enable us to measure and exactly determine the relationships between the factors temperature and humidity, both in the atmosphere and in the wood (water content) in relation to frost losses and damage, are still lacking. It may be deduced from the above, however, that at equal temperature damage is greater the higher the humidity, while under dry ambiental conditions the plant can tolerate very sharp falls in temperature.

The low winter temperatures, even though they may not in any way harm the plant, can have another effect which may, according to the circumstances, have positive or negative results. I refer to the long delay in budding brought on by the cold.

From A. Baldatori I quote the following table, in which the delay in resumption of plant-life is expressed in days beginning from 1st May, the date for budding of controls in the territory of Perugia, where the trials were carried out. Thus the Figure 26 indicates that budding has occurred on 26th May, while 48 shows that the date for budding is 17th June, etc.

The following table shows the delays in relation to temperatures of −20° C., −10° C., −5° C. for variable lengths of treatment.

Vine—Perugia.   Delay in Budding in Days after Exposure to Low Temperatures

Length of treatment.	Temperature, ° C.		
	−20.	−10.	−5.
	days.	days.	days.
½ hour . . .	20	3	2
1 ,, . . .	48	4	3
3 hours . . .	—	15	6
6 ,, . . .	—	21	14
9 ,, . . .	—	28	22
12 ,, . . .	—	—	48

The delay, which, as may be seen, can exceed the interval of a month and a half, is on the one hand advantageous, in that it protects the newly opening buds from the action of late spring frosts, but on the other hand, in regions with a short summer

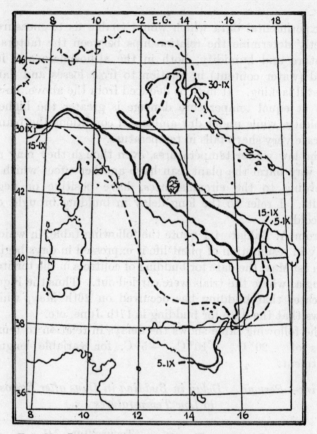

FIG. 28. ISOPHANES OF THE VINE HARVEST IN ITALY.

it is undoubtedly harmful, in that it retards the phase of maturity which can thus be so late that temperature deficiencies can hinder its accomplishment.

Thermic deficiencies during maturity show themselves throughout the whole of Italy as well as in the Alpine region, beginning from the altimetric limit to a distance of 100 to 150 metres lower.

The Agricultural Inspectorate of Aquila reports : ". . . in several zones of the province situated at a high altitude (between 700 and 980 metres) the vine with difficulty reaches the sum of temperatures necessary for the perfect maturing of the grapes, which in these zones contain small quantities of sugar and are also rather acid, thus furnishing wines of low alcoholic content."

The equivalent for deficiency between 21st September and 10th October—that is, in the last phases of maturing—is given by a mean temperature around 14–15° C.

We thus have :

Mean Temperature 21st September to 10th October

Optimal crop.		Poor crop.	
Year.	Temperature, ° C.	Year.	Temperature, ° C.
For Potenza.[1]			
1888	16·0	1897	12·1
1891	13·7	1906	12·0
1893	18·5	1912	12·6
1898	15·6	1913	13·4
1900	18·1	1914	10·5
1903	15·0		
1907	17·1		
For Perugia.[2]			
1907	18·8	1896	14·9
1908	18·8	1906	14·5
1913	18·5	1912	11·4
1936	18·4	1916	13·4

[1] According to Marchi.
[2] According to Omodeo.

Bringing these figures into the graph of the orthogonal axes, the line of the equivalent of thermic deficiency will cut the axis of the temperatures at 14·8° C.

On the (equatorial) limit for thermic excess, deficiencies in temperature during maturity are never found and, by analogy, on the cold limit (polar) damage is never encountered through excess. Similar situations, although less rigorous, are found for the dry and for the wet limits.

Moving away from the limits, the frequency of the adversities at their opposite extremes decreases gradually, until finally in the intermediate zone, although showing considerable oscillations above and below the optimum, the equivalents for excess and deficiency, especially with reference to temperature, are only rarely reached.

An intermediate (neutral) zone having more regular and steady climatic traits is thus formed.

Summarising, we can therefore distinguish six physiographic zones with well-defined bio-meteorological and enological characteristics.

I. *Dry–Hot Zone* (thermic excess and hydric deficiencies) : liquorous wines such as the muscat of Syracuse, etc.

II. *Dry Zone* (drought). (*a*) Dry wines such as Capri, Corbo, etc.; (*b*) typical alcoholic wines ("Barletta", Milazzo etc.) for blending.

III. *Humid Zone* (excessive rainfall and fog). Family wines for local consumption, not suitable for export, even if well prepared.

IV. *Cold Alpine Zone* (frost during winter period and thermic deficiencies at maturity). Light and aromatic wines are obtained if good technical control is secured (Rhine wine, Teroldico, etc.). If the wine is not prepared skilfully, the produce obtained is not of commercial value.

V. *Mountain Zone* (thermic deficiencies at maturity). Mountain wines, with high-grade acidity (they have local names : Wood wine, Striscino, etc.).

VI. *Intermediate Zone :* among these zones, each one characterised by different and quite distinct meteorological adversities an intermediate region may be found where, together with peculiar soil conditions, the meteorological adversities act with reduced frequency and intensity. We would not like to say that the factors of the atmospheric environment remain at the optimum; it is certain, however, that the equivalents for thermic excess and deficiency are only rarely reached and surpassed in this region. This region, while on the one hand not reaching the high-value musts of the dry and hot region, and on the other excluding the weak musts and wines of low alcoholic content of the humid and cold regions, does assure that equilibrium of aromatic substances which is characteristic of the " bouquet " of so many fine and estimable Italian table wines. In fact in this zone are found those localities which

FIG. 29. PHYSIOGRAPHIC ZONES OF THE VINE IN ITALY.
A = Hot dry; B = Dry; C = Humid; D = Cold; E = Intermediate.

produce the well-known table wines, such as " Chianti ", " Orvieto ", " Barolo ", " Valpolicella ", " Sangiovese ", " Prosecco ", etc., characterised by a " bouquet " and by an aromatic complex incompatible, perhaps, with any extreme ambiental situation where the environmental factors reach very high values for both excess and deficiency (see Fig. 29).

CHAPTER XII

THE METHOD OF EQUIVALENTS AND STATISTICAL METHODS OF CORRELATION

In the study of the relationships between the yields of cultivated plants and meteorological values the statistical methods of correlation have always been in use, and are still currently applied today.

We can distinguish two coefficients :

(1) coefficient of total correlation;
(2) coefficient of partial correlation.

In order to calculate the coefficient of total correlation, the following formula is used :

$$r = \frac{\Sigma D_a \times \Sigma D_b}{\sqrt{\Sigma D_a^2 \times \Sigma D_b^2}}$$

in which D_a and D_b represent the deviations from the mean of the phenomena observed in a well-defined interval of time, while Σ represents the sum of these values.

On the other hand, since

Numerator = the sum of the product of positive, negative
or mixed (positive and negative) terms
Denominator = the sum of the same terms, or values squared,
and therefore always positive
Numerator $\leqslant$ Denominator

and will have as extreme values $+1$ (positive correlation) and -1 (negative correlation) with the algebraic sign corresponding to that of the numerator.

From the geometrical point of view r represents the angular coefficient (trigonometric tangent) of the correlation line which gives the trend of the relationships between the two correlated values. The axes of the diagram (Fig. 30) correspond to the increasing or decreasing deviations from the mean for the two series of values taken into consideration.

At the origin we find the mean values (for the period considered) to which correspond $D_a = D_b = 0$. Choosing suitable scales, we obtain a straight line (line of correlation) passing

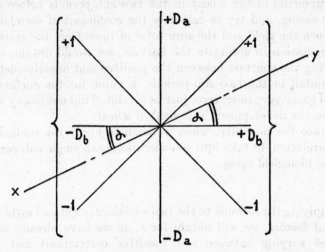

FIG. 30. GEOMETRICAL EXPRESSION OF THE COEFFICIENT OF CORRELATION.
xy = correlation line.

through the origin and contained in the two quadrants between the positive angle 45° (tangent 45° = + 1) and the negative angle 45° (tangent 45° = −1).

. . . . . .

In order that the coefficients obtained by the use of the above formula can be utilised and compared, it is necessary to divide the meteorological values into groups corresponding to the sub-periods of the vegetative life, as is done in Agricultural Ecology.

Wheat, as we have already seen, requires large amounts of water in the period between the resumption of growth in spring and earing, while after the last-mentioned stage the water requirements of the plant rapidly diminish and, at most times, rainfall is harmful rather than useful.

In extreme cases a positive-coefficient of correlation may be obtained equal to +0·8 between yield in grain and the precipitation in the interval from resumption of growth to earing, and in the same locality a coefficient of correlation, of equal value, but with a negative sign —0·8 between yield and rainfall from earing up to the harvest. Thus if we ignore the specific water requirements of the wheat in the two sub-periods before and after earing, and try to calculate the coefficient of correlation between the yield and the sum total of rains from the starting of vegetation in spring to the harvest, we would obtain, considering the contrast between the positive and negative action of rainfall in the two sub-periods, a value for the coefficient equal to, or very near, zero, just as if rainfall did not in any way act on the development and yield of wheat.

Hence the necessity, when we wish to apply the coefficient of correlation, to take into consideration each single sub-period of the biological cycle.

.   .   .   .   .

Applying the formula to the two variables, yield and meteorological factors, we will obtain for r, as we have already said, values varying between $+1$ (positive correlation) and -1 (negative correlation).

When the coefficient of correlation between the rainfall corresponding to a certain sub-period and the yield per unit area is positive and very close to $+1$, it signifies that at the situation under consideration the plant generally suffers through lack of water, so that the harvest becomes directly proportional to precipitation.

If, on the contrary, the coefficient is negative and close to -1, we shall be able to deduce that rainfall is generally excessive and, in consequence, the harvests will be all the more abundant the smaller the precipitation in that particular sub-period.

I will now give an example of the application of the correlation method in bio-meteorological research. The meteorological phenomenon which is most harmful to the development and production of sugar-beet in Italy is without doubt drought, especially in the months of June–August, which is the sub-period where root-growth is the main activity. It is actually the rains which fall in June–July which seem most decisively to influence the yield.

In the following table the root yields (quintals per ha.) in the period 1922–32 (Imola, North Italy) are divided into three yield groups : (a) abundant, (b) intermediate, (c) scarce (through drought). For each group is given the mean root yield and mean precipitations for the two months June–July.

Imola. Yield of Sugar-beet and Rain, June–July

Yield group.	Quintals per ha.	Rain, mm.
(a) Abundant harvest . . .	368	260
(b) Intermediate harvest . . .	296	81
(c) Scarce harvest	217	42

The existence of a direct relationship between total rainfall for the two months and root yields is quite evident.

In order to express in greater detail the nature of these relationships, and so render the values calculated in different localities more comparable, we may well use the coefficient of correlation to such a purpose. The figures are tabulated in the following manner :

Year.	Rain (June–July), mm.	D_p.	D_p^2.	Quintals per ha.	D_r.	D_r^2.	$D_p \times D_r$.
1922	67	−24·9	620·01	293	− 1	1	24·9
1923	72	−19·9	396·01	305	11	121	−218·9
1924	84	− 7·9	62·41	350	56	3,136	−442·4
1925	39	−52·9	2,798·41	269	− 25	625	1,322·5
1926	162	70·1	4,914·01	327	33	1,089	2,313·3
1927	66	−25·9	670·81	286	− 8	64	207·2
1928	64	−27·9	778·41	249	− 45	2,025	1,255·5
1929	29	−62·9	3,956·41	214	− 80	6,400	5,032·0
1930	142	50·1	2,510·01	355	61	3,721	3,056·1
1931	33	−58·9	3,469·21	188	−106	11,236	6·243,4
1932	253	161·1	25,953·21	399	105	11,025	16,915·5
	91·9		46,128·91 m. = 294			39,443	35,709·1

From left to right we have :

1st column : the year.
2nd   „   : sum of rains June–July.
3rd   „   : deviation from the mean of rainfall.
4th   „   : the square of deviation from the mean of rainfall.
5th   „   : root yields in quintals per ha.
6th   „   : deviation from mean yields.
7th   „   : square of deviations from mean yield.
8th   „   : product of deviations, column 3 × column 6.

Substituting the symbols of the formula with the real values, we obtain :

$$r = \frac{\Sigma D_p \times D_r}{\sqrt{\Sigma D_p^2 \times \Sigma D_r^2}} = \frac{35{,}709 \cdot 1}{\sqrt{46{,}128 \cdot 91 \times 39{,}443}}$$

$$= \frac{35{,}709 \cdot 1}{\sqrt{1{,}819{,}462{,}597 \cdot 13}} = \frac{35{,}709 \cdot 1}{42{,}655 \cdot 1} = 0 \cdot 837$$

We therefore have a very high positive coefficient of correlation, which shows us that drought is the dominant negative factor, but nothing more.

In practice all we do is to express with a numerical value a phenomenon of which farmers are already aware through their own experience. On the other hand, what we want for the evaluation of climatic conditions in order to adapt crops to the different localities is not the knowledge of the existence of the adverse phenomenon in itself, but of its mean frequency.

On the other hand, with an equal coefficient the frequency of drought, for instance, can vary within very wide limits in relation to the entity and the distribution of the deviations.

The meteorological equivalents alone give us the possibility of measuring the frequencies in that they definitely separate the normal from abnormal situations through deficiency or excess.

COEFFICIENT OF PARTIAL CORRELATION

In North Dakota the dominant meteorological phenomena affecting the yield of wheat are the rains which fall in the months of May and June, and the temperature in the month of June.

Calculating the coefficients of correlation between the different pairs of variables, we obtain a coefficient of $+0\cdot61$ for the rain in May and June and the product in grain $(r_{py} = +0\cdot61)$, a negative coefficient of $-0\cdot45$ between the temperature in June and the yield $(r_{ty} = -0\cdot45)$ and, lastly, a relationship which is equally negative between rainfall and temperature $(r_{pt} = -0\cdot38)$.

Carrying out the same calculation for South Dakota, we obtain a coefficient of $+0\cdot49$ between the rains in May and June and the yield $(r_{py} = +0\cdot49)$ and a negative coefficient of $-0\cdot62$ between the temperature in June and the yield $(r_{ty} = -0\cdot62)$.

The coefficient between the precipitation in May and June and the temperature is equally negative ($r_{pt} = -0.56$); in other words, when May and June are very wet we generally find relatively low temperatures in June.

In the states of North and South Dakota, excluding the absolute value of the coefficients, the same situation is repeated, and so we find a positive action of the rains in May and June (on the whole deficient), and a negative action of temperatures in June, which are generally excessive.

Having once established this point, an interesting question arises :

(a) In the apparent relationship between rainfall and yield (which the coefficient of correlation enables us to observe and measure) which in fact is the part due to the presence of the positive factor " rainfall ", and which is the part due to the contemporary absence of the negative factor " excessive temperature " ?   I say contemporary absence because we have in fact seen that between precipitation and temperature there exists a well-defined negative coefficient of correlation.

(b) In the apparent relationship between temperature and yield, which are we to assume as the part due to the presence of the negative factor " high temperatures ", and which the part due to the temporary absence of the positive factor " rains " ?

The partial coefficient of correlation enables us to answer these queries, furnishing us with the grade of correlation between the two variants, after having eliminated the concurring influence of the third.

To this end we used the following formula :

$$r_{ab \cdot c} = \frac{r_{ab} - r_{ac} \times r_{bc}}{\sqrt{(1 - r_{ac}^2)(1 - r_{bc}^2)}}$$

Resolving the equation, we obtain the coefficient of partial correlation between a and b, eliminating the disturbing action of c.

In the case under consideration, indicating by p rainfall in

o

May–June, by t temperature in June and by y the yield, we have :

$$r_{py \cdot t} = \frac{r_{py} - (r_{pt})(r_{ty})}{\sqrt{(1 - r_{pt}^2)(1 - r_{ty}^2)}}$$

$$r_{ty \cdot p} = \frac{r_{ty} - (r_{pt})(r_{py})}{\sqrt{(1 - r_{pt}^2)(1 - r_{py}^2)}}$$

Substituting the symbols of the formula with the real values we have for North Dakota :

$$r_{py \cdot t} = \frac{0 \cdot 611 - (-0 \cdot 376)(-0 \cdot 448)}{\sqrt{1 - (-0 \cdot 376)^2} \; 1 - (-0 \cdot 448)^2}$$

$$= \frac{0 \cdot 4425}{0 \cdot 8283} = 0 \cdot 534$$

$$r_{ty \cdot p} = \frac{-0 \cdot 448 - (-0 \cdot 376)(0 \cdot 611)}{\sqrt{1 - (-0 \cdot 376)^2} \; 1 - (0 \cdot 611)^2}$$

$$= -\frac{0 \cdot 2183}{0 \cdot 7335} = -0 \cdot 298$$

Substituting the symbols of the formula for the calculated values for South Dakota, we have :

$$r_{py \cdot t} = \frac{0 \cdot 487 - (-0 \cdot 555)(-0 \cdot 622)}{\sqrt{1 - (-0 \cdot 555)^2} \; 1 - (-0 \cdot 622)^2}$$

$$= \frac{0 \cdot 1418}{0 \cdot 6513} = 0 \cdot 218$$

$$r_{ty \cdot p} = \frac{-0 \cdot 622 - (-0 \cdot 555)(0 \cdot 487)}{\sqrt{1 - (-0 \cdot 555)^2} \; 1 - (0 \cdot 487)^2}$$

$$= -\frac{0 \cdot 3517}{0 \cdot 7266} = -0 \cdot 484$$

Summarising, we have :

North Dakota :

$$r_{py} = 0 \cdot 61 \qquad r_{ty} = -0 \cdot 45$$
$$r_{py \cdot t} = 0 \cdot 53 \qquad r_{ty \cdot p} = -0 \cdot 30$$

South Dakota :

$$r_{py} = 0 \cdot 49 \qquad r_{ty} = -0 \cdot 62$$
$$r_{py \cdot t} = 0 \cdot 22 \qquad r_{ty \cdot p} = -0 \cdot 48$$

The coefficient of total correlation between rainfall and harvest $r_{py} = 0.61$ in North Dakota is, eliminating the influence of temperatures, reduced to 0.53, while in South Dakota we pass from 0.49 to 0.22, respectively.

A considerable part of the apparent positive effect of rainfall on yield is evidently due to the absence during the same period of the negative factor " excess temperature ". Similarly, the negative action of temperature, once the effect of rain deficiency during the period has been eliminated, is reduced from -0.45 to -0.30 in North Dakota, and from -0.62 to -0.48 in South Dakota.

Without wishing in any way to diminish the interest which these statistical determinations can present in themselves, what has already been said regarding the coefficient of total correlation is here repeated : the coefficient of correlation gives us the possibility of seeing if a factor acts in the negative sense through excess or deficiency, but cannot give us the frequency of favourable or unfavourable situations through excess and deficiency, a frequency which is for us indispensable in order to be able to adapt crops to the atmospheric conditions and to represent climate as a function of a given cultivated plant.

From the point of view of the evolution of thought, the correlation method and the equivalents method do not clash, situated as they are on two different planes.

The correlation method corresponds to the concept of the continuous, and that of the equivalent to the concept of the discontinuous.

In the examination of phenomena, and in trying to co-ordinate ideas in ever wider and more organic concepts, the same question has been repeated over and over again in the history of science : Is " reality " continuous or discontinuous ? Actually it is neither continuous nor discontinuous, but is rather one and the other at the same time, and the two distinct representations which take concrete form in the continuous and the discontinuous represent for us two mental categories, due to the fact that the human mind cannot conceive of the two things existing at the same moment.

According to the trends at different epochs in the various sectors of scientific research, the resolution of problems has

been based alternatively on the continuous and on the discontinuous.

Following the " theory of numbers " of Pythagoras, who
preached the discontinuous in mathematics, come the integral
and infinitesimal calculus belonging to the continuous, until we
reach Fermat and other French mathematicians of the seven-
teenth century, who even then were insisting that certain
problems required the discontinuous for their resolution, and
this is the prelude to the modern concepts of " quanta ".

From the phlogistic theory, which inspired the alchemists
by giving a veiled vision of the continuous, since it makes one
think of the possibility of transforming one body into another,
we pass to the discontinuousness of the atom with Dalton;
while, on the contrary, in physics, from the corpuscular theory
(electrons, protons) we pass to the wave theory, and therefore
from the discontinuous to the continuous. Planck, finally,
with the discovery of quanta, has managed to show the discontinuity of energy in thermodynamics.

For the first time meteorological equivalents introduce the
concept of the discontinuous in the study of bio-ambiental
relationships in distinction to the continuous which is implicit
in the statistical processes followed up till now, and which are
identifiable as the coefficients of correlation and regression.

I shall never forget a meeting at the Centre of Scientific
Synthesis in Rome in the winter of 1942, when a heated discussion on the method of the equivalents took place, and in which
many eminent philosophers, mathematicians, physicists and
naturalists from various Italian universities participated.

The exchange of ideas, on a very high level, developed into
deep and more and more complicated questions, when Luigi
Fantappié concluded the discussion by saying : " You may
well continue to discuss. Discussion in this field is highly interesting and attractive, in that the theme is debated from
widely different points of view by intellectuals of the most
varied and widespread fields of investigation. You must,
however, remember that in the representation of bio-ambiental
relationships based on a statistical method we rely on the continuous, while Azzi, even though his method might eventually
require modification, has with the theory of equivalents, passed
to the discontinuous, and therefore to a higher level "

The words of Fantappié made me see at once, and for the first time, the proper place for my ideas in the general framework of human thought.   In the spiral which marks intellectual progress we are at a point of decision, the place in the turn which marks the passage from one level to the successive level above it, and the road to further progress undoubtedly opens before us.

PART TWO

THE SOIL-UNIT AND THE CLIMATE–SOIL COMPLEX

CHAPTER XIII

SOIL-UNIT AND SOIL SERIES

THE study of soils in Agricultural Ecology is characterised by :

(1) the determination of soil-units ;
(2) the conception of the repeated series of soils. To be quite clear from the very beginning, I must point out that for any crop and along the climatic axis going through the whole area of distribution one can find, in every locality, the complete series of soils from the best to the worst for that particular crop ;
(3) climate–soil units ; synthesis of the physical environment.

In Agricultural Ecology we distinguish soils one from another, taking into consideration their peculiar behaviour in respect of each single crop. Such behaviour is measured by the yields obtained from cultivated plants under similar meteorological and agrotechnic conditions. Each soil therefore represents a particular, indivisible entity which we could define as " soil-unit ".

The soil-unit integrates and summarises the effects of all the soil components, all the causes (known and not yet known) which determine the particular behaviour of that soil to each single crop.

The plant thus becomes an integrating instrument, and furnishes the possibility of determining the agricultural characteristics of soils and of distinguishing them one from the other.

It is an established fact that by means of what may be called a series of comparative crop trials throughout the centuries, farmers in the old world have learned to distinguish their soils one from the other and give them names. It is an imposing and complex array of observations and results, transmitted from generation to generation, outside the boundaries of official science, if you will, but based on indisputable facts.

In a first attempt to recognise and distinguish the soils, we could not but utilise this mass of information after, of course, having duly examined and co-ordinated the material.

I give here, as an example, the series of soils for the territory of Perugia. The *terra forte* (loam) is the most widespread soil in this area, being found everywhere in the most varied topographical conditions—on the plain and on hill and mountain, practically corresponding to all the geological formations of the region.

Terra forte (loam) is the result of different groups of components which converge, however, in a single soil of intermediate structure (neither too loose nor too compact), with a good water balance and well adapted both for herbaceous and ligneous plants. When mixed with lime concretions of a whitish-yellow colour, or with gravel (stones), it becomes *terra forte con concrezioni* (loam with lime concretions), or *terra forte brecciosa* (loam with stones), both poorer than the typical *terra forte* and more susceptible to drought, owing to the abundance of "skeleton" or coarse fraction.* Such soils are less suitable for herbaceous plants, but more suitable for vines and olives.

The valley of the Tiber crosses the whole territory, having on the right the limestone and sandstone masses, and on the left eocene clay-marl schists alternating with layers of sandstone. From the clay-marl formation originates the *terra bianca* (stony clay loam), derived from the disintegration of the clay-schists with which are mixed fragments of sandstone in considerable proportion originating from the weathering of this rock. It is a poor, droughty soil, rather easy to work. The olive and sainfoin, however, thrive excellently on it.

Mixed with loam (*terra forte*) and *terra bianca* is the *bianchella* (silty loam), which is very suitable for clover.

The *terra rossa* (red soil), although varying considerably from place to place in mechanical constitution, considered as a whole, and in spite of the lithologic, stratigraphic and palæontological differences of the calcareous masses of origin, represents a soil-unit quite distinct from all other soils of the neighbour-

---

* The complex of coarse material (gravel, stone and pieces of stone), which represent in a sample the skeleton remaining after the separation of the fine particles, and expressed in a percentage of the total weight of the sample.

hood. It is composed of a double hydroxide of aluminium and iron, which after the leaching of calcium remains in the form of an irreversible hydrogel.

Owing to the thinness of its layers, *terra rossa* (red soil) is on the whole a rather poor soil. Only in those particular topographical conditions in which the layers of earth reach a considerable depth, is it able to reveal its good chemical and physical characteristics in a satisfactory manner by producing abundant crops. When mixed with gravel it becomes poorer and more prone to drought, and when the gravel is composed of small limestone fragments, which corrode the farmers' working utensils in an unbelievable manner, it assumes a different appearance and the new name of *terra ferrina*.

The worst in the series of *terra rossa* is *renaro*, a mass of small fragments of limestone mixed with small quantities of fine particles and in which, with considerable difficulty, the olive alone manages to subsist.

From the sandstone, through weathering, are derived the very poor *renosa di cava* (sandy soils) and the *terra salina* (stony, sandy loam), a little richer in clay, but still rather barren, and unsuitable for both herbaceous and ligneous plants.

In the plains we find *terra di rendita* (rich loam) in the zones subject to flooding. This is a soil resulting from an accumulation of the flood deposits, rich in humus and organic substances, and the best soil in the region.

From the shores of the Tiber to the slopes of the first hills, we meet the complete series of soils, from the loosest to the most compact : sandy (*renosa di fiume*); silicious sandy loam (*sabbione salino*); humiferous sandy loam (*sabbione gentile*), loam (*terra forte di piano*) and clay (*cretone*). Lastly, when the " skeleton " abounds at the expense of the " finer particles ", stony and gravelly soils (*terra brecciosa*) are formed, which are unsuitable for all culture except olive and sainfoin.

In order to individualise and characterise the soil-units, it is necessary to be careful and discriminating. It is not sufficient to take a walk through the country and accept the opinions of farmers as considered and definite facts. Each farmer may have a good knowledge of the two or three soils on his own farm, and know their proper names; he can say which is the most suitable for wheat and which the less, but only in a generic and approximative manner—nothing more.

There is no agreement between farmers for a standard classification of their soils! The same name may apply to different soils, and a single soil may receive different names in different places. Only the trained soil scientist will be in a position to utilise the great mass of information (which, on the other hand, as quoted above, may be considered as the practical result of experimental trials carried on through the centuries), and to define and individualise the different soil-units.

Thus, with this mass of information, duly examined and co-ordinated, we move to the individualisation and classification of the soil-units.

STUDY OF SOILS

We again begin by evaluating the effects of the soils on yields, basing these effects on the usual practice of the farmer with the purpose of discovering the causes which explain the behaviour of the different soils in relation to the different crops.

The following three groups of characteristics have been considered in the study of soils :

(1) chemical capacity ;
(2) water balance ;
(3) workability (state of aggregation).

It will eventually be possible to consider other characteristics. Similarly, each of the three groups above will doubtless be capable of further division ; and the methods of investigation adopted will be bettered and perfected, thanks to the collaboration of chemists. However, the results obtained from the very beginning are sufficient for a practical application, and may be utilised because the three groups of characteristics are not isolated values, but are real factors of the soil-unit, and in large part, at least, explain the peculiar behaviour of the different soils towards each individual crop.

Chemical Capacity

From a series of preliminary experiments on several series of soils, it seems that the chemical constitution in relation to the richness of the soil can, in many cases, be identified by the content in humus, total nitrogen, potash and phosphoric anhydride, but corrected for "skeleton" and for the depth of the ploughed layer.*

In practice, the analyses are undertaken on the fine particles only, and therefore the substances which are at the disposal of the plant will be, the chemical composition remaining constant, all the more limited the more abundant the stones and other skeleton material. Similarly, under the same general conditions, the total substances which are at the disposal of the plant will increase the deeper the ploughed layer in which the roots can freely expand.

In order to illustrate the procedure, I give below the soil series for the province of Perugia with the corresponding yield for alfalfa expressed as an index with 100 the highest yield in the best soil. The graduation is valid, too, for wheat, maize, tobacco and sugar-beet—we could say for the complex of the herbaceous crop plants :

Soil Series for Perugia. Alfalfa Yields

Rich loam	100
Humiferous sandy loam	90
Loam	80
Silicious sandy loam	70
Loam with concretions	65
Clays	60
Sandy soils	50
Red soils	45
Stony clay loam	35
,, sandy loam	25
,, (or gravelly) soil	20

In Table A (below) are given the figures relative to the content in humus, nitrogen, potash and phosphoric anhydride, putting beside each analytical result the index-number obtained when the highest value is made equal to 100. †

For instance, for humus, " humiferous sandy loam " comes

* It could be objected that the chemical value of humus is included in the total nitrogen content; we have nevertheless wished to separate the terms in consideration of the influence of humus on the structure of the soil.

† This is a current statistical method to sum up values which could not be totalled directly. It is principally used at agricultural shows or in the classification of highly-bred animals where it is required to reach a value for the animal as a whole in relation to its different characteristics.

first with 3·31%. Let us consider this 3·31% equal to 100, and subsequently express as percentages of this figure the content in humus of other soils. " Stony sandy loam " has a humus content of 2·55%, which, divided by 3·31 and multiplied by 100, gives us 77, the corresponding index-number. We then add together the four indices for humus, nitrogen, phosphorus and potash, for every soil. The totals are then expressed by indices taking 100 as the highest figure, which in this series is that of *terra forte* (loam).

Table A

Soils.	Phosphorus.		Humus.		Nitrogen.		Potash.		Sum of the indices.	
	%.	Index.	%.	Index.	%.	Index.	%.	Index.	Effective.	Proportionate.
Rich loam . .	0·124	70	2·72	82	0·142	100	0·625	71	323	93
Humiferous sandy loam . .	0·119	67	3·31	100	0·131	92	0·704	80	339	97
Loam . .	0·136	76	3·02	91	0·114	80	0·870	100	347	100
Silicious sandy loam . .	0·054	30	2·45	74	0·084	59	0·290	33	196	56
Loam with concretions . .	0·108	61	2·61	78	0·141	99	0·560	64	302	87
Clays . .	0·110	62	2·39	72	0·061	42	0·810	93	269	77
Red soils . .	0·100	56	2·59	78	0·140	98	0·850	97	329	94
Stony sandy loam	0·053	29	2·55	77	0·044	30	0·137	15	151	43
,, clay loam .	0·160	90	2·69	81	0·088	61	0·440	50	282	81
Sandy soils .	0·072	40	1·86	56	0·064	45	0·386	44	185	53
Stony (gravelly) soils . .	0·177	100	2·04	61	0·103	72	0·827	95	328	94

Below are given the figures relative to production and those corresponding to the chemical content of the four main components :

Soils.	Production.	Chemical capacity.
Rich loam	100	93
Humiferous sandy loam . .	90	97
Loam	80	100
Silicious sandy loam . .	70	56
Loam with concretions .	65	87
Clays	60	77
Sandy soils	50	53
Red soils	45	94
Stony clay loam . . .	35	81
,, sandy loam . . .	25	43
,, or gravelly soils . .	20	94

We can see that no relationship seems to exist between actual production and chemical capacity. " Gravelly soil ", for instance—the worst for production—shares with " red soil " the third place for chemical capacity. We must consequently rectify the analytical values by correcting for the " skeleton ", which can be done by multiplying the analytical figures by the percentage of fine particles and dividing the product by 100.

The following table gives the amount of fine particles and " skeleton " :

Soil Type, Stones and Fine Soil. Perugia

Soil type.	" Skeleton ", %.	Fine soil, %.
Rich loam	0·0	100·0
Humiferous sandy loam . .	6·0	94·0
Loam	4·0	96·0
Silicious sandy loam . . .	3·0	97·0
Loam with concretions . .	19·0	81·0
Clays	4·5	95·5
Sandy soils	0·0	100·0
Red soils	7·2	92·8
Stony clay loam . . .	12·0	88·0
,, sandy loam . . .	4·0	96·0
,, (gravelly) soils . . .	60·9	39·1

As an example, let us consider " loam with concretions " which contains 0·108 % of phosphoric anhydride. In order to

Table B

Soils.	Phosphorus.		Humus.		Nitrogen.		Potash.		Sum of the indices.	
	%.	Index.	%.	Index.	%.	Index.	%.	Index.	Effective.	Proportionate.
Rich loam . .	0·124	88	2·72	87	0·142	100	0·625	75	350	97
Humiferous sandy loam . .	0·112	79	3·11	100	0·123	87	0·661	79	345	96
Loam . .	0·131	92	2·90	93	0·109	77	0·835	100	362	100
Silicious sandy loam . .	0·052	37	2·38	77	0·081	57	0·281	34	205	57
Loam with concretions .	0·087	62	2·11	68	0·114	80	0·453	54	264	73
Clays . .	0·105	74	2·28	73	0·058	41	0·773	93	281	78
Red soils .	0·093	66	2·40	77	0·130	92	0·789	94	329	91
Stony sandy loam	0·051	36	2·45	79	0·042	30	0·132	16	161	44
,, clay loam .	0·141	100	2·37	76	0·077	54	0·387	46	276	76
Sandy soils .	0·072	51	1·86	60	0·064	45	0·386	46	202	56
Stony (gravelly) soils .	0·069	49	0·80	26	0·040	28	0·323	39	142	39

correct for the " skeleton ", all we have to do is to multiply this figure by 81 and divide by 100, obtaining 0·087%, which is the content of phosphoric anhydride in this soil after having corrected for the " skeleton " (see Table B).

Here, too, the indices are marked in and their sum is entered in exactly the same way as for Table A.

The following indices are those for production and chemical capacity (corrected for " skeleton ").

Index-number of Soils Corrected for " Skeleton "

Soil.	Production, index-number.	Corrected for " skeleton."
Rich loam	100	97
Humiferous sandy loam . .	90	96
Loam	80	100
Silicious sandy loam . .	70	57
Loam with concretions . .	65	73
Clays	60	78
Sandy soils	50	56
Red soils	45	91
Stony clay loam . . .	35	76
,,　sandy loam . . .	25	44
,,　(gravelly) soils . . .	20	39

The contrast between the two gradings, though less marked, is still evident. One has but to observe *terra rossa* (red soils), which falls into eighth place for production, while being in the fourth for composition; and again " stony clay loam " (*terra bianca*) is still high in grade for composition, this being in striking contrast to the poor crops which are normally derived from it.

Let us therefore undertake the second correction—that relative to the " depth of the ploughed layer ". The table is given on p. 209 with the mean depth of the ploughed layer from the numerous measurements undertaken by Briccoli in five successive summers (when the stubble is ploughed up) from 1938 to 1942.

The correction for " depth of ploughed layer " is obtained by multiplying the depth (expressed by its Index-number) by the sum of Index-numbers relative to chemical constitution corrected for " skeleton ".

For " clays ", for instance (see Table B), we find a sum of

Depth of Ploughed Layer (Briccoli)

Soil.	Depth, cm.	Index-number.
Rich loam	30	100
Humiferous sandy loam . .	30	100
Silicious sandy loam .	30	100
Sandy soils	29	96
Loam	25	85
Loam with concretions . .	23	76
Clays	21	70
Red soils	17	56
Stony clay loam . . .	16	53
„ sandy loam . . .	15	50
„ (gravelly) soils . . .	15	50

281 units which, multiplied by 0·70, gives us 197, and therefore
its chemical composition corrected also for depth of ploughed
layer, as well as the correction already made for " skeleton ".
Here is the complete table :

Correction for Depth of Ploughed Layer

Soil.	
Rich loam	350
Humiferous sandy loam . . .	345
Loam	308
Silicious sandy loam . . .	205
Loam with concretions . . .	201
Clays	197
Red soils	184
Stony sandy loam	80
„ clay loam	146
Sandy soils	202
„ (gravelly) soils . . .	71

In the next table (page 210) are given the indices for production and for chemical composition corrected both for
" skeleton " and " depth of ploughed layer ".

When corrected, therefore, for the amount of " skeleton " and
"depth of ploughed layer", the grading for chemical capacity and
that relative to the production of herbaceous crops (indication
of the richness of the soil in the case considered) shows a perfect
correspondence.

P

Index-numbers of Crops from Different Soils and Corrected Chemical Constitution

Soil.	Production, index-number.	Corrected chemical constitution.
Rich loam	100	100
Humiferous sandy loam . .	90	99
Loam	80	88
Silicious sandy loam . . .	70	59
Loam with concretions . .	65	57
Clays	60	56
Sandy soils	50	58
Red soils	45	53
Stony clay loam . . .	35	42
,, sandy loam . . .	25	23
,, (gravelly) soils . . .	20	20

On the basis of chemical capacity, the series of soils may be divided into five classes, or groups :

	Index-number.
A_5 Very high chemical capacity . .	90 and more
A_4 High chemical capacity . . .	90 to 70
A_3 Intermediate chemical capacity . .	70 to 40
A_2 Low chemical capacity . . .	40 to 20
A_1 Very low chemical capacity . .	20 and less

There is one point which could cause difficulty : the interdependence, which has already been suggested, between total nitrogen : humus : potash and phosphorus. These, in reality, are independent one of the other, and their proportions could therefore vary widely, giving very different combinations of values.

A possible explanation of this alignment is that, originally, good soils were, in a general way, well provided with phosphorus and, in practice, also with potash (especially those of volcanic origin). On the other hand, being " naturally " good, these soils are given more attention by the farmer, who improves these soils first, as they will more readily respond with better yields. As a consequence, these soils produce greater quantities of fodder crops, which in their turn allow more stock to be kept : this, in turn, again allows deeper ploughing and heavier manuring. In time this naturally leads to progressive increases in the percentage of humus and of total nitrogen.

From this particular situation, natural and agrotechnic at the same time, is derived that alignment of the four substances taken as representative of the chemical capacity of the soil—a suggestion made by my friend the late Prof. Tommasi.

The relationship between chemical composition and amount of the crop cannot, however, be considered a fixed one. For a plant requiring large quantities of water, it may well be that in droughty environmental conditions the best results will be obtained in a soil poorer in chemical constituents, but able to preserve water reserves for a longer period. The second group of characteristics, which we have called " water balance ", thus comes into play.

Even if chemically perfect, an excessively compact soil is not suitable for the cultivation of tubers (potato) or bulbous (onion) plants : a third group of characteristics, which we have called " workability ", is thus involved. Workability is the practical effect of a greater or lesser degree of compactness which makes itself felt by the ease or hindrance in working the soil, with evident negative consequences both from a technical as well as from an economic point of view when the workability is bad.

Of the three groups of factors, the chemical capacity holds first place, because in rich soils (such as soils suitable for a kitchen garden) the high percentage of organic matter, besides making the soil naturally more productive, is directly correlated with a favourable state of aggregation (loose earth) and with a positive water balance : humidity is preserved for longer intervals and at the same time the damage from waterlogging is lessened.

Water Balance

The behaviour of soils in regime of drought or in regime of excessive moisture (waterlogging) has been studied.

Resistance to Drought

In order to assess the resistance of soils to drought we have, in this first experiment, used a biological reaction, taking maize as an indicator. Maize is a very sensitive instrument : it reacts to a considerable extent, and in an easily comparable manner, to the various negative situations which characterise the hot–dry regime.

The experiment consisted in noting when the leaves of maize had permanently wilted after a rainless period.

Now, the length of the period of endurance from the last rains (sufficient to saturate the soil) varies in notable measure from one soil to another, and can be taken as an indication of the resistance of such soils to drought.

The experiments were carried out at Imola (northern Italy). From a maximum tolerance of 30 days for *terra laguna* (rich loam), one passes to the other extreme of the series with " yellow sands ", which are in a droughty condition 8–9 days after rain has fallen.   The following grading was adopted :

B_5 : highly resistant to drought   .   . 30 or more days
B_4 : resistant   .   .   .   .   . 30 to 23 days
B_3 : intermediate .   .   .   .   . 23 to 16 ,,
B_2 : susceptible to drought   .   .   . 16 to 9 ,,
B_1 : very susceptible to drought   .   . 9 days or less

This scale is based on the behaviour of the plant in a regime of deficient rainfall. We have not, however, yet managed to single out those soil characteristics which explain its capacity to conserve water for a longer or shorter period.

The content in clay and in organic matter and the proportions of sand and clay are in many cases in direct relation to the soil's resistance to drought, but not with that constancy and exactitude which would permit one to formulate a well-defined rule. There are notable exceptions which make the application of any general rule (which at first sight and for many soils seemed to be simple and clearly defined) difficult, or at least doubtful.

Decidedly positive, on the other hand, are the results of experiments on resistance to drought in relation to the capacity of retention of water and contraction in volume of the soil passing from the humid state to the dry, when cracking takes place.

In pot trials the clays, in a restricted space, thanks to their high capacity of retention, allow the plant to resist a lack of water for a long time, while in open country under natural conditions these soils are rather droughty in the summer period.

This happens because in passing from the wet to the dry state the clay contracts considerably, and the superficial layer is split up into separate blocks by deep cracks which further increase the evaporating surface and act as suction-pumps by drawing the evaporating water towards the open.

Let us study a group of soils from this point of view, taking the following four points into consideration :

First : Length of the period of drought resistance in days (index plant : maize).

Second : Capacity of retention in litres per cubic metre measured by the usual methods. From 250 litres for *rossolina* (stony sandy loam) we pass to 379 litres for *grossa di piano* (clay loam tending to compact).

Third : Adhesion water : the limit beyond which the soil will no longer surrender its water to the plant. It is well known that when moisture drops to 8% of the weight of the pure clay it no longer yields water to the plant, while pure sand yields up to 1·5%. From the total capacity of retention we must therefore subtract the quantity not available for the plant—namely, the adhesion water.

For the different soil-units mentioned, I quote the effective capacity of retention and the same figure corrected for the water of adhesion.

Soil Series and Water Retention

Soil-unit.	Capacity of retention, l. per m³.	Water of adhesion, %.	Corrected capacity of retention, l. per m³.
Rich loam	282	4·5	270
Humiferous sandy loam .	287	4·3	275
Loam	300	5·7	283
Clay loam	379	4·9	360
Stony clay loam (with lime concretions) . . .	294	5·6	278
Stony sandy loam . .	250	5·5	236

Fourth : Contraction in volume. When on a section of a particular soil one linear metre long (100 cm.) we find a crack 25 cm. deep, it is evident that the evaporating surface (since the cracks appear in all directions forming a network) is increased by 50 cm., making in all 1·50 metres.

Dividing 100 by 150, we have 0·66, being the coefficient D, which can be used to measure the effect of cracking. We have only to multiply the capacity of retention by this coefficient.

It is evident that with the total absence of cracks the quotient will be equal to unity ($\frac{100}{100} = 1$), so that the capacity of retention remains unaltered. The higher the divisor, on the other hand, and therefore the more numerous and deep the cracks, the lower will be the coefficient and the lower the capacity of retention.

We have :

Soil Cracking and Resistance to Drought

Soil-unit.	Coefficient of cracking = D.	$D \times$ capacity of retention.	Resistance to drought, days.
Rich loam	0·92	248	31
Humiferous sandy loam .	0·90	247	30
Loam	0·81	229	25
Clay loam . . .	0·61	220	19
Stony clay loam (with lime concretions) .	0·65	181	17
Stony sandy loam . .	0·67	158	11

The correlation between the endurance in days on the one hand, and the capacity of retention corrected by the coefficient of contraction on the other, is therefore well brought out.

There are, however, particular cases in which resistance to drought is in relation to more complex conditions. On the island of Ischia (Neapolitan Gulf), on the soil locally called *lapillosa*, the vine does not suffer in the least through drought during the long summer, in spite of the abundant gravel and stones and the consequent high degree of permeability of this soil.

Here the " skeleton " is represented by *pomiceous lapilli*, which absorb and withhold large quantities of water in the rainy season that can be utilised subsequently by the plant during the dry season. The hairy roots closely adhering to the small stones absorb the humidity from them, and can thus supply the water requirements of the plant. These *lapilli*, as the local vine-growers so expressively put it, " drink in the winter and sweat in the summer ", yielding to the plant the water previously absorbed.

Similar conditions are found in Malta. Here a layer of *terra rossa* 20 cm. deep is found, having a substratum of calcareous, porous and spongy rock which stores up considerable amounts of water during the winter. Despite the complete lack of rain from April to October, not only woody plants, but even herbaceous ones, such as the tomato, prosper magnificently; this plant develops and extends its roots to the wet surface of the under-lying calcareous rock, yielding abundant harvests during the torrid summer period, with no need of irrigation (according to Borg).

Resistance to Waterlogging

The behaviour of soils to the opposite phenomenon, and more precisely to excess water in the soil, will now be examined.

The oxygen in the atmosphere passes freely from the air into the soil, penetrates deeply through the cracks and pores and reaches the layer in which the roots develop, bringing about those processes of oxidation which are indispensable for the life of the plant. When this flow of oxygen is interrupted, for one reason or another, the soil will first become neutral, and then, with a gradual increase in the process of reduction, those abnormal conditions which comes under the generic name of asphyxia will prevail.

One of the causes which can prevent the easy access of oxygen into the soil is brought about by the overloading of the soil known as " waterlogging ".

It is unnecessary to repeat that for this reason in badly drained places, and after long spells of uninterrupted rainfall, the plants turn yellow and the freshly sown fields have a squalid and impoverished look.

The negative consequences of stagnation do not, however, make themselves manifest at the same time for all soils. As for drought, there are certain soils which resist flooding more and others which resist it less.

For the soil series of Perugia, it has been observed that bean plants give signs of distress owing to immersion after a minimum of 2 days for *cretone* (clay) soil, while others in *terra rossa* have a maximum endurance of 24 days. The series is as follows :

Clays	2 days
Stony or gravelly soils . . .	8 ,,
Sandy soils	12 ,,
Humiferous sandy loams . .	21 ,,
Red soil	24 ,,

On the basis of these results, and since the two extreme soils are so far apart, we propose a general grading for resistance to flooding in the following terms (symbol B') :

B'_5 = very resistant to immersion . . .	23 or more days
B'_4 = resistant to immersion	22 to 18 days
B'_3 = mean resistance to immersion . .	17 to 13 ,,
B'_2 = little resistant to immersion . .	12 to 8 ,,
B'_1 = very little resistant to immersion . .	7 and less

What is of particular interest is the fact that resistance of soils to immersion appears to be directly related to the oxidation-reduction potential ($= rH_2$).

When the latter is equal to 27·3 (at 25° C.) the phenomena of oxidation and reduction are balanced. Figures above 27·3 signify a decrease in pressure of the hydrogenation and therefore an accentuation of the processes of oxidation, while lower figures indicate the gradual increase of the reducing powers of the soil, so that more and more unfavourable conditions are created for the plant.

Here are the oxidation-reduction potentials for the series of soils under review :

Oxidation-reduction Potentials

Soil-unit.	After 1 day.	After 14 days.	After 1 month.
Red soil	30·6	27·2	23·5
Humiferous sandy loam .	25·3	24·6	23·0
Stony (and gravelly) soils .	24·2	20·1	17·0
Sandy soils . . .	23·1	20·2	17·4
Clays	20·5	14·5	12·5

The behaviour of *cretone* (clay) is characteristic. It begins at a very low quota, and then falls rapidly, while *sabbione gentile* (humiferous sandy loam) begins at a relatively high mark and decreases slowly, so justifying its high grade of resistance to immersion.

Below is a grading for resistance based on the number of days necessary to create obvious damage through excess moisture, and the corresponding values for the oxidation-reduction potential after immersion for 1 day, and after immersion for 1 month :

	Number of days.	Potential of oxy-reduction.	
		After 1 day.	After 1 month.
B'_5 . . .	23 or more	20	23
B'_4 . . .	22 to 18	26	21
B'_3 . . .	17 to 13	23	18
B'_2 . . .	12 to 8	20	15
B'_1 . . .	8 and less	17	12

The agreement between the two groups of values is quite clear, and makes us believe in the possibility of measuring, with reasonable accuracy, the resistance of soils to waterlogging by simply determining the oxidation-reduction potential.

Workability

In order to determine the resistance of the soils to working, we have made use of a dynamometer spade made of a rectangular steel blade 25 cm. high and 15 cm. in width, having a hollow iron handle attached to the blade, which is graduated in cms. : along it runs a steel weight of 10 kilogrammes.

The use of the instrument is very simple : the only thing an observer has to do is to count the number of strokes necessary to sink completely the blade into the ground, allowing the weight to fall from a height of half a metre (each beat corresponds to 5 kg.).

The resistance of the soil will be greater the higher the content in clay; but it is more especially the gravel and stones contained in the soil which offer the greatest resistance to the penetration of the dynamometer blade, and of work-a-day tools in general.

In the series of Umbrian soils one passes from a minimum of seven strokes in a sandy soil, to a maximum of forty-eight in *terra ferrina* (red soil with abundant "skeleton"), while for *cretone* (compact clay) nineteen strokes are sufficient.

In the study of workability in general, the resistance to "cutting" of the soil was overcome by the use of a common plough pulled by two oxen and six cows working at a depth of 25 cm. with a furrow 40 cm. wide.

Placing the dynamometer between the plough and oxen, we calculated the kilogrammes necessary to carry out the work.

From 400 kg. in the loosest soils, we reach 1,200 kg. in the most difficult to work.

The following grading may be adopted :

C_5 = very easy to work	.	.	Effort of 450 kg. or less
C_4 = easy to work	.	.	.	„ from 450–600 kg.
C_3 = intermediate	.	.	.	„ „ 600–800 „
C_2 = difficult to work .	.	.	„ „ 800–1,200 kg.
C_1 = very difficult to work .	.	„ „ 1,200 and more kg.

Sandy soils can be worked at any time, I would almost say, when they are very dry and when saturated with water. However, as the content in clay increases, the opportunity and, in pure clay soils, the necessity of working the soil when it is fit (neither too dry nor too wet) become more and more evident. In clayey-sandy soils, for instance, the easily workable limits of soil moisture vary from a minimum of 6·5% (dry) to a maximum of 14% (wet). Within these limits, an effort of approximately 750 kg. is necessary when ploughing. Above and below the dry or moist limit, the necessary effort increases rapidly, and at 5% and 16%, respectively, is 900 kg.

For compact clays the most favourable condition is found within the restricted limits of 9% and 12·5%, to which corresponds a mean effort of 850 kg.

However, above and below these limiting values the situation worsens rapidly, until at 6% and 15·5%, respectively, we reach 1,200 kg.; it then becomes necessary to employ a tractor so as not to harm working animals by putting them under an excessive strain.

Besides this, if tilled at the wrong time owing to excess water, not only do clays need a very great effort in ploughing, but their structure undergoes alterations, with consequent symptoms of sterility for the next 1 or even 2 years.

Representation of Soils by Symbols

Any soil-unit can thus be conveniently represented by four symbols : A (chemical capacity), B (resistance to drought), B' (resistance to waterlogging), C (workability), and has for each of these characteristics a scale of five exponents, from 5 (the most favourable situation) to 1 (the most unfavourable).

I illustrate below the use of the symbols with some examples from soils in Umbria :

Terra rossa (red soil) has the following formula :

$$A_3 \ B_2 \ B'_5 \ C_3$$

to which correspond the following characteristics :

(1) intermediate chemical capacity ;
(2) susceptible to drought ;
(3) highly resistant to immersion ;
(4) intermediate with regard to workability.

The formula $A_3 \ B_2 \ B'_5 \ C_3$ equally represents all soils having the above characteristics, whatever their constitution, their denomination or aspect.

For *renosa di cava* (sandy soil) we have the formula :

$$A_1 \ B_1 \ B'_2 \ C_5$$

and the following characteristics :

(1) very low chemical capacity ;
(2) highly susceptible to drought ;
(3) susceptible to immersion ;
(4) very easy to work.

For *sabbione gentile* (humiferous sandy loam) we have :

$$A_4 \ B_5 \ B'_4 \ C_4$$

with the following characteristics :

(1) high chemical capacity ;
(2) very resistant to drought ;
(3) resistant to immersion ;
(4) easy to work.

For *cretone* (clays)

$$A_3 \, B_3 \, B'_1 \, C_{2-1}$$

and therefore the following characteristics :

(1) intermediate chemical capacity;
(2) medium resistance to drought;
(3) highly susceptible to immersion;
(4) from difficult to very difficult to work.

These are all soils of the Umbrian series (Perugia). The characteristics indicated above correspond perfectly, and explain the behaviour of the same soil in regard to the different cultivated plants.

      .   .   .   .

The soil-unit with its relative symbol must not be taken to represent a fixed and invariable value. The soil-unit, pinpointed, singled out and circumscribed on the basis of its behaviour towards the various crops, also has a contingent value and significance in relation to the agrotechnic situation of that particular locality.

But if we now modify the agrotechnic conditions of a particular soil, it will necessarily undergo a transformation, so that it will no longer in fact belong to its original denomination.

By increasing the chemical constituents with continued applications of manure and working it more deeply, we will evidently pass to a different formula, while the yield on which the evaluation and appreciation of the soil-unit are based is altered in a positive direction. In the " red soils " when the depth of the furrow was increased from 17 cm. (actual mean, a very modest depth owing to the generally unfavourable topographical conditions of this autochthonous soil) to 25 cm., the chemical capacity passed from A_3 (intermediate) to A_4 (high). The increased depth of the furrow also increases the soil's resistance to drought, which so passes from B_2 (susceptible) to B_3 (medium resistance). A new soil will thus come into being with the formula $A_4 \, B_3 \, B'_5 \, C_3$ (as against the previous $A_3 \, B_2 \, B'_5 \, C_3$).

" Red soil " with the new formula is no longer the *terra rossa* of before, and could be distinguished with the name " improved *terra rossa* ", for instance. This is a perfect analogy to what happens in Romagna for the " recent sandy alluviums " which can be rapidly improved by generous applications of dung. We thus get two separate soils : *sandy-arid*, $A_1 B_2 B'_5 C_5$ (recent alluviums) and *sandy-fresh* soil, $A_3 B_3 B'_5 C_4$ (improved or bettered sands).

Repeated Series of Soils

In the territory of Perugia we have numerous (no less than fifteen) soil-units, and the same can, more or less, be said for all the other provinces in Italy, and what has been said for Italy is also true of all other countries. We are therefore faced with an enormous number of names (given to the different soils) which are different not only in the various languages, but even in single dialects. At first sight this appears to be a tangled web, a mass of words and an extraordinarily numerous collection of soil-units all jumbled together and impossible to sort out and co-ordinate into a harmonic pattern of values. Actually this is not so. In effect, in spite of the difference in aspect, colour, structure and origin, it can be said that the same soils are found in the different countries of the world, from the richest (suitable for a kitchen garden) to the worst (gravel, stones, shale, etc.), from the most compact (clays and conglomerates) to the loosest (sands), from the driest to the wettest. In exactly the same manner, for each cultivated plant and in every sector of the area over which it has spread we can more or less trace out the complete series of soil-units, from the most to the least suitable. In this lies the repeated series of soils.

In every country a grading of all the different soil-units will have to be made, from that giving the highest yield to the soil giving the poorest yields.

These grades naturally vary from plant to plant; this, of course, because the needs of the single species differ, and a soil which is good for wheat may prove to be negative for the potato and vice versa.

In the territory of Reggio Calabria, the soil known as *terra pillosa* is the best for the potato (150 quintals per ha.), while being the worst for wheat (6 quintals per ha.), *Mato pignataro*, on the other hand, which is the worst for the potato (70 quintals) is intermediate for wheat (13 quintals). *Mato pignataro* is richer in chemical constituents but more compact (restricting the growth of tubers) and susceptible to drought, while *pillosa* although chemically poorer, is more resistant to drought and is extremely loose.*

The following is a grading for several soils of the series found in Perugia relative to yields of wheat and olive (according to Briccoli) :

Perugia.   Soil-units, and Wheat and Olive Yields

Soil-unit.	Wheat quintals per ha.	Soil-unit.	Olive Kg. per ha.
Loam . . .	16·0	Stony (and gravelly) soil	515
Loam with concre- tions . .	14·5	Stony clay loam .	478
Stony red soil. .	10·0	Stony red soil. .	432
Stony clay loam .	9·5	Loam with concre- tions . . .	386
Stony (and gravelly) soil . . .	7·0	Loam. . .	294

The two series, as may readily be seen, are practically the reverse of one another, confirming that the needs of the plant in respect of the soil vary widely and that the relationship of soil to yield can differ in notable measure for the different species.

For the production of grain, the most important characteristic is represented by the chemical capacity (which is inversely proportional to the " skeleton " content), while in Umbria, where thermic deficiencies at maturity and excess rainfall in winter constitute the most harmful group of phenomena, the olive prospers, and is especially planted on slopes facing south in gravelly, loose and very permeable soil, so as to avoid harmful stagnant water.

* " Terra pillosa " and " mato pignataro " are both derived from the degradation of gneiss and mica-schists, the first being a sandy-clay-siliceous soil and the second a clay-sandy soil.   The contents are :—

	Pillosa	*Mato pignataro*
Skeleton . . .	18·0%	34·8%
Fine particles . .	92·0%	65·2%
Siliceous sand . .	91·6%	49·4%
Clay	23·2%	44·5%
Calcium . . .	0·5%	0·0%
Humus . . .	3·3%	5·0%

Of particular interest, although foreseeable, is the inversion of grading with regard to the quantity and quality observed for numerous crops. The fresh, deep soils of the plains of Romagna assure a very high grape production, while the quality of the musts is often poor. The yellow sands of the Pliocene, however, when mixed with considerable quantities of gravel, give an extremely poor soil, on which the production of grapes is greatly reduced in comparison with that obtained in the fertile soils of the *bassa* (plains) : the wine, however, has an excellent aroma, high alcoholic content and fine taste.

Here is the grading for several soils on the island of Ischia in regard to quantity and quality of the wine : *

Quantity Soil-unit.	Yield, hl. per ha.	Quality Soil-unit.	Alcoholic graduation, %.
Padule.	71	Terra rossa	16
Arenella	66	Lapillosa	15
Terre forti	56	Terre forti	15
Pappamondo	52	Cenere .	14
Lapillosa	50	Pappamondo	12
Pozzolana	44	Pozzolana	10
Terra rossa	42	Arenella	9
Cenere .	35	Padule.	8

Just as for those years in which there is a plentiful harvest the musts are of low graduation, so do the soils richer in humus and rather humid, where the mean produce is abundant, give us the worst wines from every point of view : in years hit by drought and in airy, dry soils, the produce in grapes is scarcer, but the quality much improved.

* " Terre forti " : volcanic sediment.
  " Arenella " : volcanic alluvium (along river banks) of various lithological origin (lava, *tuff* etc.).
  " Padule " : of volcanic alluvium origin as in the preceding case but richer in humus, situated in coastal depressions.
  " Pappamondo " : clayey tuff.
  " Lapillosa " : mass of lapilli.
  " Pozzolana " : soil derived from the degradation of the rock bearing the same same (*pozzolana*)
  " Terra cenere " : volcanic cinders more or less elaborated by the waters and mixed with plant remains.
  " Terra rossa " : red soil with sub-soil formed by a mass of pumice which absorbs water during winter and yields it up in summer to plant roots.

In the two gradings given above there is a typical and almost complete inversion.

Similar situations are found for the sugar-beet, which in rich, deep and well-manured soils yields an imposing root mass : this mass has a low sugar content, while in less productive and drier soils root production is lower, but the sugar content higher.

·   ·   ·   ·   ·

The symbols adopted for the representation of soil-units as based on the chemical capacity, resistance to drought, water-logging and the state of aggregation (workability), enable us to explain the behaviour of the different soils in the most varied conditions of atmospheric environment.

These symbols may, up to a certain point, be compared to the formulæ in chemistry. " Water " is chemically represented by H_2O, but its name varies in the different languages of the world, and it impossible to replace the name by the simple formula. If we consider wine, for instance, the matter would be more complicated still. Suppose we wished to substitute the name " Wine of Orvieto " on the label with the complete chemical analysis.

So it is with the soil-units. We cannot abolish local denominations, for the following reasons :

(1) They correspond to the soil-unit in its contingent, concrete reality, and the result of all the pedological components (the cause of the behaviour of the soil versus the different crops), including those not yet studied or defined.

(2) They are understood by the farmer, and the link between applied science and practice is thus more solidly established.

In studying and representing soil units in the various localities, besides giving the appropriate symbol (formula), we shall always, where possible, supply the local name, even in dialect.

Determination of Pedological Characteristics for Each Crop

The determination of the chemical capacity, water balance and workability, completed by the study of the granular structure may explain, partially at least, the behaviour of the soil-units of a region in relation to the different cultures.

But this is not all. These determinations represent only the first phase in our work. It is only after we have defined all soils, not only for Italy, but for the whole area of distribution of each plant, that we may start the second phase—undoubtedly the most important in this line of research.

We have to distinguish the pedological factors which characterise the soil series (for each species) from the best to the worst for each species considered.

We may distinguish five classes of soil values in relation to each species, as we have done for maize. (See Ch. XIV.)

(1) very good;
(2) good;
(3) intermediate;
(4) bad;
(5) very bad.

Basing ourselves on at least 50 units for each of the extreme groups (1 and 5), we have to determine :

(1) which are the attributes common to all soils, which are considered *very good* for a given species, and
(2) which are the attributes common to all soils which are considered *very bad* for a given species.

This simple and well-defined procedure leads directly to the second and conclusive phase of our research.

This conclusion could in no way have been reached without the initial discernment and recognition of the soil-units.

For the first time the problem may be faced squarely and its resolution made in a concrete manner, within the framework of agricultural research.

In this second phase, a collaboration with agricultural chemists, pedologists, microbiologists and even agronomists becomes not only useful but I should say indispensable for the complete study and integral solution of such a difficult and complex problem as is the scientific and practical understanding of the soil, considered from a purely agricultural point of view.

Q

CHAPTER XIV

CLIMATIC AXES AND SOIL SERIES FOR MAIZE

THE general order of relationships between plant and climate can now be summarised in the following four typical situations, where by limiting conditions are meant those which cause the yield to drop below the limit of economic husbandry :

(1) optimal climate and soil conditions;
(2) optimal climatic conditions and limiting soil conditions;
(3) limiting climatic conditions and optimal soil conditions;
(4) limiting conditions for both climate and soil.

In the first place we shall find the highest mean general yields and in the fourth, quite naturally, the lowest.

With better climatic conditions, the number of soils able to give yields above the economic limit is naturally increased. With a worsening of meteorological conditions, on the other hand, the number of soils which can be used economically for the cultivation of a particular plant gradually diminishes, until at last, on the climatic limit of expansion for the species considered, the crop can be economic only in the best soil of the series.

To illustrate this point we can study the yields of maize along a profile (axis of frequency for drought) crossing the area of the crop's distribution from the point at which optimal pluviometric conditions are encountered to the point at which, through successive and gradual increases, drought reaches a frequency of 100%.

Let us examine the following four regions, indicating for each of them the frequency of drought in summer for maize :

(1) Lower Lombardy . . . . 20% to 30%
(2) Central Umbria . . . . . 50% to 60%
(3) Tuscan Maremma . . . . 70% to 80%
(4) South-western region of Reggio Calabria 90% to 100%

Along the axis joining the two extreme conditions we find at practically every point the complete series of soils, from the most fertile and fresh to the most sterile and dry, thus giving us the possibility of trying out the most varied combinations between climate and soil and their effects on yield.

Basing our calculations on the characteristics of chemical capacity and water balance, we divide the soils into five categories, from the best to the worst for maize and using the symbols : X_5 (very suitable), X_4 (suitable), X_3 (intermediate), X_2 (unsuitable), X_1 (most unsuitable).

Let us now examine each of the zones mentioned above :

In the territory of Stagno Lombardo (Cremona) along the course of the River Po, maize is hit by drought twice (at the most, three times) in 10 years.

Under these conditions the most suitable soils, i.e. the clayey-sandy tending to a compact structure, reach the high productive levels of 46·5 quintals per ha.   We can, with good approximation, on the basis of this result, deduce that in total absence of drought the yield would easily reach 60 quintals per ha.

In the clayey-sandy soils of a loose nature the product is still very high : 41 quintals, while in sandy soils there is a sudden drop to 26 quintals.   Lastly, in the worst soils of the series X_1 (sands and gravel), on which maize is practically never sown, the yield in grain is of approximately 13 quintals per ha.

It is, however, opportune to observe that the soils of the X_1 group cannot be defined and limited in any absolute way. Through them, with the progressive reduction in " fine particles ", there is a gradual passage to gravel and stones, completely sterile and almost devoid of vegetation.

In the most humid regions of central Italy only the olive keeps in step with the progressive impoverishment of the substratum and is able to develop its roots even in gravels where with the fine particles reduced to 10% the cultivation of all other herbaceous and ligneous crops is impossible.

We could perhaps say that to the X_1 group are assigned those soils which would not of themselves justify an agricultural enterprise, but which are cultivated because of the presence on the farm of those better soils which thus compensate and balance the enterprise.

For the first zone we therefore have the following series of yields :

Soil.	Maize, quintals per ha.
X_5	46–47
X_4	32–38
X_3	24–28
X_2	18–20
X_1	12–14

On the whole the yields are pretty high.

It must be borne in mind, however, that this happens to be one of the most progressive regions, in which, besides a rational use of chemical fertilisers and a good rotation, the large production in fodder—over 5 quintals per ha.—and the consequently increased stocking with cattle, assure abundant quantities of manure and a deep and accurate working of the soil. The depth of the furrow, from a minimum of 26 cm. in the most compact soils, passes to 30–32 cm. and more in the looser ones, while its width is approximately 35 cm.

In the territory of Perugia the rich loams (*terra di rendita*) and the humiferous sandy-loam (*sabbione gentile*), which are considered of excellent quality, give high yields reaching 32 quintals of maize and more. These yields, however, are not strictly comparable with those obtained in Lower Lombardy, owing to the lower fodder production and upkeep of cattle, the consequences of which are a reduced quantity of manure at the disposal of the farmer and the less accurate and shallower working of the soil. In the more developed farms, where a progressive technique is employed, the mean yields rise to 38 quintals.

In the said region, where drought occurs five to six times in 10 years, the following series of yields may be adopted :

Soil.	Maize, quintals per ha.
X_5	30–33
X_4	23–25
X_3	16–18
X_2	9–11
X_1	8 or less

In Perugia, where, to fix a figure, the economic limit is 12–14 quintals, the cultivation of maize is practically excluded in soils of the X_2 and X_1 groups.

In the Tuscan Maremma drought reaches a frequency of no less than seven to eight times in 10 years, so that in the excellent *terra di golena* (rich loam) similar to the Umbrian *rendita* and to the *laguna* of Romagna, 25 quintals are just reached, while, owing to drought, the cultivation of maize drops below the economic limit in the silicious soils in general, and therefore into the groups $X_3 X_2 X_1$. We find :

Soil.	Maize, quintals per ha.
X_5	23–25
X_4	15–20
X_3	10–12
X_2	7– 9
X_1	5 or less

Finally, in the territory of Reggio Calabria, where drought recurs with a frequency of nine times in 10 years, the minimum economic yield, 12–14 quintals, is reached only in the best soils—*limico* and *fior di china* (rich loams)—in which, as confirmation of their natural productivity, we find yields of 45 quintals and more obtained in irrigated crops where drought is totally eliminated.   We have :

Soil.	Maize, quintals per ha.
X_5	12–14
X_4	9–11
X_3	7– 8
X_2	5– 6
X_1	3 or less

In the soil of the groups $X_4 X_3 X_2 X_1$ maize cultivation is not normally undertaken.

In South Morocco, on the extreme limit for the dry (non-irrigated) culture of maize, the highly resistant variety " Abda " gives a mean yield of a mere 5 quintals of grain, and this only in the best soils.

.   .   .   .   .   .

In order to determine the frequency of drought, we have not considered the sum of rainfall from sowing to harvest (middle of April to end of August), but only the precipitation in the interval June–July which includes the critical period.

Around the limit for hydric deficiencies, when drought during the critical period occurs every year, we can, notwithstanding this, obtain a passable, although very low yield, thanks only to the rains falling between sowing and the beginning of the said critical period.

. . . . . .

The above figures have been used to construct a table in which all the possible combinations of pluviometric and soil conditions are represented in regard to maize yields. The frequencies of drought from 30% to 90% are given on the ordinates, while on the abscissæ we have the series of soils X_5; X_4; X_3; X_2; X_1.

The figures in the table are those corresponding to the different soil and drought frequencies.

Yield of Maize

Quintals per ha.

Frequencies of drought, %.	X_5.	X_4.	X_3.	X_2.	X_1.
30	46	34	26	19	13
50	31	24	17	10	8
70	24	17	11	8	5
90	13	10	7	5	3

These figures are not perfectly inter-comparable, but in every case they represent a complex of more or less harmonious values which can be perfected by mathematical techniques without altering the table and the general relationship between the factors taken into consideration.

REPRESENTATION OF SOIL AND CLIMATE AS A WHOLE (CLIMATE–SOIL UNIT)

The series of soils repeated along the climatic axis furnishes us with a fair representation of the physical environment as a whole.

Below is given one of the simpler examples relating to maize in Italy for which the only adverse meteorological phenomenon is drought. In the table we found the frequencies of drought from 0, never in 10 years, to 10 in which drought occurs every year—*i.e.* rainfall always remains below the drought equivalent of 46 mm. in the critical period. On the abscissæ the soils are divided into five groups : X_5, very good for maize; X_4, good; X_3, intermediate; X_2, poor; X_1, very poor.

Thus the series of soils repeated among the climatic axis gives us fifty-five combinations (see table). These fifty-five combinations integrate the physical environment.

Climate–Soil Units for Maize

Drought frequency, %.	Soil series.				
	X_5.	X_4.	X_3.	X_2.	X_1.
0	1	5	10	18	28
10	2	6	12	21	31
20	3	8	15	23	34
30	4	11	17	25	37
40	7	13	20	30	39
50	9	16	24	33	43
60	14	22	29	38	44
70	19	27	36	42	49
80	26	32	41	47	51
90	35	40	46	50	54
100	45	48	52	53	55

By construction, situations worsen, going down the scale as regards drought frequency, and from left to right as regards soil conditions.

Taking into consideration the resultant soil–climate, we will find a worsening of conditions along the diagonal which from the top left-hand corner of the graph reaches the right-hand bottom corner.

We can distinguish the following fifteen series :

Series.	Combinations (*i.e.* possibility of same yield for all combinations in same series).
1st	1
2nd	2– 5
3rd	3– 6–10
4th	4– 8–12–18
5th	7–11–15–21–28
6th	9–13–17–23–31
7th	14–16–20–25–34
8th	19–22–24–30–37
9th	26–27–29–33–39
10th	35–32–36–38–43
11th	45–40–41–42–44
12th	48–46–47–49
13th	52–50–51
14th	53–54
15th	55

Conditions obviously worsen in the progression from the first to the fifteenth series, while each series contains relatively homogeneous and balanced values. These fifteen series give a good picture of the physical complex as a function of the yield of maize and could be a sure guide for any practical use or research. Thus, for instance, as far as genetical research and plant-breeding are concerned, it is evident that in relation to a productivity-resistance combination (the two essential components of yield) the degree of productivity on which we can rely will gradually diminish from the first to the fifteenth

Drought frequency, %.	Soil series, quintals per ha.				
	X_5.	X_4.	X_3.	X_2.	X_1.
0	62	46	35	26	18
10	57	42	32	23	16
20	51	38	29	21	14
30	46	34	26	19	13
40	40	30	23	16	11
50	35	26	19	14	9
60	29	22	16	12	8
70	24	18	13	9	6
80	18	14	10	7	5
90	13	10	7	5	3
100	7	6	4	3	1

series, while the characteristics of hardiness will be more and more necessary.

If we bring into the table the yields corresponding to the fifty-five climate–soil units, we find a complex of continuous and harmonious values, rationally associated and arranged, thanks to the two combined series of components, soil and climate, of which they are an expression.

An examination of the preceding table will reveal a number of interesting details which help to show how the table itself could be used for the solution of problems where cognisance of physical conditions is necessary.

Without undertaking any profound analysis of the relationships between drought frequency and soil series as regards yield, it is sufficient to recall that any yield on the table (say 18 quintals) might well correspond to two completely different situations :

(1) very good climatic conditions, but poor soil conditions ;
(2) very good soil conditions, but poor climatic conditions (drought frequency of 80 %).

It becomes clear that to move to a better situation in the first case we do not have to consider the water factor, but rather to concentrate on fertilisation and the deep working of the soil. In the second case, however, what is of importance besides irrigation is the adoption of dry-farming, *i.e.* those means which tend to maintain water in the soil, and so combat lack of rainfall. The example here considered might seem at first sight perfectly obvious and easily found without recourse to our table. This is not the case.

In current statistical reports the yields are given per surface unit with reference to different administrating areas without, however, discriminating between the different soils, and without considering drought frequency. But, as has been shown above, the same yield can be derived under entirely differing conditions.

It is needless to say that accurate statistical observations are not considered useless, for, on the contrary, they are necessary to evaluate agricultural production in the various zones in order to establish a basis for buying and selling, for problems of taxation, etc. But when from the yield we want to obtain exact information which will help in the choice of the agro-technic means for bettering the said yield (*i.e.* bettering conditions in the locality), then it becomes necessary to discover those factors having a direct relationship to yield (production).

We can, in the same way, report at the corresponding places of the table of climate–soil units, the cost of production, man-hours, effort of production and other items which thus become co-ordinated into a single harmonious complex similar to the faces of a well-defined polyhedron rather than a loose mass of chaotic fragments of individual observations : the scattered fragments of a broken looking-glass !

What has been said concerning climate, soil and the soil–climate unit, can without doubt serve as a good guide for the determination of positive and negative factors for any locality.

This representation of the physical environment will be of great advantage for the agronomist, the economist and the geneticist in the solution of those problems (and they include the majority of problems of agriculture) for which an understanding of physical environment is necessary.

PART THREE

THE YIELD AND ECOLOGICAL CHARACTERISTICS OF CULTIVATED PLANTS

THE plant should be considered as a machine transforming the environmental availabilities at its disposal into products which directly or indirectly are needed by man for his own requirements.

This machine, according to the physical and agrotechnic environment, should be chosen and constructed (by cross-breeding) to obtain the highest possible yield.

The yield of cultivated plants has three aspects :

(1) quantitative (quantity of the product);
(2) qualitative (quality of the product);
(3) generative (character of the seed).

Yield is not an absolute value, but the result of a relationship between productivity and resistance to ambient adversities.

CHAPTER XV

QUANTITATIVE YIELD

Productivity

The productivity of a plant is its capacity to utilise the environmental means at its disposal so that, in favourable ambiental conditions, to the increase of these availabilities corresponds successive increases in product up to a maximum yield, the entity of which is in direct relationship to the degree of productivity.

The " Nostrano dell' Isola " variety of maize (as has been ascertained by widespread trials organised throughout Italy by the Ministry of Agriculture) yields up to 65 quintals of grain per ha. in very favourable environmental conditions, while, with identical conditions, the yield from " Trenodi di Campiglia " does not rise above 48 quintals.

We can therefore say that " Nostrano dell' Isola " possesses a degree of productivity superior to that of " Trenodi di Campiglia ".

Resistance

The resistance of a plant to a particular adverse factor is its capacity of developing in the unfavourable conditions brought about by this factor in such a way that, with increases in the negative intensity of the phenomenon, the decreases in yield will be smaller the higher the degree of resistance.

So with soils which are unsuitable for the cultivation of maize, scarcely manured and in a regime of drought, " Nostrano dell' Isola ", highly productive but with little resistance to these adverse factors, produced a mean of 5 quintals of grain per ha., while " Trenodi di Campiglia ", less productive, but more resistant, yields 12 quintals.

A resistant variety will thus give a modest product, of course, but which represents the maximum obtainable under these conditions, conditions which would cause complete failure in a highly productive variety.

Hardiness

By hardiness is meant the sum of resistances, that is, the capacity of the plant to develop in adverse conditions, both natural and agrotechnic, reacting to the gradual worsening of environment with successive decreases in yield, which will be smaller the higher the degree of hardiness. *There is a certain incompatibility between productivity and hardiness.* However, if between productivity and hardiness there is found an understandable state of intolerance beyond certain limits, a similar situation shows itself, though less evidently, between productivity and the various categories of resistance : that is to say, resistance to any single adverse factor.

The incompatibility between productivity and resistance, however, is quite different according to whether it is resistance to deficient or to excess rainfall.

While, in fact, resistance to drought can be reconciled only with a relatively low degree of productivity, resistance to excess rainfall can exist together with a high capacity for production. These differences are understandable when one considers that :

(1) Drought acts in an exclusively negative sense, limiting the water at the disposal of the plant, and the possibility of high yield is therefore excluded.

(2) Excess rainfall, on the other hand, although negative in its ultimate effects, does assure the plant the necessary water fully to satisfy the requirements of those varieties having a high capacity of utilisation.

Excess rainfall can therefore be said to act both in a positive and in a negative sense.

. . . . .

From the above, the conception of relativity of yield clearly emerges : moreover, it is easily seen that this representation of the facts is natural and in itself deducible from the available evidence.

Yet, in spite of this evidence, the idea of yield as we have defined it is still far from being grasped by many agronomists, and the consequence of an inadequate representation of this fundamental phenomenon is to slow down the results obtained from research in genetics and selection, which are invariably directed towards an increase in productivity. One hears of good, medium or poorly productive varieties, as if these expressions held good anywhere, and at any time, without taking into account the fact that yield, as was seen when speaking of " Nostrano dell' Isola " and " Trenodi di Campiglia " varieties of maize, is always the result of a compromise between productivity and resistance to adverse factors.

How can we explain this imperfect picture of the phenomenon " yield " ? Before geneticists came to modify and rapidly transform a plant's genotypical framework by creating new types with the most varied combinations of characteristics in every country, only local varieties were found. These local varieties had remained *ab illo tempore* unaltered in the autochthonous sphere of their natural area, where they appeared to be fairly well adapted to the physical environment, constituting true " ecotypes ".

In such conditions, the factor " plant " remaining constant, new agricultural methods (which are the result of progress in agriculture) could evidently only improve environmental conditions, and so increase the yield. In such situations yield and productivity varied always in the same direction, so creating confusion in evaluating the effects of each particular factor.

But when we begin to introduce varieties from foreign countries with different climatic conditions, and when by crossing it becomes possible to obtain new genotypes, the relationship between plant and environment is greatly altered and the two values " yield " and " productivity " become independent.

The necessity of considering the yield not as an absolute entity, but as the result of two components " productivity " and " resistance " should therefore have been insisted upon half a century ago. However, in spite of the noticeable modifications in the concept of bio-ambiental relationships brought about by the progress of genetics, one concept has remained firmly rooted to the old ideas.

I recall a hybrid, " Carlotta Strampelli ", created by Strampelli, which was considered, by such an authority as Prof. Cuboni, as the type of wheat which, as he affirmed in my presence, would solve the problem of cereal production, increasing the nation's crop by 12 million quintals. In this estimate it was naturally implied that " Carlotta Strampelli " could be grown advantangeously throughout Italy in spite of considerable differences in the conditions of the physical and agrotechnic environment of the various regions. As is well known, Prof. Cuboni's hopes were not confirmed.

In order to obtain the maximum yield, the characteristics of productivity and of resistance must, in each single case, be adjusted and regulated so as best to fit environmental conditions. In zones having fertile deep soils, a favourable climatic situation and particular agrotechnic provisions, a variety having a high degree of productivity is well suited, though this might be accompanied by a low resistance of the variety in question to adversities which do not occur in this particular case, and which are therefore not considered. On the other hand, in zones having shallow soil, frequent and intense adverse meteorological factors and deficiencies of plant food, it is essential that a variety with low productivity but high hardiness be chosen, in order to obtain a yield, not of course a very high one, but one representing the maximum obtainable in those particularly unfavourable conditions.

We give below the details of a series of experiments undertaken many years ago, the results of which are very useful as an illustration.

These are from the 245 cultural experiments carried out under the auspices of the Italian Farmers' Association having as their aim the measurement of the yields of three varieties of wheat obtained under the most varied conditions of rainfall in the month before earing. The values are expressed as percentages of the highest mean yield which was obtained from the " Gentil Rosso " in the most favourable rain conditions (*i.e.* over 80 mm.).

Wheat Variety Experiments. Index Number.

Rainfall in the month before earing, mm.	Coccitta.	Realforte.	Gentil Rosso.
Less than 20 . .	16	12	4
21–50 . . .	32	36	20
51–80 . . .	40	60	48
80–115 . . .	60	80	100

(Base : " Gentil Rosso " over 80 mm. = 100.)

If in a particular region we find rainfall below 20 mm. 8 years in 10, once between 21 and 50 mm., and once only between 51 and 80 mm., we shall find :

"Coccitta" . . $(8 \times 16) + (1 \times 32) + (1 \times 40) = 200$
"Realforte" . . $(8 \times 12) + (1 \times 36) + (1 \times 60) = 192$
"Gentil Rosso" . . $(8 \times 4) + (1 \times 20) + (1 \times 48) = 100$

In these conditions Coccitta, evidently the most resistant to drought, has the right of preference.

In another region with rainfall at or below 20 mm. for 5 years, between 20 and 50 mm. for 2 years, between 51 and 80 for 2 years, and once above 80 mm., we find :

"Coccitta" . $(5 \times 16) + (2 \times 32) + (2 \times 40) + (1 \times 60) = 284$
"Realforte" . $(5 \times 12) + (2 \times 36) + (2 \times 60) + (1 \times 80) = 332$
"Gentil Rosso" $(5 \times 4) + (2 \times 20) + (2 \times 48) + (1 \times 100) = 256$

"Realforte" takes first place.

Lastly, let us examine a third region in which rainfall between 21 and 50 mm. fell once, three times between 51 and 80, and 80 and more for no less than 6 years. We find :

"Coccitta" . . $(1 \times 32) + (3 \times 40) + (6 \times 60) = 512$
"Realforte" . . $(1 \times 36) + (3 \times 60) + (6 \times 80) = 696$
"Gentil Rosso" . . $(1 \times 20) + (3 \times 48) + (6 \times 100) = 764$

In these conditions, the more productive "Gentil Rosso" is the first choice.

In this first tentative experiment, the idea of geographical trials is already implicit, trials which can well serve for a measurement of the grade of productivity and resistance of the different varieties of a cultivated species.

In geographical trials, the whole area of distribution of a plant is considered and utilised like a gigantic laboratory in which, in a single year, are found all the conditions under which the species considered is cultivated, from the limit for excess to the limit for deficiency for rainfall and temperature, from the best soils to the worst, from the most primitive agricultural practices to the most progressive and developed.

Operating throughout the total area of distribution, we shall therefore obtain in a single year all the yields which a variety produces under the most varied natural and artificial ambiental

R

conditions. We may visualise a central point at which climatic
conditions are around the optimum, the agrotechnic organisation perfect, and the soils the best for the crop considered. In
these conditions the highest yield for all varieties will be obtained, the first in yield naturally being that with the highest
degree of productivity.

In the four directions radiating from this central nucleus,
the situations gradually worsen as the four extreme cardinal
points of the bio-atmospheric complex are reached : here the
hot–dry, dry–cold, wet–hot and wet–cold regimes, respectively,
lower the yield below the economic limit. In these extreme
situations the lowest yields will be reached for all varieties
irrespectively, but the first in grading will be the variety
having the highest degree of resistance to the group of limiting
adversities.

In 1928 a series of trials was organised along the north/south
meridian, chosen in such a way that the extreme localities,
polar and equatorial, were in places which were decidedly
abnormal through deficiency or excess temperature respectively
(above and below the equivalents for deficient or excess temperature during the sub-period from earing to maturity). In
this way the mean temperature during earing from a minimum
of 12° C. in Oslo reached the maximum of 26° C. in Cerignola
(Italy), while all the intermediate values were registered and
their effects studied. This enabled us to evaluate the complete
series of bio-thermic reactions (naturally limited to the places
in which wheat was able regularly to complete its cycle and
reach complete maturity). In this way we can obtain the complete series of bio-thermic reactions in a single year, an achieve-
ment which would not have been attained even in several
centuries if the trials had been concentrated on a single point
or station on the chosen longitudinal axis. In reality, and if
we consider the station of Cerignola only, it would not have
been possible to register there such low temperatures as those
obtained in Oslo during the interval earing–harvest, neither is
it possible to register at Oslo such high temperatures as those
at Cerignola, always considering the period earing–maturity.

The varieties adopted for this trial were chosen to provide
the most complete range of the various types of spring wheat
and, at the same time, to show high and low degrees of produc-

Timilia.   Marzatico.

Wagenburg.   Janetzky.   Gelchsheimer.   Börsum.   Halland.

Fig. 31. Types of Wheat.

tivity and resistance with all the intermediate graduations, as also different degrees of earliness.

The following varieties were taken (Fig. 31) :

(1) " *Timilia* ". On the extreme equatorial limit of expansion of spring wheat in the Mediterranean region (Sicily); it is characterised by its earliness and resistance to drought.

(2) " *Marzatico* ". From central Italy (Apennine range). Quite productive and appreciated for its great hardiness and the good quality of its flour.

(3) " *Wagenburg* " (Swiss). Obtained by selection from the Canadian " Manitoba ", is distinguished, like the mother variety, by the excellent quality of the product.

(4) " *Janetzky* " (Silesia, Germany). Obtained by selection from the Austrian variety " Kolben ", is very productive and considered early in Germany's physical environment.

(5) " *Gelchsheimer* " (Germany). Obtained by crossing the " Argentinicher Braunweizen " (not better specified) with the Scottish " Squarehead "; it is distinguished by the very great productivity derived from " Squarehead ".

(6) " *Börsum* ". At the time in which the trial was undertaken it represented one of the best Norwegian varieties, thanks especially to its earliness, which permits it to mature in regions where the cold–wet summer excludes practically all other varieties.

(7) " *Halland* " (Southern Sweden). Early and not very exigent with regard to heat.

(8) " *Dala* " (Central Sweden). Considered very early and able to push its way up to the polar limit of expansion of spring wheats; locally it is, or was, considered a quite productive variety. (Not illustrated.)

The evaluation of the different wheats in their zones of origin which we have noted has a purely local significance, so that it would be impossible to compare the varieties solely on the basis of information gathered at their original source. On the other hand, cultivating together all the said varieties in the most varied ambiental conditions, from the most favourable to the limiting, we shall be in a position to formulate a more exacting judgment.

The yields for all the varieties, without distinction, obtained from all the stations along the longitudinal network, were plotted on a graph bearing the yields, expressed in quintals per ha., on the ordinate, and on the abscissa the mean temperatures during the interval from earing to harvest (beginning from undoubtedly deficient temperatures, and reaching excessive ones). Each yield is marked at the point of intersection on the axes. The curve which geometrically co-ordinates all the

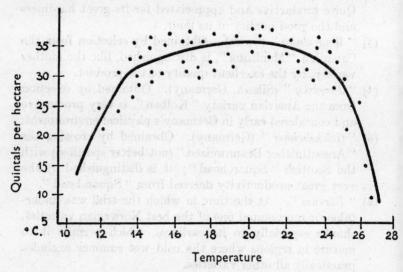

FIG. 32. YIELD OF SPRING WHEAT IN RELATION TO TEMPERATURE.

points on the graph is a true representation of the yield's course in respect of temperature (Fig. 32).

This curve may be divided into three parts : a central and practically horizontal part comprising what we may call the favourable situations and two laterals in rapid decline corresponding to unfavourable situations through excess and deficiency. It is a flat curve of the fourth order.

In order to simplify the demonstration, we shall now choose three stations which evidently summarise and integrate the bio-ambiental situations as a whole.

(1) *Schackensleben* (Germany). Found in the horizontal sector of the segment with temperature during the earing

period, around the theoretical optimum of 18° C. and in which the other meteorological factors proved to be the most favourable. The trial was undertaken on very good soil and employing all the methods of a perfected agricultural technique.

(2) *Cerignola* (Italy). With thermic excesses and water deficiencies.

(3) *Skara* (Sweden). With excess rainfall and thermic deficiencies at maturity.

There is no doubt that at Schackensleben, owing to the extremely favourable ambiental conditions, the highest yields were recorded.

The grading for varieties is :

Variety.	Quintals per ha.	Index-number.
Gelchsheimer	48·58	100
Marzatico	44·60	92
Wagenburg	40·90	84
Timilia	40·50	83
Halland.	38·25	79
Janetzky	37·50	77
Dala	36·75	76
Börsum	30·00	62

" Gelchsheimer " takes first place : its high productivity is without doubt derived from the parent " Squarehead ".

For the two stations of Cerignola and Skara during earing and maturing (fourth sub-period), we have :

Station.	Rainfall, mm.	Temperature, ° C.
Cerignola	3·3	25·52
Skara	261·6	12·35

The higher the yield of a variety at Cerignola, the greater must its resistance be to the extremes of a dry and hot regime. On the other hand, the higher the yield of a variety at Skara, the greater must its resistance be considered due to the extreme situations of a wet and cold regime.

Table for Yields Obtained at Cerignola (in Decreasing Order)

Variety.	Quintals per ha.	Index-number.
Timilia	12·80	100
Marzatico	10·09	79
Wagenburg	9·57	75
Janetzky	9·45	74
Gelchsheimer	9·00	70
Halland	8·10	63
Börsum	6·04	47
Dala	5·55	43

The yields for Skara, in decreasing order, are :

Variety.	Quintals per ha.	Index-number.
Dala	22·13	100
Halland	21·86	99
Börsum	21·00	95
Janetzky	21·00	95
Gelchsheimer	20·00	90
Marzatico	19·50	88
Wagenburg	18·40	83
Timilia	13·90	63

The tables for the yields in the three localities considered thus supply a grading for the eight varieties relative to productivity and resistance to the two groups of adverse phenomena.

Comparing the three gradings, and as confirmation of what was said previously, we observe that between productivity and resistance to thermic deficiencies and rainfall excesses, there is greater compatibility than that found between productivity and resistance to thermic excesses and insufficient rainfall.

" Gelchsheimer's " yield of 20 quintals in the cold–wet station of Skara represented 41% of the yield obtained at Schackensleben (48 quintals), while the yield of 9 quintals in the hot–dry station of Cerignola is only 18% of the yield obtained at Schackensleben.

Although it was to be expected, we would like to remark on the diametrically different behaviour of Italian and Scandinavian wheats : the latter occupy the first place in a grading for resistance to thermic deficiency (and to excess rainfall),

while " Marzatico " and " Timilia " are decidedly at the head
of the list in a hot–dry environment.

. . . . . .

Once the degree of productivity and of resistance, based on
the yield which each variety produces in favourable and unfavourable conditions, is determined by means of geographical
trials, it becomes easy to establish which of the varieties considered has the right of preference in this or that region, using
the method already illustrated for " Coccitta ", " Realforte "
and " Gentil Rosso ".   To do this we shall take a place where,
let us say, the absolutely dominant adversities are thermic
excesses and lack of rainfall, having for favourable and unfavourable situations frequencies of 6 and 4, respectively,
(considering a 10-year period).   Multiplying yields by frequencies, we find :

Dala	.	.	.	.	$(36 \cdot 7 \times 6) + (5 \cdot 5 \times 4) = 242 \cdot 2$
Börsum	.	.	.	$(30 \cdot 0 \times 6) + (6 \cdot 0 \times 4) = 204 \cdot 0$
Halland	.	.	.	$(38 \cdot 2 \times 6) + (8 \cdot 1 \times 4) = 261 \cdot 6$
Gelchsheimer	.	.	.	$(48 \cdot 6 \times 6) + (9 \cdot 0 \times 4) = 327 \cdot 6$
Janetzky	.	.	.	$(37 \cdot 5 \times 6) + (9 \cdot 4 \times 4) = 262 \cdot 6$
Wagenburg	.	.	.	$(40 \cdot 9 \times 6) + (9 \cdot 5 \times 4) = 283 \cdot 4$
Marzatico	.	.	.	$(44 \cdot 6 \times 6) + (10 \cdot 0 \times 4) = 307 \cdot 6$
Timilia	.	.	.	$(40 \cdot 5 \times 6) + (12 \cdot 8 \times 4) = 294 \cdot 2$

With these conditions, " Gelchsheimer " occupies first place
and has the right of preference, while " Börsum " comes last.

By varying the frequency of favourable and unfavourable
years, first one variety then another will acquire the right of
preference.   Based on the results of all the trials carried out
with wheat as a whole up to the present day, we can distinguish
the following five categories, or degrees of productivity and of
resistance :

Productivity (P).	Yields, quintals per ha.
$P_5 =$ Very high . . .	45 and more
$P_4 =$ High . . .	45 to 40
$P_3 =$ Intermediate . .	40 to 30
$P_2 =$ Low . . .	30 to 25
$P_1 =$ Very low . . .	25 and less

These yields come from completely favourable environmental

situations (climate, soil and agrotechnic conditions). For this reason they are, on the whole, rather high.

The yields in hot and dry, wet and cold regimes were obtained at stations where the meteorological factors alone acted negatively, while agrotechnic and soil conditions proved to be decidedly favourable.

	Quintals per ha.
Resistance in wet–cold regime (rWC) :	
rWC_5 = Highly resistant . . .	21 and more
rWC_4 = Resistant	21 to 19
rWC_3 = Intermediate . . .	19 to 16
rWC_2 = Susceptible	16 to 14
rWC_1 = Highly susceptible . .	14 and less

	Quintals per ha.
Resistance to hot–dry regime (rHD) :	
rHD_5 = Highly resistant . . .	12 and more
rHD_4 = Resistant	12 to 10
rHD_3 = Intermediate . . .	10 to 7
rHD_2 = Susceptible	7 to 5
rHD_1 = Highly susceptible . .	5 and less

As was done in the evaluation of soil characteristics here, too, a quinary system has been adopted : very much—much—intermediate—little—very little.

When a more detailed graduation or analysis is required, the base n may be multiplied by any number. For instance, $n \times 2$ (from a maximum of 10 for the most favourable condition to a minimum of 1 for the most unfavourable); $n \times 4$ (from a maximum of 20 to a minimum of 1), etc.

With this as a basis, we may now establish the formula for some of the spring wheats used in those trials. Under favourable conditions, " Gelchsheimer " produces 48·58 quintals per ha., as we have seen; in a hot–dry regime this figure is reduced to 9·0 quintals, and to 20·0 quintals in a cold and wet environment. This variety may thus be represented with the formula P_5 rHD_3 rWC_4. " Gelchsheimer ", according to the formula, is highly productive, has a medium resistance to drought and excessive heat, and is resistant to the adversities of the wet–cold group.

" Timilia ", in favourable conditions, produces 40·50 quintals, 12·80 quintals in a hot–dry environment, and 13·90 quintals in a wet–cold regime. This variety is therefore productive, highly resistant to the hot–dry regime and highly susceptible to the conditions of a wet–cold environment : $P_4 \, rHD_5 \, rWC_1$.

" Dala " in favourable ambiental conditions produces 36·75 quintals, 5·55 quintals in the hot–dry, and 22·13 quintals in the cold–wet, regimes. It thus has an intermediate productivity, is highly susceptible to rainfall deficiency and to excess temperature and highly resistant to thermic deficiencies and excess humidity : $P_3 \, rHD_1 \, rWC_5$.

With an increase in the frequency of adversities, the degree of resistance necessary to face the situation also rises, while, quite naturally, the necessary degree of productivity is lowered. Similarly, with the bettering of general conditions it is convenient to rely more and more on productive varieties, while hardiness becomes less and less important.

With reference to the five classes of frequency for adversities, we may represent the corresponding combinations of the degrees of productivity and hardiness (resistance in the broad sense) in the following manner :

Adversities (Y)	Mean frequency, %.	r.	P.
Y_1 = Very frequent .	80	r_5	P_1
Y_2 = Frequent .	45	r_4	P_2
Y_3 = Intermediate frequency .	22	r_3	P_3
Y_4 = Rare . . .	10	r_2	P_4
Y_5 = Very rare . .	2·5	r_1	P_5

The frequency of favourable conditions is, of course, given by the difference between 100 and the frequency of the adversities.

In order to calculate the yields corresponding to each of the five combinations of productivity and of resistance, the frequency of the adverse and of the favourable situations are multiplied by the corresponding yields, bearing in mind that in unfavourable years yield is a function of resistance, and in favourable ones a function of productivity.

With reference to the hot–dry group of adversities, a frequency Y_2 (see preceding table) corresponds to a mean yield of 20·07 quintals per ha. To the degree of productivity P_2 there corresponds a yield of 27·50 quintals, which multiplied by the frequency of 55% (frequency of favourable situations) gives 151·25; to a grade of resistance r_4 there corresponds a yield of 11·0 quintals which multiplied by the frequency of 45%, gives 49·50 quintals. Summing up the two products and dividing by ten, we get the 20·07 quintals noted above.

In relation to the hot–dry group, with very favourable agrotechnic and soil conditions, we therefore have the following yields in relation to frequency :

Very frequent	14·60 quintals per ha.
Frequent	20·07 ,, ,,
Intermediate frequency .	29·17 ,, ,,
Rare . . .	38·85 ,, ,,
Very rare . . .	44·02 ,, ,,

We have here the series of yields obtainable in the different harmonic combinations of favourable and unfavourable situations through excess temperatures and deficient rainfall.

The example is simple but even in the most complicated cases the same procedure may be adopted.

VARIETIES WITH GREAT PRODUCTIVITY (HYBRIDS): LOCAL VARIETIES: WILD VARIETIES

Referring to the productivity–resistance binomial we must first of all note how the progress made by agricultural research, diminishing at least in part the negative effect of environment, provides a possibility of taking advantage of higher and higher degrees of productivity.

This clearly emerges especially in those countries which are thinly populated and where the soil has been first cultivated in relatively recent times : in these cases agriculture is mainly concentrated where the conditions of soil and climate are most suitable. In contrast to this, in densely populated countries, where the earth has been tilled for thousands of years, it has been found necessary in the course of time, as a consequence of the ever-increasing demand for food, to spread the cultivation of the most important species to zones in which the conditions of the physical environment, soil and climate are decidedly not very favourable.

In this case it is not possible to rely on varieties with a high degree of productivity, and therefore highly exigent; instead, it is found better to adopt hardy types capable of developing normally in poor and adverse environments.

Having established these points, we can distinguish the following three groups :

(1) Wild varieties obviously possessing a maximum degree of hardiness which has enabled them to survive in competition with other living plants without the aid of man.

(2) Cultivated local varieties which have been able to survive because of being protected by man, but which, at the same time, through natural selection through the ages, have ended up by forming ecotypes which are particularly resistant and suited to the peculiar conditions of the particular localities.

(3) The selected races and hybrids obtained through the technique of geneticists whose principal aim is to get the greatest possible increase in productivity. In these forms the inherent resistance and hardiness are reduced to a minimum in relation to the environmental conditions, which become more and more favourable, enabling us to rely more and more on high levels of productivity.

. . . . .

By means of selection, and by isolating from a population those strains which possess a higher degree of productivity, we will obtain a complex of individuals which presents a degree of productivity (in greater or smaller measure) superior to that of the original population. The advantage so gained is, however, relatively modest, especially when compared with the high degree of productivity of the hybrids. The fusion of different germinal plasmas acts powerfully (heterosis), increasing the plant's reactivity and its capacity to utilise the environmental availabilities in the highest measure. We could say that the liaison between plant and environment is enlarged, multiplied and intensified.

In this manner, and by simultaneously using the new agricultural techniques, it has been possible to obtain yields which until 20 or 30 years ago would have been considered pure fantasy or, at the most, the consequences of a concentrated effort on a small lot. Now, however, yields in wheat of 50–60 quintals per ha., or of 90 quintals per ha. of maize, are not at all exceptional, even on a large holding.

However, such high degrees of productivity and such high yields will be obtained only if the plants find themselves in an environment where the conditions, both natural and agrotechnic, are absolutely favourable.

Moving away from these optimal conditions of environment, the highly productive varieties and hybrids no longer find conditions which favour their perfect development, and so local varieties may assume importance, varieties which, through the effects of the continued action of adverse factors in the course of time, have ended up (as has repeatedly been said) by forming ecotypes which are particularly resistant and suited to the specific conditions of the different zones.

The further we move from the optimal situation into less favourable conditions, the more the highly productive form will feel the negative consequences of their high degree of productivity and their lack of resistance, while, vice versa, in some cases the local races will, on the contrary, still show an excess of hardiness and a deficiency in productivity.

The cross, therefore, between the highly productive varieties and local races in order to obtain a more effective combination of values of productivity and resistance, constitutes the basis for the work of the most important plant-breeding stations, a typical example of which is Svalöf. The varieties produced by this station which have met with the greatest favour are in general the result of crosses between the Scottish " Squarehead " and local Swedish varieties.

Lastly, on the geographical limit of a species, the utilisation of the total degree of resistance of the local varieties will be necessary to overcome the adversities of the physical environment, while in such conditions the corresponding degree of productivity drops to a very low level.

Primitive man and the most backward populations of to-day feed on fruits which grow wild in the forests. I remember a trip to the northern part of the Caucasus, where, in the territory of Maikop, I was able to visit forests entirely composed of plum, pear, apple, cherry and vine, all in the wild state. The product, of course, is of very low quality, with the exception of the plum, which I was able to sample and found sweet and well flavoured. However, the wild varieties have the advantage of being very hardy, inasmuch as they are able to compete with other species without the help of man—that is, without being cultivated.

It is not always possible to distinguish between wild varieties and those which have returned to the wild state; certain varieties of potato, for instance, which are found both in the wild state and cultivated by man, present the same physiological and morphological characteristics.

The races of wild potato found in the equatorial region of the Andes, having a very high degree of hardiness, were used by Soviet geneticists as a " genofond " to increase hardiness. By means of crosses with *Solanum tuberosum*, they obtained new forms of potato which were particularly resistant to cold and to *Phytophthora infestans*, De Bary.

In the hot–wet zones, *peronospora* marks the expansional limit for the European vine (*Vitis vinifera*, *L.*). In the hot and rather wet regions of Minas Geraes, and especially at Montes Claros (Brazil), *Vitis labrusca*, *L.*, having a high degree of resistance to *peronospora*, manages to develop and give a good yield of grapes or, better still, as has already been said, gives two harvests a year.

The vines of the *Muscadinia* group (*Vitis rotundifolia* and *Vitis munsoniana*) grow in the wild state throughout the southeast region of the U.S.A. from Florida along the coastal regions of the Gulf as far as Texas, and then push into the interior, following the Mississippi along its course as far as the banks of Tennessee. The *Muscadinia* wood is hard, and varies in colour from an ash-grey to a greyish-brown or yellowish-brown. The bark adheres closely to the surface of the stem on young branches, while it peels off annually from the older ones and the trunks. With the passing of the years, the stem splits up longitudinally into separate cordons, although examples of

century-old plants with a whole and tree-like trunk are not
rare (Fig. 33).

The leaves are long, petiolated with entire or slightly lobed
blades, round or subcordate; the sinus is not very pronounced.
The surface on both sides is smooth and shiny, while the margin
of the blade is dentate. The vine tendrils are simple instead
of bifurcated, a distinguishing characteristic compared with
the European vine. Inflorescences are globose, more or less
compact, generally bearing a limited number of grapes—from
four to ten—but which can reach a total of forty. The size
of the grape varies widely, as does the colour, which can be
green, pearl, bronze red or black, with a uniform tint or with
patches of variegated colour; the skin is rather thick and the
grape-stones are large.

From the time of the European colonisation the pioneers
knew and made use of the products of the wild vine for both
food and drink, and began to cultivate it in their garden plots
and near the populated centres. The best results were obtained
with *Vitis rotundifolia*. This species grows in sectors where
the plentiful rainfall and the very high relative humidity,
with, at the same time, a constant high mean temperature,
make profitable cultivation of the European vine absolutely
impossible.

In a hot–wet environment, therefore, no species of the *Vitis
vinifera* genus can compete with *Vitis rotundifolia*, and the
races derived from it. As regards the product, on the other
hand, although the better crops obtained by selection are by
no means to be neglected, they are always well below the grapes
and wines of Europe (Figs. 34 and 35).

(1) The bunches are small, with watery berries, have a viscid
   pulp and an uncertain sweet taste.
(2) To give an idea of the wine obtained from *muscadinia*,
   for instance, it is sufficient to recall that the Brix has a
   mean value of 14·8 (corrected to 16·5° C.), and that the
   acidity is of a mean 6·7 gm. of tartaric acid per litre.

Rather than speak of a wine, it would be better to consider
it as a scarcely alcoholic drink when fermented, sweet in the
fresh state, and then acid, and always with highly questionable
taste and characteristics.

FIG. 33. OLD TRUNK OF *VITIS ROTUNDIFOLIA*.

FIG. 34. LEAF AND FRUIT BUNCH
OF *VITIS ROTUNDIFOLIA*.

FIG. 35. *VITIS ROTUNDIFOLIA* LOADED WITH FRUITS.

FIG. 36. *PYRUS BACCATA*.

However, the extraordinary resistance to *Peronospora* and the capacity of prospering in an extremely wet–hot climate remain as a statement of fact, and this suggested to Hausmann and Dearing the possibility of crossing *Vitis rotundifolia* and *V. vinifera*. The hybrids which resulted were morphologically perfect, but sterile; there are individuals with stamens but with sterile pollen and others which have the pistil but which cannot be fertilised even with the best pollen. There is, therefore, incompatability.

The importance of the experiment is not, however, in any way diminished, in that, although the desired result was not obtained, the limits of possibility have been clearly shown, suggesting that when the trials were continued we should rely on *Vitis labrusca* for the crosses with *V. vinifera* instead of *V. rotundifolia*.

The apple tree cultivated in Canada does not push its way beyond 50° N., where, in any case, only the most resistant and hardy varieties are found to resist the harshness of the winter, and to mature their fruits each year in the brief sub-arctic summer. Typical of this category is the " Yellow Transparent " apple, which develops its fruits in June–August with mean temperatures around 22° C., and which reaches maturity in September with mean temperatures of 14° C., while from the end of the harvest until the fall of the leaves the conditions of the atmosphere allow the perfect maturing of the wood, thus enabling the plant to withstand minima of −30° C. and more in the winter. Beyond the 50th Parallel the cultivated races are no longer able to withstand the intense ambiental adversities. A wild type, *Pyrus baccata*, then makes its appearance. Its continent of origin is Asia, where it is found in large numbers on the banks of Lake Baikal in Siberia. It is a dwarfish tree with smooth bark and compact wood; it branches from the base, with short, robust stems, and these enable it to withstand the violent winds which blow in the prairies of the northwest. Its resistance to the cold is notable as shown by trials undertaken at Brandon (Manitoba) and Indian Head, Saskatchewan, for many years. New shoots spring up each year (Fig. 36) from the terminal branches, and the natural and vigorous pruning, which so greatly harms cultivated varieties which are less resistant to cold, has no harmful effect. However, the quality of the fruit is not at all good; it is of a yellowish-red colour, small and about the size of a cherry (mean diameter, 1·8 cm.), astringent and acid, sometimes with an unpleasant and bitter taste.

The thermic requirements of *Pyrus baccata*, however, are much more limited than those of *P. malus, L.* In the period of development and maturing, mean temperatures of 13° C. and 11° C., respectively, are sufficient.

Saundersen tried to cross *Pyrus malus* and *P. baccata*, and was successful in that he obtained hybrids which were widely distributed beyond the 50th Parallel under the name of Crab-apple. In certain places they reach the 56th Parallel, and bring their fruits to maturity with mean temperatures of 15° C. during development, and 13° C. during maturity.

With reference to thermic requirements, therefore, hybrids possess intermediate characteristics when compared with the parents; the small fruits 4·5 cm. × 4·0 cm. are edible and worth cultivating for the market, even though being, as regards productivity and quality, well below the standards of *P. malus*. Their resistance to the cold is nevertheless clearly superior to that presented by *P. malus*, and has permitted the culture of the apple to extend further north.

The wild species can also be considered a " genofond " for " resistance " and " hardiness " to be utilised in crosses with the purpose of extending the area of distribution of many cultivated plants beyond their present limit of existence.

The order of relationships between productivity and hardiness in the progressive decrease of productivity, and the corresponding increase in hardiness, may be represented by the following five forms as one moves further and further away from the optimal sectors towards the limits :

(1) Hybrids and highly productive varieties in general.
(2) Crosses between highly productive varieties and local varieties.
(3) Local varieties.
(4) Crosses between local varieties and wild varieties.
(5) Wild varieties.

CHAPTER XVI

QUALITATIVE YIELD

THE favourable ambiental conditions which lead to a plentiful yield very often have a negative influence on the quality of the product. The large masses of grapes obtained in rich humiferous soils in wet and cool years furnish wines having a sugar content, and alcoholic graduation inferior to those obtained in drought years and on the stony slopes of the mountain-sides, where the grape-yield is not very high, but where the quality of the musts and of the wines is excellent. To demonstrate the different requirements of the plant with reference to a quantitative and qualitative product, the figures relative to yield obtained in hectolitres per ha. and the alcoholic graduation of wines in the various soil-units on the island of Ischia are given again :

Quantity.		Quality.	
Soils.	Yields, hl. per ha.	Soils.	Alcoholic graduation, % by volume.
Padule	71	Terra rossa	16
Arenella	66	Lapillosa	15
Terre forti	56	Terre forti	15
Pappamondo	52	Cenere	14
Lapillosa	50	Pappamondo	12
Pozzolana	44	Pozzolana	10
Terra rossa	42	Arenella	9
Cenere	35	Padule	8

With an increase in the skeleton content of the soil (and with a decrease in precipitations within certain limits at least), the quality of the product undoubtedly improves, while the quantity decreases.

Before the 1914–18 war the activities of the plant-breeding station at Svalöf were directed towards the creation of types of wheat able to give the highest possible yield by means of crosses

S

between the highly productive Scottish " Squarehead " and the local, not very productive, but early wheats that also were resistant to cold, and distinguished by their excellent quality.

The hybrids so obtained gave an excellent result contributing towards the increase of grain production by over a third in many provinces. During the war, however, it was brought home to the experts that the higher quantitative yield had worsened the quality : the content of gluten was greatly reduced, so that Swedish flour had become very poor, and not very suitable for bread- and pastry-making. In normal times these defects would have been eliminated by mixing the local flour with Canadian flour, easily obtainable and at economic price. But when submarine warfare made imports of " Manitoba ", (very rich in gluten) difficult, the deficiencies of the Svalöf hybrids became apparent, with all their inherent inconveniences.

If in wheat-importing countries such as Sweden and Italy, with some exceptions, quantity has right of preference over quality to an extremely advanced point of tolerance, in exporting countries such as the Argentine, Canada and Australia, the varieties richer in gluten are preferred to the poorer ones, even if yield in grain is lower. Below are given the figures relative to two Argentine varieties, " Universal II " and " Favourite " :

Variety.	Grain, kg. per ha.	Gluten, %.	Gluten, kg. per ha.
Universal II . .	1,584	13·0	205·9
Favourite . . .	1,708	11·4	196·7

" Favourite " comes into first place for quantity of grain, but yields its place to " Universal II " when considering the gluten factor which makes the demand higher on the market for this latter type.

It is the rains and low temperatures during maturation that hinder the formation of gluten in the kernels; while dry and clear conditions, although often having a negative influence on the quantity of the product, undoubtedly improve its quality.

Here are two groups of typical stations for which are given the figures of gluten percentage, mean temperatures and precipitation from earing to the harvest for winter and spring varieties :

Winter and Spring Wheats : Gluten, Temperature and Rainfall

Station.	Gluten, %.	Temperature, ° C.	Rainfall, mm.
Winter Varieties.			
Roseworthy, 1932 .	13·5	25·5	19·0
Volbu, 1932 . .	10·6	11·9	80·0
Voll, 1931 . .	5·6	10·4	262·0
Volbu, 1931 . .	0·3	9·4	121·0
Spring Varieties.			
Cerignola . .	15·6	24·1	5·6
Rastatt . . .	14·5	20·8	72·6
Skara . . .	12·8	12·3	261·0
Volbu . . .	0·7	8·4	162·0

Bringing to the abscissæ the mean temperatures from earing to harvest, and to the ordinates the percentage in gluten, the curves of the relationship between gluten and temperature for spring and winter varieties show the same trend. One must remember, however, that the winter forms contain less gluten than the spring varieties.

From approximately 12° C. onwards, the percentage in gluten tends to increase progressively with increases in temperature. Below 12° C., which may well be considered a thermic threshold, the formation of gluten is reduced, and between 10° C. and 9° C. it becomes practically nil.

If the plants are kept in a hot-house, the quantity of gluten tends to increase with rises in temperature up to a temperature of 35° C., as experiments now being conducted clearly prove. However, this is somewhat unreal, since in no position in the area of distribution of wheat are such high mean temperatures recorded (Fig. 37).

With a constant temperature, but making humidity in the soil vary within wide limits, gluten percentage varies noticeably, and is lower the greater the moisture in the soil. From experiments carried out by Briccoli we have (with a constant temperature of 20° C.) the following mean percentages of gluten :

Dry series   .   .   .   .   .   17·0%
Normal series .   .   .   .   .   14·9%
Wet series   .   .   .   .   .   12·2%

In consideration of this obvious action of the soil moisture, it is evident that, with reference to gluten percentage, highly

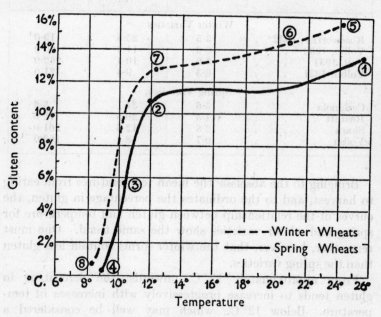

FIG. 37.   EFFECT OF TEMPERATURE ON THE FORMATION OF GLUTEN IN WHEAT.

differing results may be obtained in different types of soil, according to their water content. With regard to the chemical composition of soil, although the action is not so evident, Briccoli has demonstrated the undoubtedly positive action exercised by nitrates. In effect, applying this fertiliser in varying doses to a very poor soil in the period between earing and milk maturation, a series of decidedly positive results was obtained :

Treatment.	Calcium nitrate, kg. per ha.	Gluten, %.
No fertiliser added . . .	0	7·0
Fertiliser added once . .	130	7·6
,, ,, twice . .	260	16·4
,, ,, three times .	390	19·7
,, ,, four ,, .	520	20·6
,, ,, five ,, .	650	23·5

Between the non-fertilised series, and one that had the maximum application of nitrate, the great difference of 16·54% was observed. On the whole, it seems that conditions of the physical and agrotechnic environment acting positively on the quality of the product, differ completely, especially in respect to temperature and water availability, from those acting favourably on the quantity of the product.

At constant yield, any flour is considered all the better from the nutritive point of view the higher its calorie content. This latter, on the other hand, depends in part on the physical environment, and in part on the specific aptitudes of the individual varieties. The experimental results obtained by A. Dimič are of interest.

The calorific value of flour is a character which can vary only slightly. Experiments at numerous places throughout the world, and in the most different thermic and pluviometric conditions during the period of development and of maturing of the grain, show the calorific value of the kernel of the variety " Turkey " to have a minimum of 3,833 and a maximum of 3,981 large calories at the places where conditions were respectively, very favourable and very bad, for the development of this character.

The coefficient of variation obtained by dividing the standard deviation from the mean by the mean itself is very low : $\frac{\sigma}{M} = 0·09$. Variability therefore has a value which is below 1% of the mean. The low intrinsic variability is without doubt accentuated by the contrasting action of the fundamental factors, rainfall and temperature, in connection with calories production.

In reality rainfall can act simultaneously in the positive and in the negative sense.

(1) It acts negatively, in that with increase in rainfall, the gluten content, which is the biggest calorific component of the grain, is diminished. Besides a certain quantity of water, the grain contains starch, cellulose and gluten—substances possessing different calorific values : 3,200 for starch, 4,400 for cellulose and 5,800 calories for gluten.

(2) It acts positively, in that, since an increase in rainfall causes a fall in temperature, the interval between fructification and maturity is lengthened. This period, all other conditions remaining constant, is directly correlated with the calorific value.

Thus in certain years the negative action can prevail, in others the positive, according to meteorological conditions. In the case examined here, the quantity of rain is directly related to yield in calories, as Dimič observed for the years 1940 (very rainy) and 1942 (relatively dry) at Perugia :

	1940.	1942.
Rainfall, mm. . . .	151·8	49·5
Calories	3,951·5	3,909·2

In 1940, with plentiful precipitation, a higher number of calories was registered. The difference, however, is very small (but quite definite in every case), due to the fact that rainfall acted also in the direction of lowering the gluten content.

Temperature also behaves in two different ways :

(1) with an increase in temperature, the gluten percentage is increased : positive effect;

(2) with an increase in temperature the length of the 4th sub-period is shortened : negative effect.

Here, too, according to whether the positive or negative action prevails, we shall have a direct or an inverse relationship between mean temperature and the calorific value of the grain.

In the case considered, the negative action prevailed. In fact :

	1940.	1942.
Temperature, ° C.	16·19	18·99
Calories	3,951·5	3,909·2

In the warmer year, 1942, the sum total of calories proved to be lower. The difference between the two years is in any case relatively small, for the reason given above.

On the whole, it is evident that the length of the fourth sub-period has a dominant, positive action in every case on the calorific value.

In experiments for the determination of gluten, it is indispensable that only normally developed and perfectly mature grain be used. Grain damaged by either a hot spell or a cold wave gives a very high percentage of cellulose, which, as we have seen, has a calorific value superior to that of starch. Cellulose, although a negative component as regards the quality of the product, contributes, however, towards an increase in the number of calories obtainable from the yield.

Below are given the figures relative to the calorific value for normal and shrivelled grain of the " Wagenburg " spring variety, taken from two places whose meteorological characteristics are completely different. At the station Roseworthy (Australia) the processes of development and maturing were interrupted by hot spells, while at Volbu (Norway) low temperatures cut these processes short. The result was a badly developed, wrinkled and shrivelled grain, poor in starch and gluten, but, in contrast, very rich in cellulose. We have :

Calorific Value of Normal and Damaged Wheat : " *Wagenburg* "

Roseworthy :	Shrivelled kernels	.	.	.	4,027 calories
	Normal kernels	.	.	.	3,940 ,,
Volbu :	Shrivelled kernels	.	.	.	3,929 ,,
	Normal kernels	.	.	.	3,895 ,,

Effect of Temperature on the Composition of Ferments in Musts

It is well known that the nature and composition of ferments have a considerable influence on the quality of wines. It is for this reason that in this chapter, dealing with yield from a qualitative point of view, we regard it as opportune to refer to the experiments of Castelli and his collaborators. The question particularly interests us because Castelli started his work from the concept of climatic axes, and developed his research along a longitudinal axis (from polar to equatorial limit) which tended to reach to the extremes of vine cultivation—that is, the limits for deficient and excess of temperature, respectively.

In his research, extending from northern Italy down to Sicily and in the State of Israel, Castelli has first and foremost observed that the asporogenic forms of ferments diminish from north to south, while, on the contrary, the sporogenic ones diminish from south to north. As an example, here are the figures gathered from genus *Kloeckera* as an asporogenic form, and for *Hanseniaspora guilliermondii* Pijper as a sporogenic one : the figures represent the percentage for all strains :

Regions.	Kloeckera.	Hanseniaspora guilliermondii.
Umbria, Toscana and Marche .	13·8	0
Latina	13·6	0
Puglie and Calabria . . .	9·6	48·5
Sicily and State of Israel . .	0·0	77·5

In considering the total for all sporogenic and asporogenic forms, the law of latitude is confirmed by the figures for the Puglie region, from the most southerly zone to the Capitanata, in flat and uniform topographical situations, and in homogenous conditions for the vine and enological products. We give below the respective percentages of asporogenic and sporogenic strains for the northern, central and southern districts of the region :

	Asporogenic strains.	Sporogenic strains.
Puglie : Northern . . .	53·3	46·7
Central . . .	21·4	78·6
Southern . . .	5·6	94·6

Castelli explains the variations for latitude as being due exclusively to the thermic factor, and his statement finds convincing confirmation in the experiments carried out by Capriotti on material taken at the 30° N. latitude at heights ranging from 10 to 620 metres above sea level.

Altitude, m.	Kloeckera.	Hanseniaspora guilliermondii.
620	+	−
600	+	−
270	+	−
68	+	+
67	−	+
62	−	+
10	−	+

While certain forms of *Kloeckera apiculata* (Reess) Janke, within the limits in which the research was carried out, do not exactly correspond to the law of variations in latitude, in that they are, we might say, more or less widely represented in all sectors from the extreme north to the extreme south, other species, on the contrary (in the group of the asporogenic ones), decrease from north to south, while others (in the group of the sporogenic) increase the nearer one gets to the hot regions.

Two extreme and typical cases are represented by *Hanseniaspora guilliermondii*, absent in northern districts, and *Kloeckera magna*, which is never found in vineyards in the south. Under extreme conditions—that is to say, near the hot and near the cold limits—the number of forms directly participating in fermentation processes tends to become restricted to those which are most adaptable in a hot, and in a cold environment, respectively.

In intermediate zones, on the other hand, are mixed together the species incapable of reaching the extreme limit, as well as the forms found in these extreme positions.

CHAPTER XVII

GENERATIVE YIELD
(Characters of the Seed)

As has been repeatedly observed, ambiental conditions favourable for a quantitative yield and decidedly unfavourable for a qualitative one can often be found. Similarly, conditions favourable to quantity and quality can hinder the attainment of good seed for planting. We refer to the interesting communications received from Todeschini (Tripolitania) and from Parodi (San Remo). The radish (*Raphanus* spp.) reproduced with seed obtained in Africa degenerates. The shape of the root changes, the original globoid form becomes elongated and the flesh is so hot to the taste that it becomes practically impossible to put it on the market.

The behaviour of the cantaloup melon is worthy of note. If it is made to reproduce in Libya (North Africa), it rapidly degenerates from one year to another. The crop, which is always excellent when the seed is renewed by importing it from its original birth-place (Colorado), is, in fact, scarce and of poor quality if locally grown seed is employed. The pulp loses its colour, it contains less juice, it is less aromatic and, lastly, it is more fibrous.

The dwarf bean of America, made to reproduce in Aziziah in irrigated culture, becomes a climber and reduces its productive capacity to a quarter of normal, in spite of the greater development of the aerial portions. Here again, by making use each year of seed directly imported from the zone of origin, the plant keeps its form and mode of growth, furnishing an abundant yield, and this in spite of the peculiar conditions of the new African environment.

The seeds of tomatoes from the Riviera, according to Parodi, give an excellent result in Ecuador (South America) : on the other hand, plants grown from seed locally reproduced in Ecuador develop badly, giving small, tasteless fruits, and the crop worsens rapidly from year to year. In any case, the

practice of renewing cereal seed, and the seed of certain garden
or fodder plants, from time to time by importing directly from
the countries of origin, has been adopted for quite a long time,
and we have many examples of it all over the world.

It suffices to recall that the farmers in the north of Great
Britain often obtain the seed for their wheat from the south of
the country, where the relatively dry, hot regime is more
favourable for the development of the embryo.

In Perugia, experiments were undertaken with certain
varieties of wheat reproduced *in loco* (matured in a wet year),
and with the seed of the same varieties obtained from Messina
(matured in a dry–hot environment). As will be seen from the
table given below, the seed from the last-named locality gave
by far the best results :

Station.	Variety, quintals per ha.			
	Oberdan.	Aziziah.	Milazzo.	Ardito.
Messina . .	36·8	19·4	30·7	28·0
Perugia . .	32·8	13·9	22·2	24·2
Difference .	4·0	5·5	8·5	3·8

The negative effect of rainfall and low temperatures on the
quality of the seed is evident.

From these observations and preliminary determinations, we
felt justified in beginning a methodical study into the influence
of the physical environment on yield from a generative point
of view—that is, in relation to the quality of the seed.

Meteorological factors are all-important in this connection.
This shows itself in two distinct ways :

(1) in being favourable or unfavourable for the formation of
the embryo ;
(2) in causing the poorer, or less resistant, individuals to be
eliminated by natural selection.

With reference to the first point, I always quote an experiment which I undertook in Rome from the year 1919 onwards,
when I wanted to try out a type of local wheat from the Alpine

regions, and which had been sent to me in considerable quantity with the assurance that it was a pure line—this from the " Cattedra ambulante di Agricoltura " of Domodossola.

In the first year the results proved to be excellent in respect of both quantity and quality. In the second and successive years, when the seed obtained from plants reproduced locally was employed, there was a progressive worsening of the situation, and the yield reached a very low standard. In control plots, where the original seed (from Domodossola) was utilised, the yield always remained good for quantity and quality.

We have explained this phenomenon with the assertion that while the climatic conditions in the Lazio region are compatible with a satisfactory quantitative and qualitative yield for the variety considered, these conditions are, however, contrary to the normal development of the embryo.

The consequence is that the plant grown in Lazio from the original seed bears a sound ear, with kernels large and rich in gluten. These kernels, however, contain a defective or weak embryo. If this material is used as seed, it will give a plant having an imperfect development, and this, if the seed reproduced locally is employed for successive sowings, will naturally aggravate the situation in each subsequent year.

The geographical trials subsequently carried out with great care in many countries have fully confirmed the accuracy of our interpretation.

In 1930–31 the " Turkey " variety of wheat from the U.S.A. (*T. v. erythrospermum*) was sown at numerous research stations distributed in such a manner as to have the most varied combinations of temperature and rainfall—from Volbu (Norway), where the development of the wheat and maturing took place in a regime of excessive rains and thermic deficiency, to Tunis, where, on the contrary, the regime was a typically dry–hot one, and Lincoln (New Zealand), where decidedly favourable meteorological conditions were encountered.

The grain obtained from the various stations was sown at Perugia in November 1932, and care was taken to see that all plots contained the same number of plants—namely, 100 per square metre. That same winter, differences in the intensity of tillering, pigmentation and habit of growth (erect and prostrate) were already noticeable in the different plots.

From the resumption of growth in spring, in spite of the evident identity between general conditions of soil and climate, we began to observe considerable differences between one plot and another in relation to the country of origin of the seed. These differences were accentuated up to the maturity phase, so that in the qualitative and quantitative sense, as also with reference to the length of culms and ears, the modes of growth, etc., quite different data were registered for the various plots. Since the plants, I repeat, had grown under absolutely identical meteorological and soil conditions, the differences encountered in the various plots are evidently to be attributed to the conditions of the atmospheric environment which had acted on the development of the embryo in the different stations of origin (see page 285).

The material gathered at Perugia in 1933 was re-sown the same year. In 1934 all the differences observed the preceding year disappeared completely. The experiment and its confirmation could not have been more convincing.

. . . .

In considering the effects of natural selection on the quality of the seed, I limit myself to giving a brief outline of recent preliminary trials which go under the name of " meridionalization " (Tallarico).

A variety of wheat from a province in central Italy (Grosseto), in which drought occurs in three years out of ten, was made to reproduce for several years in the southern coast of the peninsula, where drought is observed eight years out of ten. The seed obtained from plants grown in such hard conditions was returned and sown in the place of origin; a considerable increase in the mean yield was noted over that obtained with the wheats which had always been reproduced locally.

This undoubtedly positive result was attributed to the beneficial action on the embryo of the luminous radiations of the Mediterranean sky, where, in the hottest and unclouded sectors, the embryos appeared to reach a more perfect development and to have improved structure.

However, similar experiments undertaken in Scandinavia and north Russia, where wheats of the south were moved towards the polar limit, and therefore placed in diametrically opposite conditions to those encountered in the Mediterranean region (rainfall and considerable nebulosity), gave identical results. In fact, utilising the seed of wheats reproduced at the polar limit in the places of origin further south, yields superior to those of the locally reproduced plants were obtained.

Without wishing to exclude a possibly favourable action by the luminous radiations or, better, of certain radiations on the formation of the embryo, we cannot but notice how in these cases the results obtained could be attributed to a natural selection which, in an adverse environment, causes the least adaptable and defective individuals to be eliminated : a general improvement in the mass, a concentration of " chosen " individuals and, in consequence, an increase in mean yield, is thus obtained.

Once accepted that environmental conditions contrary to a quantitative and qualitative yield can give rise to good seed, the problem of the discovery and delineation of the zones most suitable for the production of good seed for each species becomes one of the most attractive tasks of Agricultural Ecology.

The Puglie region in Italy is the most suitable for the attainment of excellent cauliflower seed, which is exported to Germany. In the latter country meteorological conditions give rise to bad seed, but are highly favourable for a quantitative and qualitative end product. In Puglie, on the contrary, the plant develops badly and yields a crop of inferior quality : this region is therefore a typical example of a centre for the exclusive production of good seed.

In the plains of the Mediterranean region, in a regime of high and ascending temperatures, and with sufficient water in suitable soils, the potato gives an abundant yield of tubers which are of good quality for the market, but unsuitable for planting. Good tubers for planting are obtained only on the mountains, where the formation and development of the tubers (contrary to the situation in the plains) take place in a regime of low and descending temperatures, and this combination appears to be indispensable for the production of good tubers for planting. Identical observations were made in Peru, with particular reference to the irrigated coastal region and to the range of the Andes, where the best tubers for planting for the plain are obtained close to the altimetric cold limit of cultivation of the potato. In practice, tubers gathered in the coastal plains are not good for planting.

One must not, on the other hand, forget that high temperature may favour the development of the virus, so contributing to make the tubers less suitable for planting.

CHAPTER XVIII

VERNALISATION OF SEED

WITH reference to the problem of the quality of seed, I do not think it out of place to allude briefly to the theory and technique of vernalisation put forward by Lysenko, though still the subject of much speculation and controversy.

At the beginning of its cycle of development, every plant presents according to Lysenko two successive and very brief stages.

These are : (1) thermic stage; (2) photoperiodic stage.

Giving the plant, during these short intervals, the thermic and photoperiodic quotas which are not to be found in the natural environment the plant grown from vernalised seeds can develop regularly, even under contrary ambiental conditions. On the other hand, plants raised from seed which has not undergone the treatment would not be able to accomplish their development, or would, at least, greatly delay the date of flowering, with the result they are more exposed to eventual adversities—to hot spells, for instance, whose frequency increases towards the summer.

· · · ·

In considering this technique we must differentiate between growth and development.

(a) *Development* is nothing more than the series of successive transformations of form, structure and composition through which the plant must pass in order to complete the cycle from germination, or budding, to maturity of fruit or seed.

(b) *Growth* is the simple increase in weight and volume independent of any motive of *evolutionary activity*.

Winter wheats sown in hot-houses in a short-day regime during winter display a vigorous growth presenting a large mass of tillers and leaves, but remain indefinitely at the tillering phase without progressing further in their development. On the whole the works of Gassner (artificial transformation of winter forms of wheat into spring ones) and of Hallard and Garner (the phenomena of photoperiodism) converge in the general conception of Lysenko, which takes the name of " stadial theory ".

After subjecting pre-germinated seed in a state of very slow growth to a particular thermic and luminous treatment, a normal development of the plant may subsequently be obtained in the open field, even in unfavourable conditions of the thermic and photoperiodic environment.

By the term " vernalisation " is meant the physical and chemical treatments as a whole to which the seed in subjected before sowing in order to obtain a normal development of the plant in those ambiental conditions under which, we repeat, the complete development up to fructification and maturity would not have been possible.

Integration of the Thermic Stage

The credit of having laid the foundations of this new technique goes to Gassner. Seedlings of rye, barley and wheat belonging to winter and spring forms were put to grow at different temperatures : from 1° to 2° C.; from 5° to 6° C.; up to 12° C.; up to 24° C., and for varying intervals beginning from a minimum of 48 hours. The material so treated was then sown at different times, from January to late spring.

While the spring forms, independently from the time of sowing and from the thermic treatments, behaved in much the same way, the winter forms reacted quite differently. The plots treated with temperatures from 5° C. upwards, and sown in April, developed in a purely vegetative sense, while those treated with temperatures from 1° to 2° C. during the first stages of development eared regularly, and the grain matured just as if they had been spring forms.

The difference, therefore, between winter and spring forms, according to Gassner, does not lie in the different lengths of the vegetative period, but in the fact that the winter forms, in order to complete their cycle and form the reproductive organs, necessitate low temperatures which, in the open field, act on the plants during the autumn and the cold winter from

T

the very first stages of development until resumption of growth in spring. A similar effect may be artificially obtained, satisfying the " Kältebedürfnis " of the plant by treating the seedlings with low temperatures, which are thus put in the position of being able to complete their cycle, even if sown in spring, as Gassner has demonstrated.

Taking as his basis the ideas and conclusions reached in this research, Lysenko greatly developed these experiments both in a scientific and in a practical direction, founding, within the Institute of Genetics at Odessa, a school whose activities had wide repercussions in the scientific and agricultural worlds. Moreover, Lysenko applied the cold treatment not to " seedlings ", but to " pre-germinated seeds ", which can then be directly employed for sowing, which would not have been possible in the case of the treated seedlings. Vernalisation by treatment of seed with low temperatures enables the spring sowing of winter wheats, which is of considerable importance in Soviet Russia (where the severity of the winter renders the autumn-sown crop in many regions difficult and uncertain) to take place.

On the other hand, however, the winter forms are more productive and, thanks to their earliness in ripening, they to some extent are spared from the hot spells so frequent in the south-eastern territory of the U.S.S.R. For winter, semi-winter and spring wheats, we have the following temperatures of vernalisation :

Type.	Temperature, ° C.
Winter wheat	From 0– 2
Semi-winter wheat . . .	„ 3– 5
Spring wheat	„ 5–10

The lower the necessary temperature (and keeping the temperature constant), the longer the duration of treatment necessary to obtain vernalisation, and the more accentuated is to be considered the grade of autumnality. (With reference to spring forms, vernalisation induces early earing.)

With temperatures from 0 to 2° C., the time necessary to accomplish vernalisation shows notable differences between one variety and another.

Variety.	Duration of treatment, days.
Strain 808/1/26	18
Erythrospermum 917 . . .	36
Ukrainka	41
Hostianum	46
Bianco aristato 040	52
Erythrospermum 1325/5 . . .	57

" Erythrospermum 1325/5 " therefore represents the highest degree of autumnality, and requires a lengthy treatment of no less than 57 days in order to be transformed into a spring form, always according to Lysenko.

Besides temperature, however, we must consider the other environmental factors, particularly the moisture or percentage of water in the grain. Under natural conditions in the open field, the grade of humidity is always sufficient. In material kept in storage, however, the water content is approximately 12%, and this percentage is insufficient for the vernalisation process. On the other hand, in wetting the seed, one has to take great care, and limit the application of water to the quantity which is strictly necessary for the embryo to initiate its development. In this way the seed will be susceptible to the vernalising action without, however, reaching that excess growth which would render impossible the utilisation of the vernalised material for planting.

This optimal humidity is directly related to the various temperatures necessary for the realisation of the vernalisation process.

For winter wheats requiring temperatures from 0° to 2° C. we must regulate the humidity in the grain so that it is 55%, this being obtained if 35 kg. of water are added to 1 quintal of seed.

The semi-autumnal seed needing temperatures of from 3° to 5° C., requires 33 kg. of water to increase the humidity or water content to 50%. Lastly, the early spring wheats, which require temperatures up to 10° C. and more, necessitate 31 kg. of water to reach a moisture grade of 48%.

Summing up briefly : For the vernalisation of seed, and in order to overcome the thermic phase, the following preliminary treatment is necessary, this being the technique given by Lysenko :

Variety.	Temperature, ° C.	Humidity, %.	Kg. of water needed per quintal.	Duration of treatment, days.
Autumnal .	0– 2	55	35	40
Semi-autumnal	3– 5	50	33	25
Spring . .	5–10	48	31	10

So much for vernalisation by low temperatures. With regard to high temperatures which would, in certain cases, furnish the plant with those temperatures lacking in its natural environment, the technique to be employed is not yet, according to Lysenko, perfectly established.

Integration of the Photoperiodic Phase (Vernalisation of Buds)

In order to illustrate this thesis, I find it best to refer to experiments carried out by Lysenko on the potato, and to research by Rocchi on the effects of the artificial variation (reduction) of the photoperiod on the buds of the vine.

If potato plants be subjected to continuous illumination during growth by the employment of powerful electric lamps throughout the night, it is observed that those individuals treated with uninterrupted illumination rapidly develop their aerial portion, and bloom with great precociousness; these, however, produce few tubers, which turn out very small and malformed. If the length of day is artificially reduced to 9 hours by means of suitable screens, the epigeous portions develop very slowly, the internodes on the stem are notably contracted, and the plants do not bloom, while a good harvest of large and numerous tubers is obtained. All this was foreseeable because we know that the potato is a long-day plant, so that the best results for tuber production will naturally be obtained with a short-day regime, which delays or excludes flowering, while favouring the formation of tubers.

However, in complete contrast with these observations, and with the results of the above experiments, is the fact that close to the polar limit for the culture of the potato, where in summer the length of day is, as we well know, very long, harvests are obtained which are superior to those at lower latitudes, and therefore where the day is shorter. Lysenko gives the following explanation : " Being a long-day plant, the potato develops with greater rapidity the longer, quite naturally, the interval between sunrise and sunset and, better still, in a regime of continued illumination. Under such conditions the development of the aerial portions proceeds with the greatest velocity, the products of photosynthesis being thus all directed to bloom and fruits, while on the subterranean portions of the plant, the development of the tubers is hindered, either in part, or completely. However, once the development of the fruit has been completed (and this rapidly), the plant does not die, but continues to assimilate. Having completed the development of the aerial portions, the products of assimilation go towards increasing the weight of tubers. It is in this manner that the abundant production of tubers at the polar limit of the potato may be explained."

On these deductions and observations is based the vernalisation of tubers to be employed for planting (photo-vernalisation of eyes) tried by Lysenko with positive results. The technique is very simple : the tubers, linked together by a string in rows 1 metre long (2 kg. of tubers per row), are hung vertically in a closed chamber for a period of from 20 to 30 days before planting, at a temperature of 15–20° C. The eyes are all exposed to sunlight during the daytime, and to artificial light (by means of electric lamps) throughout the night.

The tubers so treated rapidly integrate the photoperiodic phase, so that at the beginning of tuberisation the vernalised plants have already formed their fruits; at the same time, they present a mass of leaves, and therefore a photosynthetic capacity far superior to that of plants derived from tubers which have not had the luminous treatment. On the other hand, with the formation of the berries, the cycle of the aerial portions is completed, and these can no longer compete with, and hinder the development of the subterranean portions. It happened, therefore, that the mean yield obtained from the treated tubers was of 370 gm. per plant, while in a regime of normal day length 260 gm. were obtained and, lastly, the tubers used as seed, kept in an artificially-shortened regime of 9 hours illumination, produced plants whose mean yield was of only 241 gm. per plant. The vernalisation of eyes therefore presents the advantage of enabling the plant to anticipate blooming and at the same time favours the development of a large mass of leaves which, having completed the cycle of development with the formation of fruits, contribute, as we have seen, towards the accumulation of an abundant quantity of starch in the tubers whose volume rapidly increases, thanks to the intensity of photosynthetic processes. This, as far as I know, is the only described case of vernalisation of eyes.

.   .   .   .

An artificial reduction in length of day to 8 hours in the period between budding and the blooming of the vine (treatment for approximately 30 days) does not bring forward the date of the appearance of blooms, which remains the same both for treated and control plants.

The abbreviation of the day's length, however, if we act during the photoperiodic or luminous stage, brings about vernalisation of the buds, the subsequent effects of which are quite evident later in a very advanced stage of the cycle of development.

The results are :

(1) A more abundant development of the stem and leaf-masses in consequence of the vernalising stimulus in the first stages of the biological cycle.

(2) A marked anticipation (10–12 days) in the beginning of maturity, while, as stated, the date for flowering remains the same.

(3) In consequence of the earlier maturity, the treated plants come to make use of a greater number of degrees of temperature, which helps to complete maturity, increasing the sugar content in the musts and reducing the acidity.

The following varieties were used in the experiments :

(a) *Table grapes*—" Luglienga nera " (very early) and " S. Jennet " white and late.

(b) *Wine grapes*—" Pinot bianco " (early), " Nebbiolo nero " (late).

Here is a synopsis of the results obtained, beginning with the early varieties :

The weight of branches and leaves is expressed by index-numbers, taking as equal to 100, the weight of branches and leaves of the control plants.

For " Luglienga " we find :

	Sugars, %.	Acidity, gm. per litre.	Weight of branches and leaves, index-number.
Plant in shortened day regime . .	19·5	5·17	122
Controls . . .	17·5	6·00	100

For " Pinot bianco " we have : 18·5% of sugar and 6·1% of acidity for the plants kept in a shortened-day regime, while the controls give, respectively, 17·5% (less sugar) and 7·5% (greater acidity). The greater sugar content and decreased acidity are therefore evident in the musts of treated plants.

Let us now pass to an examination of the analytical results for the late varieties : " S. Jennet " and " Nebbiolo ".

	Sugars, %.	Acidity.
" S. Jennet " :		
Plants in shortened day regime .	18·8	6·80
Controls	16·2	8·60
" Nebbiolo " :		
Plants in shortened day regime .	21·3	6·90
Controls	19·1	7·20

Here, too, as for the early varieties, but with even more marked differences, an increase in sugar content and a decrease in acidity are noted for plants kept in a shortened-day regime. We may therefore conclude that the artificial reduction in length of day between budding and blooming does not act in a photoperiodic sense (bringing forward the appearance of reproductive organs), but in a vernalising manner, with after-effects which result in an anticipation of the first stages of maturity and, as a consequence, an increase in sugar content and a reduction in the acidity of the musts, with bigger and richly developed branches and leaves.

.   .   .   .   .

With regard to the integration of the photoperiodic state for seeds themselves, the treatment will naturally have to be different according to whether it is meant for long-day or short-day plants. For the former, a continued illumination for a few days immediately after the thermic phase should enable the plant to complete its development, even in an environment where the natural length of day would be too short.

For short-day plants, on the other hand, the treatment consists in exposure in a shortened-day regime and, in certain cases, to a subjection of 120 hours of continued darkness before sowing. Plants arising from seed which had been so treated would then be able to accomplish their cycle even in an environment in which the length of day was too long (Lysenko).

Effect of the Shortening of Length of Day on the Development of Winter and Spring Forms of Wheat

During the photoperiodic stage the effect of artificially shortening the length of day causes quite different and opposite actions in winter and spring forms, as is brought out by an experiment of Salvatori.

Two Swedish varieties were used :

Winter form : " Sammet ", derived from the polar limit of expansion of wheat and characterised by maximum degree of autumnality, which accentuate the photoperiodic reaction.

Spring form : " Local Spring Wheat ", from Halland, where the long and very cold winter determines a clear separation between winter and spring forms.

During the trials the temperature was always above that necessary to realise the vernalisation of the seed, which is 0–2° C.

We report the daily mean temperatures, ° C., in the corresponding interval :

11th March	.	7·5	21st March	.	8·6	31st March	.	12·1
12th ,,	.	8·7	22nd ,,	.	8·8	1st April	.	12·0
13th ,,	.	10·4	23rd ,,	.	9·8	2nd ,,	.	11·3
14th ,,	.	10·9	24th ,,	.	8·5	3rd ,,	.	12·9
15th ,,	.	8·8	25th ,,	.	10·4	4th ,,	.	14·4
16th ,,	.	8·9	26th ,,	.	12·2	5th ,,	.	15·0
17th ,,	.	10·5	27th ,,	.	13·7	6th ,,	.	13·0
18th ,,	.	11·0	28th ,,	.	9·2	7th ,,	.	14·3
19th ,,	.	12·0	29th ,,	.	10·1	8th ,,	.	13·0
20th ,,	.	10·6	30th ,,	.	10·9	9th ,,	.	11·3

The sowing was made on 1st March, 1954, and on 11th March
the young plants were all above ground. From germination
and for a period of 30 days the plants were kept in a regime of
an 8-hours-long day, by means of screens.

For " Sammet " variety we have :

	Date of earing.	Difference.
Shortened day (8 hours) . .	26th June	—
Normal day	7th July	11 days

It is further to be noted that while the plants submitted to
treatment eared with 100% of their culms, the plants of the
control eared with only 40% of their culms, which were reduced
while the ears were malformed.

These results bring further into evidence the difference
between the controls and the treated plants, so confirming the
decidedly positive action of the shortened day in the first stages
of development, when it is desired to sow winter forms in spring.

For the " Halland " variety we have :

	Date of earing.	Difference.
Shortened day (8 hours) . .	8th June	8 days
Normal day	31st May	—

Here we find quite the opposite to what was observed for the
winter forms—i.e. the culms kept in a short-day regime eared
with notable delay in respect of the controls. The true interpretation of this phenomenon is that the spring forms for their
normal development do not require a stage of very slow velocity
of growth, so that the reduction caused by shortening of the
day has only a negative effect.

To sum up :

(1) The artificial reduction in the length of day determines a vernalisation of autumnal forms which ear in anticipation, so demonstrating that the plant would have no need of low temperatures (" Kältebedürfnis "), but simply of an interval of very slow growth which is obtainable both by means of low temperatures and a shortening of the length of day (remember that wheat is a long-day plant).

(2) Gassner and Lysenko had explained in different manner the effects of temperature on the so-called transformation of winter into spring wheats. Gassner maintained that winter forms need low temperatures in the first stages of development, while Lysenko says that it is not the low temperature in itself that is important, but the slow growth which goes with it. The above experiments, conducted in temperature conditions which were insufficient to cause vernalisation, would tend to confirm Lysenko's interpretation.

Integration of Both Stages by Crossing

The problem of integrating the two stages by means of crosses is undoubtedly very attractive. In relation to a particular genotype, or mass of hereditary material, we can, according to ambiental conditions, distinguish two extreme cases together with all the intermediate situations. These are :

(1) The mean ambiental conditions perfectly suiting the requirements of the genotype in connection with the development of the organism, which therefore proceeds normally and at an optimum rate.

(2) Ambiental conditions are in contrast to the genotype, and limit the rate of development. The plant intensifies its growth without, however, completing its biological cycle, or delays to a considerable extent the formation and maturing of the seed.

Thus ambiental factors may be divided into two groups : (a) inert mass; (b) dynamic mass.

With reference to the thermic stage, the dynamic group of

ambiental factors is represented by temperature and by water (in relation to the water contained in the seed), while the photoperiodic factor belongs to the inert mass, since the variations in length of day in no way have an influence on the surpassing of the thermic stage.

During the photoperiodic stage the essential factor is, on the other hand, represented by light and darkness, and may be realised in variable conditions of temperature, excepting, naturally, those which are harmful to the vegetable organism through excess or deficiency be not reached. In this case, temperature behaves as an inert mass. How, we might now ask ourselves, is this complex of characteristics, which result in a greater or lesser velocity of development, transmitted ?

Let us take two varieties of wheat which, in certain environmental conditions, will behave in a late and in an early manner, respectively. Now let us cross them :

The first generation of hybrids, the heterozygote, carries with it the two possibilities—earliness and lateness. Given, however, according to Lysenko, that earliness is dominant over lateness, the hybrid will, when developed in the same environment as its parents, behave like the early variety in harmony with the characters of the plasma which have been transmitted to it by the early parent.

Let us now take two varieties of wheat *aaBB* and *AAbb* in the same region :

Variety aaBB is late because the ambiental conditions are contrary from the thermic side (*aa*); there is therefore a certain friction with regard to temperature which acts as a brake during the thermic stage, leading to a general delay in development. On the other hand, the photoperiodic factor is very favourable for the development of the plant. If the seed is vernalised by means of some convenient thermic treatment, we obtain a normal development, even in ambiental conditions which are unfavourable from a thermic point of view (temperatures are too high).

Variety AAbb is late (*bb*) because the relative lengths of day and night are in contrast with the requirements of this variety, for which the thermic conditions in the locality considered are undoubtedly favourable. The contrast between genotype and environment—contrast represented by a length of day not corresponding to the exigencies of the organism—acts like a brake retarding the development of the plant. However, if the pre-germinated seeds (or small plants) at the very first stage of development are subjected to artificial illumination for several days, the development of the plant will take place up to the full maturing of the seed, even in not altogether favourable conditions of the natural photoperiod (too short).

Crossing now the *aaBB* and *AAbb* varieties, the genotype of the *AaBb* hybrid, owing to the dominance of the characteristic " early habit ", will find favourable conditions both from a thermic and from a photoperiodic point of view; it will behave like an early form without being subjected to any previous treatment, namely, without having recourse to vernalisation.

Following such principles the Institute of Physiology and Genetics of Odessa directed its breeding trials along lines which gave undoubtedly positive results by producing wheats which were particularly suitable for the thermic and photoperiodic conditions of the Ukraine.

Two couples were used :

T.v. erythrospermum 534/1 × Girka 0274.
T.v. erythrospermum 534/1 × T.v. lutescens 062.

T.v. erythrospermum adapts itself well to the photoperiodic conditions for southern Russia, but does not find suitable thermic values, and therefore behaves as a late variety, giving poor yields. However, if the pre-germinated seeds are treated with low temperature, the plant ears with a considerable anticipation and gives a good yield.

While adapting themselves well to the thermic conditions of the zone, " Girka " and *T.v. lutescens* have an adversity in the relative length of day and night, so that they become late and supply a scarce and poor-quality product. With the elimination of this condition by treating the pre-germinated seed with light, the plants arising from this seed develop normally, ear early, mature and give a satisfactory and good quality yield.

· · · · ·

Having crossed the said varieties, the late individuals were eliminated through three successive generations until constant forms were obtained. These, without in any way treating the seed, eared notably early, and so produced a good yield from a qualitative and quantitative point of view, appearing particularly suited to the conditions of the physical environment of the Ukraine, where the frequency of hot spells which are the most harmful adversity, increases towards the summer.

In connection with the above, there is no doubt that the effect of ambiental factors on the formation and development of the embryo is of fundamental importance in studying and tabulating problems of vernalisation.

The " Turkey " variety (*T.v. erythrospermum*) cultivated in Perugia under absolutely identical conditions of soil and climate, presented quite different characteristics, according to the ambiental conditions of the numerous places of origin spread throughout the world. Significant is the fact that plants obtained from grain derived from the cold–wet station of Voll (Norway) presented stems and leaves which were decidedly larger in size than those obtained from the seed of the hot, dry zone of Cerignola. Care had naturally been taken to choose seed in perfectly healthy condition, and of the same weight and dimensions, so as to eliminate all sources of error.

We have the following figures (index-numbers are given for the plant characteristics) :

Station.	Rainfall, mm.	Temperature, ° C.	Length of culms.	Length of ear.	Length of leaf.
Voll . .	262·0	13·3	100	100	100
Cerignola .	8·5	25·6	70	80	65

The action of the ambiental factors at any point of the plant's development necessarily shows itself in greater or smaller measure in the successive phases of life up to the formation and maturing of the seed. Furthermore, when this action is exercised on the embryo, it will naturally make itself felt throughout the whole cycle of development of the plant derived from the said embryo.

The embryonic mass, at the beginning of its development, may be exposed to one of the four fundamental situations :

dry–hot; dry–cold; humid–hot; humid–cold. The action of the environmental factors just at this moment makes itself evident throughout the whole cycle. In other words, once pushed on to one of the four rails, the plant tends to run along it, showing the characteristics corresponding to the first stimulus, even if transferred into an indifferent, neutral environment.

We can now easily explain why it is that in the " indifferent " environment of Perugia, the seed derived from cold–wet localities tends to manifest the morphological characteristics of a cold–wet environment and, similarly, the seed derived from hot–dry localities tends to manifest the morphological characteristics of the hot–dry environment.

It is in any case demonstrated that the factors which have acted positively and negatively on the formation of the embryo later show their action on the plant developed from this embryo throughout the whole vegetative cycle.

Within the great framework of bio-ambiental reactions, the embryonic stage evidently precedes the first two stages of development of the plant : the thermic and photoperiodic stages. A study on the biological cycle must begin, therefore, from the moment in which the embryo is formed on the mother plant of the preceding generation, so that the following stages can, as a whole, be envisaged :

(1) Prestadial (embryonic).
(2) First stage (thermic).
(3) Second stage (photoperiodic).

We would almost be tempted to add a fourth stage in relation to the effects of the lunar phases during germination; however, scientific documentation on this subject is still too incomplete.

CHAPTER XIX

ECOLOGICAL CLASSIFICATION OF CULTIVATED PLANTS

WE repeat that, to all intents and purposes, cultivated plants are to be looked upon as living machines able to produce wine, flour, sugar, oil, spices, etc. The classification of the said plants will, from this point of view, have to assume a highly specific character, quite different from that of a botanical classification, since it naturally becomes necessary to base ourselves on those morphological and physiological characteristics which are in direct relationship with productivity and resistance, the two components of yield.

We must now disintegrate and single out the pieces of this machine which produce flour, or fats, or sugar.

At the beginning of our study of this problem we adopted a scheme of classification which, although very simple, can well serve to give a preliminary but sufficiently clear idea of the agricultural characteristics of each single variety. This scheme was accepted by many colleagues, and among them Prof. Emanuele De Cillis, who wrote an excellent monograph on Italian wheats.

With reference to productivity and resistance, and to the quality of the product, we take a scale of values $n \times 4$ (see page 248) from 1 (minimum of productivity and resistance, worst quality of the product) to 20 (maximum of productivity and of resistance, optimal quality).

As examples, we give two ecological tables for some Italian and British wheat varieties :

Variety.	Lodging.	Rust.	Cold.	Drought.	Preco-ciousness.	Produc-tivity.	Quality.
Biancuccia	5	7	6	16	17	9	18
Civitella	12	10	13	8	7	19	3
Rieti	4	19	10	15	10	9	18
Mentana	19	14	8	14	18	20	15
Gentil Rosso	10	9	12	8	9	12	16
Inallettabile 96	16	4	18	4	5	14	12

" Biancuccia " is evidently indicated for hot–dry regions, thanks to its resistance to drought and to its earliness which protects it from hot spells. The " Mentana " type at present predominates in the greater part of central and northern Italy, where, owing to the splendid combination of characters, it gives a yield which is superior by at least two-fifths to that of pre-existing varieties. " Mentana " is a hybrid obtained from the cross (" Wilhelmina " × " Rieti 21 ") × " Aka Komughi " : its high productivity comes from the European " Wilhelmina ", while the earliness and resistance to lodging are derived from the Japanese parent. In those same regions in which " Mentana " to-day predominates, the most widely diffused variety was, until a few years ago, " Gentil Rosso ", which, although possessing a notable number of positive characteristics, is in every case (exception made of quality) inferior to " Mentana ". " Civitella " met with great favour during the First World War, thanks to its high productivity. With a return to normal conditions, a fundamental defect in its structure, the poor quality of the product, soon lead to the disappearance of this type. The lodging-resistant " Inallettabile 96 " was introduced into Italy from France, for its productivity and resistance to lodging, but this wheat was unable to make headway in Italy due to its lateness and susceptibility to rust. " Rieti ", quite frankly negative in many points, gives a good-quality product and has a peculiar resistance to *Puccinia graminis*. Regarding this characteristic, we recall that "Rieti" has served as the basis for the series of hybrids in British East Africa and in Peru ; the aim was in fact to obtain new rust-resistant varieties. Among these, " Kenya Governor " stands out : it is able to develop regularly in the hot and humid equatorial regions where rust would completely destroy European and American wheats.

Resistance to excessive humidity and to lodging, the faculty of maturing the grain in a damp and sparsely lit environment are the essential characteristics of a good wheat in Great Britain and Ireland.

We give the figures relative to some British varieties of wheat in Table on page 289.

Squarehead Master and Standard Red. These two varieties, derived from a common stock, are distinguished by the high productivity and good quality of the grain from a milling point

Variety.	Produc-tivity.	Resistance to :			Quality.
		Excess of hu-midity.	Lodging.	Rust.	
Squarehead Master	17	14	13	5	14
Browick Gray Chaff	18	15	16	10	12
Yeoman . .	14	8	14	13	18
Local Irish . .	8	19	10	12	8
Wilhelmina . .	16	10	16	14	15

of view; they also have a good resistance to lodging and to excess humidity in winter. The weak point in this type of wheat is susceptibility to rust.

Browick Gray Chaff. Superior to the two preceding varieties both for the resistance to lodging and for productivity. It is, however, inferior in the quality of the product (milling quality), and is also much later, in that it reaches maturation with a delay of one to two weeks.

Yeoman. Presents high resistance both to rust and to lodging, satisfactory with regard to productivity and the very good quality of the product. It does not stand up well to excess of humidity.

Local Irish. Superior to all other wheats for its resistance to waterlogging, which in certain zones of Great Britain, but more especially in Ireland, is decidedly the most harmful phenomenon. It is, however, a poor producer, and the quality of the seed is also inferior.

Wilhelmina. Among the imported varieties it leads in productivity; this is combined with a good quality of the product and a notable resistance both to rust and to lodging, a positive complex of characteristics which justify the favours reserved for this variety in Great Britain.

The ecological scheme thus furnishes an adequate notion, at first sight, of the virtues and defects of the single varieties, and constitutes a sound basis on which the farmer may make his choice of varieties adaptable to particular conditions of the estate under his care : the geneticist, too, can benefit in choosing the most suitable parents for the construction of new geno-types by means of cross-breeding.

U

THE ECOLOGICAL BASIS OF WHEAT EVOLUTION

For many cultivated plants, it has been possible to establish their centre of origin—that is, a limited area characterised by the prevalence in the hereditary material of the said plants of dominant genetic factors and by extraordinary polymorphism. There we find herded together and represented all the forms which are distributed over the surface of the earth, plus a certain number of endemic forms which may be observed only in this restricted territory.

For soft wheats, the centre of origin is a very limited area in the zone in which the boundaries of Turkestan, Afghanistan and North-west India meet. For *durum* wheats, on the other hand, the centre of origin occupies a more extended area (perhaps because this centre is not well defined)—namely, Abyssinia and the larger part of the Mediterranean coastal region, in Africa, Europe and Asia.

Other species of *Triticum* are either found together with those above or, being in a state of regression, are found only in isolated spots so that it is not easy exactly to define their place of origin (Fig. 38).

On the great mass of wheats natural selection has, from the start, greatly exerted its directive and formative action, action which makes itself manifest in two ways :

(1) Somatic selection : this acts directly on the organism eliminating the less suitable individuals.
(2) Genetic selection : this acts on the hereditary material in the course of phylogenesis, resolving itself in a natural selection of adaptation to ambiental conditions.

Acting in the same direction, the two forms of selection have a powerfully formative effect in the course of time : they steer the evolution of the hereditary material, whatever its original composition, towards a well-defined point of convergence—the ecotype.

From this comes the fact that different botanical forms subjected to the continued and intense action of certain ambiental factors over a period of time tend to adapt themselves to the

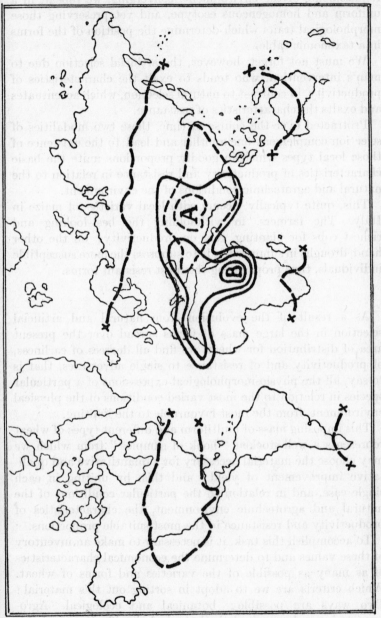

FIG. 38. GENETIC CENTRES OF (A) *Triticum vulgare* and (B) *T. durum.*

requirements of the environment, converging, we repeat, in a uniform and homogeneous ecotype, and yet preserving those morphological traits which determine the position of the forms in a taxonomic table.

We must not forget, however, the artificial selection due to man's intervention, who tends to exalt the characteristics of productivity, in contrast to natural selection, which accentuates and exalts the characteristics of resistance.

Protracted over the course of time, these two modalities of selection complement one another and lead to the existence of those local types which in goodly proportions unite the basic characteristics of productivity and resistance in relation to the natural and agrotechnic conditions of the environment.

This, quite typically, occurs with local varieties of maize in Italy. The farmers, in withholding the best-looking and richest cobs for planting, rely on productivity; on the other hand, drought in summer tends to suppress the more susceptible individuals, thus propagating the most resistant forms.

.   .   .   .   .

As a result of the evolution from natural and artificial selection in the large mass of forms spread over the present area of distribution for wheat, we find all degrees of earliness, of productivity and of resistance to single adversities, that is to say, all the physio-morphological expressions of a particular species in relation to the most varied conditions of the physical environment, from the most favourable to the limiting.

This imposing mass of multiform and different types of wheat represents a well-stocked " book of samples " from which we may choose the material necessary for a quantitative and qualitative improvement of yield; and this, by uniting in each single case, and in relation to the particular conditions of the natural and agrotechnic environment, the characteristics of productivity and resistance in the most suitable proportions.

To accomplish this task, it is necessary to make an inventory of these values and to determine the economical characteristics of as many as possible of the varieties and forms of wheat. Which criteria are we to adopt in sorting out this material ? Two ways are possible : botanical and ecological. Agronomists have always used the botanical classification, and this explains the reason why the problem of the individualisation of forms has, up to the present day, been badly done and imperfectly understood.

The species of *T. vulgare* Vill. were, as is known, divided by Körnicke into sixty-seven botanical species which are distinguished from one another through the combination of the following characteristics : colour of the ear, kernels and beards : dimension and form of the ear; form and dimension of beards; presence or absence of beards; pubescent or glabrous glumes; presence or absence of ligules; form and structure of grain, and habit of growth. All these characteristics can in no way serve to explain the behaviour of the plant in respect of ambiental factors as a function of yield, because they are in no way correlated with productivity and resistance.

Tr.v. erythrospermum, which constitutes the principal wheat variety cultivated in the Punjab, from where it has widely extended into the Indo-Ganges plain as far as Madras, presents the most varied aspects when considering its characteristics of productivity and resistance. Besides being highly resistant to drought—a necessary requirement for all Indian wheats— the degree of earliness, productivity, resistance to rust and lodging differ widely.

For instance, the Punjab No. 4 line is easily prone to lodging and to shedding, but is resistant to rust; the Punjab No. 15, on the other hand, is late and susceptible to attacks from rust, but resists shedding and possesses a well-developed, robust and elastic culm.

A single botanical variety can therefore contain different ecotypes; conversely, from two or more botanical varieties can come a single ecotype through the converging and intense action of ambiental factors. So it is that *T.v. milturum*, *T.v. erythrospermum*, *T.v. lutescens*, in the peculiarly harsh meteorological conditions of the Province of Irkutsk, constitute a well-defined homogenous ecotype characterised by great earliness and by exceptionally reduced thermic requirements for the accomplishment of maturity.

.   .   .   .   .   .

Leaving aside the botanical classification, therefore, in ecology we follow a path which is diametrically opposed to that trodden to the present day for the individualisation and sorting out of different types. Instead of beginning from a study of the plant, we begin with a study of the environment, basing ourselves on the following argument and referring to what has been mentioned above regarding selection. In a typically dry–cold zone for instance, where deficiencies in rainfall and temperature reach a notable intensity, the varieties of wheat grown will evidently possess a common denominator for their natural existence—namely, a high resistance to drought and to low temperatures, and this whatever their botanical characteristics may be. Environmental conditions therefore serves as the guide for our evaluation of the forms and varieties of wheat.

We have divided the area of distribution of wheat into four natural physiographical zones :

(1) Humid–hot.
(2) Humid–cold.
(3) Dry–cold.
(4) Dry–hot.

The more intense in each of these four zones is the representative meteorological phenomenon, the more marked will be the characteristics of adaptation for the varieties of wheat there cultivated.

Siberia is for the greater part included in the cold zone. However, the other groups of adverse phenomena also are present, so that in a single year a locality can report thermic excesses and deficiencies and rainfall excesses and deficiencies, alternatively (Fig. 39).

A fundamental characteristic of the " wheat climate " in the larger part of Siberian territory is in fact represented by the winter adversities, which sorely try winter forms, marking the expansional limit towards the pole.

Both for the autumnal as for the spring varieties, moreover, two periods with contrasting meteorological characteristics are found in the spring–summer interval.

The first, generally very droughty, hinders the sprouting of spring forms and the tillering of the young plants, which are

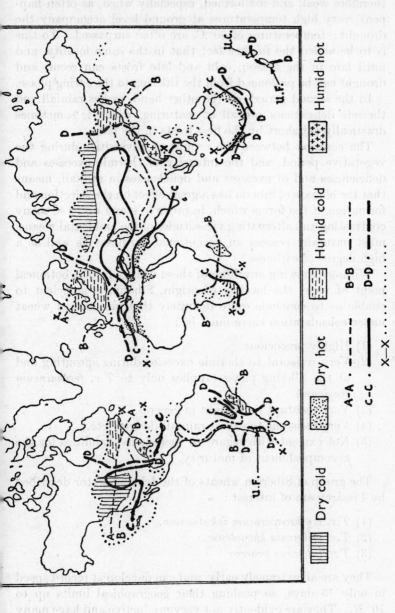

FIG. 39. PHYSIOGRAPHIC ZONES OF WHEAT.

Humid hot ++++

Humid cold

Dry hot

Dry cold

A-A B-B ·-·-·

C-C D-D ·······

X—X

therefore weak and malformed, especially when, as often happens, very high temperatures at ground level accompany the drought; temperatures of 60° C. are often surpassed. To this is to be added the further fact that in the same locality, and until late in the season, cold and late frosts can recur, and drought can be prolonged from the tillering to the earing phase.

In the second period, on the other hand, excess rainfall and thermic deficiencies prevail at maturing, which is sometimes drastically cut short by the first frosts in the fall.

The contrast between the groups of adversities during the vegetative period, and the intensity of thermic excesses and deficiencies and of excesses and deficiencies in rainfall, means that the climate of Siberia has a great effect on the selection and formation of the forms which, in order to stand up to so many contrasting and alternating vicissitudes of the ambiental means, must naturally possess an exceptional hardiness as well as a high degree of earliness.

Without knowing anything of these wheats from a botanical point of view, the locality of origin, Siberia, is sufficient to enable us to conclude quite definitely that varieties of wheat under consideration there must be :

(1) Highly precocious.
(2) Very resistant to thermic excesses during sprouting and at the tillering phase (applies only to *T.v. ferrugineum rossicum*).
(3) Very resistant to drought in general.
(4) Very resistant to excess rainfall (lodging etc.).
(5) Not exigent with regard to thermic availabilities for the accomplishment of maturity.

The group of Siberian wheats of the Irkutsk sector described by Pissarev are of interest :

(1) *T.v. erythrospermum irkutianum.*
(2) *T.v. milturum khogotense.*
(3) *T.v. lutescens praecox.*

They are all extremely early, and can develop at record speed in only 75 days, so pushing their geographical limits up to 70° N. They are evidently not very productive and have many weak points, susceptibility to rust and lodging and they easily let the grain drop. However, these wheats in general resist excess humidity and can bring their grain to maturity in an environment with limiting low temperatures.

It is on this last character especially, and on the earliness, that the adverse ambiental conditions have, on the polar limit of culture, exercised their selective and formative action in full. *T.v. milturum khogotense* has undoubtedly contributed towards the improvement of wheat culture in Alaska : " Small quantities of seed of certain spring wheats, of rye and barley, were sent to us by the Director of Agricultural Experimental Station of Irkutsk, but none of the varieties were able to reach maturity owing to the adverse meteorological conditions; one only, and that *khogotense* reached perfect maturity of its grain on the 26th August." (From a letter of the Director of the Agricultural Experimental Station, Fairbanks, Alaska.)

Among the spring forms also endowed with a high degree of earliness and with a considerable hardiness is *T.v. ferrugineum sibiricum*, which reaches the extreme polar limit of culture for wheat.

Further to a marked resistance to drought, *T.v. ferrugineum rossicum* also presents a peculiar tolerance to thermic excesses (up to 60° C.) on the soil surface during the initial stage of development of the young plants and at the tillering stage. Under such conditions, not only the exotic varieties, but also many Siberian ones are in no condition to develop.

. . . .

With reference to the resistance to winter adversities, it is impossible to go beyond a generic judgment, of an assuredly very high degree of resistance, for the winter forms cultivated on the extreme limit of expansion.

It is well known that Swedish wheats (the " Svalöf " hybrids) are not sufficiently resistant to the colds of Finland and of Baltic territories. This deficiency will make itself felt more and more as continentality becomes accentuated. In any case, before making final judgment we should—and this has not yet been done—possess comparative results between Siberian races and the local Swedish " Sammet " (not the hybrids of " Svalöf ", " Pansar ", " Thule ", etc.), which on the limit of culture for winter forms has demonstrated its possibility of resistance up to

—18° C. on soil uncovered by snow, and this without any loss through freezing of the plants.

It is true that in Siberia temperatures of −40° C. are reached, but if in these conditions the young plants are not killed, it is without doubt due to the layer of snow which maintains on the surface of the soil a much higher temperature than that found in the open air.

.   .   .   .   .

From the centre of origin of soft wheat, access to China is across deserts and high mountain ranges, so that along this route selection acts in the direction of allowing only very hardy resistant types to pass. In the south-east provinces of China, where the extremes of wet and hot climate are found, the varieties of wheat cultivated are not very productive, in spite of rich soils and irrigation in many places. These varieties are, however, distinguished by their resistance to excess rainfall and to high temperatures, which are the cause of lodging and widespread attacks of rust. In the Szechwan (as I learned from an oral communication from Father Vincent, S.J.) there exists a wheat having a small ear and minute grain, but endowed with such a low, thick and resistant culm as to be able to stand up to sudden downpours and strong gusts of wind without giving way to lodging (*T.v. triste sunpani*). In general, for Chinese wheats it is officially stated :

" None of the European, Australian or American varieties could reach maturity in Southern China as opposed to local types which form their ears and produce regular harvests even in a regime of continued rainfall and in a hot and wet environment, two factors extremely favourable to the diffusion of rust and cryptogamic attacks in general."

The wheats of the Island of Formosa are also very early and resistant to lodging. Here two types of soft wheat are found, one with yellowish-brown grain and the other with reddish-brown grain : an intense pigmentation is nearly always a marked characteristic of hardiness. Similar characteristics of resistance are possessed by the local strain of Cao-bang (Tonkin), the " Red of the Jun-nan " and those of the isle of Kiu-sciu (south of Japan). We recall further that Prof. Strampelli obtained the earliness and resistance to lodging found in his worthy set of hybrids from the indigenous types of the wet Sino-Japanese zones.

Westwards the centre of origin of soft wheat is surrounded by extensive deserts where the culture of wheat is possible only by irrigation. In such conditions the forms migrating along the route to the extreme boundaries of a dry–hot regime in the Mediterranean region and of a humid–cold one in North-west Europe could, in crossing the desert area (thanks to irrigation !), keep their original degree of productivity and the character-istics correlated with it. Here is the reason for the superiority of the European varieties from which are derived the best type for use in America and Australia.

From an ecological point of view, durum wheats, in spite of their botanical polymorphism, are less differentiated than soft wheats. Owing to the meteorological characteristics in their area of distribution, they are practically all resistant to rainfall deficiency and could in fact be divided into two categories only : late and early. The latter are naturally better able to protect themselves from hot spells in those sectors of the dry zone in which these adversities have a tendency to manifest themselves with greater frequency. On the whole, durum wheats resist very high mean temperatures well throughout the whole vegetative cycle, as may be seen in the Indian penin-sula, where, proceeding towards the south, durum wheats completely substitute the soft wheats. Here too, however, be-yond a certain limit the thermic complex becomes excessive and the various forms of *T. dicoccum* Schr. make their appearance. This species is without doubt the most resistant to extremely accentuated thermic conditions, and should furnish forms par-ticularly suited to the conditions of the hot physiographic zone. It is true that there are soft wheats which prosper in this zone, but in this case it is not their specific resistance to high tem-peratures which comes into play, but rather the great earliness which allows them to mature before the hot waves arrive.

From their centre of origin, the *T. durum* have pushed their way in a north-easterly direction as far as Russian Central

Asia. There we single out *T. durum hordeiforme* for its particular ecological characteristics : it presents two distinct forms of adaptation in different environments. We have *T. durum hordeiforme laxiusculum*, relatively late, of notable size with a long and lax ear, a tendency towards the macrocellular structure and gifted with a high degree of productivity which naturally shows itself only in the most favourable ambiental conditions, owing to the fact that for its structure and mass it turns out to be less resistant to drought and hot spells.

The *T.d. hordeiforme densiusculum* form, less productive, smaller in size, earlier, with a compact ear and a tendency towards the microcellular structure, resists drought very well and also hot spells, although naturally it is less productive than the former.

The existence of these two forms for a single variety is of considerable interest and should be more closely studied.

Durum wheats are not, on the whole, very adaptable, and they are therefore less apt to diffuse; they stop at the first bouts of cold and before the first rains, habits which are decidedly against the quality of the crop, as also against the quantity (see also page 349).

.   .   .   .   .   .

Soft wheats, however, as we have seen, are capable of adapting themselves to varied conditions, and we thus find them largely diffused in four extreme conditions : dry, wet, cold and hot. As an example, we now give a list of some typical varieties for adverse weather conditions :

(1) *Dry.*—As varieties which are very resistant to drought we recall : " Cooperatorka " (from Khivinka), *T.v. graecum* (in the U.S.S.R.), " Cervenoklasa Zagaria " (*T. durum hordeiforme*) in Bulgaria, " Banatka " (*T.v. erythrospermum*) in Jugoslavia, " Mauragani " (in Greece), " Rossarda " and " Capinera " (durum, Italy), " Touzelle " and " Saissette " (soft) (France).

(2) *Wet.*—For resistance to lodging we find : " White Stand Up " (Great Britain); " Hatif Inversable " (France); " Rosso Olona " (Italy); indigenous variety from Timok (Jugoslavia); " Gorri-Gariya " (Spain). The indigenous

variety from Galicia (Spain) is outstanding for its resistance to continual downpours and to excess humidity
in the soil. These are all soft wheats. In the scale of
resistance, however, the local varieties of South-east
China take first places (resistant to lodging and cryptogamic diseases).

(3) *Cold.*—The following are locally considered very resistant
to cold : " Brkulja " (Jugoslavia); " Blé d'Alsace "
(France); " Braunweizen " (Germany). In the scale of
resistance the local varieties of Scandinavia, Russia and
Siberia (close to the polar limit of distribution of wheat),
take first places.

(4) *Hot.*—*T. vulgare oasiculum*, studied by A. Chevalier,
cultivated in the oases of the Sahara desert.

The other species of *Triticum* are found scattered as separate
islets in the area of distribution of *Triticum vulgare*.

We distinguish two principal isolated groups : (A) *T. spelta, L.*
and (B) *T. turgidum, L.* :

(A) *T. spelta.*—In the most climatically harsh zones of
Switzerland, where thermic deficiencies and excesses of
humidity prevail, *T. vulgare* yields its place to *T. spelta*,
resistant to low temperatures and to excessive humidity
and, thanks to the great adhesive power of the glumes to
the kernels, is also resistant to shedding and to attacks
from birds.

Two types are known :

(1) " Langkorn "—long kernels, less resistant to
lodging.
(2) " Schlegelkorn "—a compact ear, low and robust
culms ; more resistant to lodging.

With *spelta*, in the same zones, are mixed *T. monococcum, L.*
and *T. dicoccum*, represented by forms which are extremely
resistant to ambiental adversities and which are also characterised by the good quality and whiteness of the flour. It is to be
noted that *dicoccum* also distinguished itself in India by its
capacity of adaptation to an extremely hot environment, clear

confirmation of its high grade of hardiness (multiple resistances). On the whole, however, the *spelta* varieties (together with *dicoccum* and *monococcum*) represent typical forms within the framework of a primitive agriculture and in an environment which is adverse through its thermic deficiencies and rainfall excesses : they are decidedly inside the wet–cold zone.

(B) *T. turgidum*.—Turgid wheats are found in isolated groups all over Europe. For instance, there are the " Cintarola " of Nicastro and the " Cinta " (Cotrone in Calabria) : " Biancolino " in Upper Garfagnana : " Balin Bianco " and " Balin Rosso " in Liguria, none very resistant to meteorological adversities, but reasonably productive, even though found in zones in which agricultural practice is backward.

In Spain, " Redondillo " is quite diffused. It stands up reasonably to cold and dampness, but is susceptible to rainfall deficiency, although at the same time being capable of adapting itself and of giving a reasonably good yield in extremely poor soils.

At one time, turgid wheats (the same may be said for *spelta*) were spread over a much wider surface, as archaeological findings in Germany (Neolithic) and North Italy (bronze age) show.

Now reduced to limited centres and on their way towards extinction, turgid wheats present a relatively good productivity, accompanied, however, by a bad-quality product, while resistance to environmental adversities is not on the whole very accentuated. Turgid wheats can thus be considered as " the representatives of a poor and primitive agriculture in an environment which, from a meteorological point of view, is not too unfavourable ".

So far we have referred to forms which are particularly adapted to the different physiographical zones and suited to those places where the adverse phenomenon reaches a notable intensity. We wish now to see what happens when we move away from this locality along a route on which the adverse phenomenon gradually diminishes.

Let us consider resistance to cold. On the polar limit in Sweden we find the "Sammetsvete" variety, which in a particularly cold year managed to resist −18° C. on unprotected ground, without harm (as already stated). This extremely high degree of resistance is absolutely necessary in those places where environment completely dominates the genotype, and where it has directed and still directs the formation of local types, thus obtaining a better adaptation of the local varieties to these limiting ambiental conditions. All those possibilities of resistance which are together necessary to counteract the action of the cold are so mobilised.

With reference to the plant's behaviour in respect of thermic minima, we have instituted, as usual, five grades : (1) very resistant, (2) resistant, (3) medium resistance, (4) susceptible, (5) very susceptible to cold. Quite evidently the fourth and fifth categories are not to be taken into consideration inasmuch as those refer to susceptible forms.

"Sammetsvete" can therefore be taken as representative of the first category (very resistant to cold).

Moving away from the polar limit, the resistance of the local type becomes partly superfluous and may be substituted by a proportional dose of productivity. This, in synthesis, is the work of Swedish geneticists who have crossed very resistant and poorly productive local varieties with the Scottish "Square-head", less resistant but more productive, and obtaining, as we have already said, a series of hybrids ("Pansar", "Thule", "Stal", etc.) which have contributed towards the raising, by at least a third, of the local grain production of Sweden, as also of Norway, Finland and northern Germany, in addition to the Baltic countries.

At lower latitudes, in the mountains of central Germany, we meet with indigenous races having a resistance to cold which is lower in comparison to that of the Scandinavian races, but which is still conspicuous. These also have served as a basis for crosses : the results obtained, with the same end in view, were analogous to those obtained in Sweden. One of these indigenous wheats is "Braunweizen" which we can take as representative of the second category (resistant to cold). Lastly, in the Franco-Italian Alpine valleys and in certain sectors of the Northern Apennine range we find, under different names and botanical forms, a reasonably homogenous ecotype which is locally considered very resistant to the cold. These are : " Blé Mouton ", " Petit Rouge de Montagne ", " Rosso " from Piedmont and " Vernacchio " (Upper Garfagnana). All these varieties can be included in the third category of resistance to cold (medium resistant). Once the valley of the Po is reached, the problem of resistance to low temperatures does not arise and, at the same time, thermic excesses do not yet make themselves felt.

From the cold limit we have thus reached the intermediate (neutral) zone.

. . . . . .

In this zone natural selection, both somatic and genetic, has a greatly reduced and enfeebled action, so that its directive action towards well-defined physio-morphological complexes loses its force. The organism may be said to detach itself from the environment. The characteristics are no longer " shepherded " towards a single physio-morphological objective, and diverge and converge in groups of the most varied combinations.

An ecotypical indifference seems to correspond to an ambiental indifference, represented by the confused medley of atypical forms tending towards a same level by the integration of a proper state of enthropism.

To the original botanical polymorphism, which is naturally preserved, correspond little differentiated ecotypes, a flat and colourless whole where no character assumes clear and well-defined expression. In such conditions there is a large margin for an increase in productivity, and this because the low intensity of ambiental adversities means that the characteristics of resistance can be neglected.

In the levelled and enthropic neutral zone the geneticist can therefore come decisively into action again and be able to impress a physio-morphological directive action, tending, by opportune crosses and for each single locality, to bring to a focal point those combinations of productivity and resistance which assure the maximum yield possible.

Within this zone of low potential we still meet, however, with isolated areas (islands and mountain masses) which can still have the characteristics of secondary centres of distribution and which sometimes harbour local varieties distinguished by a particular and very marked grade of resistance. Here are a few, as an example : " Biancone " of the isle of Elba, about which we will speak in greater detail later on, is the only variety of wheat among the great number which I have studied possessing a specific resistance to hot spells. " Rieti ", an indigenous variety of a restricted mountainous region of central Italy, and on its way to extinction, has (as previously seen) a specific resistance to rust and has served for crosses which, in Peru and East Africa, have produced the types of wheat more resistant to rust. " Coccitta ", from the mountainous interior of the province of Messina, occupies a greatly restricted residual area, is very early, small in size and with a compact ear, being very hardy in general and resistant to drought. The local wheats of the Alpine valleys and of Upper Garfagnana constitute an ecotypical entity characterised by great resistance to cold. From them, with intelligent discernment, Prof. Oliva has obtained his "mountain wheat "; " Richelle Hative ", with its sufficient productivity, notable resistance to drought and earliness, which enables it to push its way victoriously into North Africa, overcoming the competition put up by durum wheats, the only varieties cultivated in that part of the world until very recent times. The " Indigenous " from Eire and " Browick Gray Chaff " (Great Britain) are remarkable for their resistance to excessive humidity in the soil (waterlogging) during the winter period. " Hen Gymro " (Wales) presents extraordinarily reduced thermic requirements during the fourth sub-period, and matures even in a cold summer and in a regime of scarce sunlight. In certain mountain zones swept by wind we find local races which stand up well to shedding, one of the gravest consequences of gusts of wind (" Castiglione " in Sicily, etc.).

Lastly, we mention " Marzatico ", a splendid spring variety of the Abruzzo, gifted with great earliness and a goodly combination of the characteristics of resistance which are accompanied (a rare case) by good productivity.

In geographical trials with spring wheats, as has already been said, the mean yields for all places, from the polar to the equatorial limits, reaches a maximum value for " Marzatico ", so confirming its multiple capacity for adaptation. We have

x

limited ourselves to a few examples, but illustrations of this nature are plentiful.

With the exception of " Richelle Hative ", however, all these praiseworthy local types are disappearing under the avalanche of new hybrids. I cannot say with what joy, after having long waited in vain, I received at the end of 1950 a small quantity of seed of the " Coccitta " variety which, I believed, had already disappeared.

In any case, even admitting that in every country these local varieties give a product inferior to that furnished by the hybrids, they must be preserved as historical documentation of the evolution of wheats which can in no way be substituted. It is these local varieties which summarise and integrate in their hereditary material, through the selection of adaptations, the history of wheat. We should not allow so many beautiful and interesting forms to be destroyed which, once lost, can never be built up again.

Nor must we in any case forget that the most intelligent geneticists have always taken as the basis of their crosses a couple of parents, the one very productive, even though of foreign origin, the other represented by a local type carrying with it the characteristics of resistance and particular adaptation to the peculiar conditions of the environment. It is in this manner that the hybrid is fused into the environment.

I admit that the hybrids, so obtained, practically always give yields superior to those of the local races, but this is not a good reason for totally suppressing the latter, as though all the possibilities had been exhausted by a single cross.

In Sweden during the First World War it was noted (as stated elsewhere) that hybrids which furnished an excellent yield from a quantitative point of view were considerably wanting in the quality of their flour, which in local varieties is excellent. With the hybrid " Squarehead " × " Local Swedish ", the function of the latter had evidently not yet been exhausted, and in fact it became necessary to return to the local Swedish variety to better the quality of the grain by new hybrids.

I would like here to quote a passage written by the late Prof. R. Pirotta and myself in 1924 : " From what has been summarily said, there emerges the necessity of also extending botanico-agrarian research to rare varieties and to those of low economic importance, lost in regions far from the great centres of culture : these varieties could, perhaps in virtue of their isolation, contain treasures of ignored genetic factors, and give rise to new and very interesting bio-ambiental reactions when crossed with other varieties, or brought into a different environment."

.   .   .   .   .

The characteristics on which the botanical classification of forms of *Triticum* is based are in no way correlated with the various degrees of productivity and resistance, the two basic components of yield. A study, therefore, of the varieties and forms of the single species from a botanical point of view cannot serve in the evaluation of the economical characteristics of the multiple forms and varieties of wheat.

In agricultural ecology, as has been said before, we follow a path which, instead of beginning with a study of the plant, begins with a study of the environment whose characteristics, especially meteorological, can with good approximation indicate the degree of productivity and the degree of resistance to each adversity for each form.

It is in fact evident that the greater the yield obtained from a certain variety under the most favourable conditions, the higher will be its degree of productivity. Similarly, the higher the yield in a place where drought was very intense, the higher will be the degree of resistance to water deficiencies.

The exact evaluation of bio-ambiental relationships as a function of the yield opens the way and represents the main line for the preliminary evaluation of forms of wheat spread over the face of the world in the most different conditions of natural and agrotechnic environment. The unit of measurement is the yield in quintals per hectare.

.   .   .   .   .

The yields in quintals per hectare (or other unit of measurement) correlated with detailed information on the nature of the soil, agrotechnic provisions, the factors (biological and meteorological) which, during the cycle of development relating to single phases and vegetative sub-periods, have exercised a negative and positive action on the plant, represent what we call the " reasoned yields ". It is from them that we must begin, in order to single out the intrinsic causes of yield and, therefore, those different morphological and physiological values which are correlated with the different grades of productivity and resistance, and which we have called " ecological characteristics ".

CHAPTER XX

ECOLOGICAL CHARACTERISTICS

Analysis of the Intrinsic Components of Yield

ECOLOGICAL characteristics as defined above can concern the whole plant or show themselves only in certain organs, or even only in minute details of structure, composition or aspect.

We shall therefore have characteristics of productivity and of resistance. At first we attempted to individualise and evaluate these characteristics directly. I would like to quote a few : photosynthetic activity, which may well be presumed correlated with productivity ; the thickness of the hypodermis, which in cereals would vary proportionately with resistance to drought ; the concentration of sugar solution in the cell sap, which increases the resistance of tissues to thermic depressions. These correlations seem obvious and in certain cases agree very well.

However, extending the research and broadening the field of inquiry, it has been observed that *different* degrees of resistance to cold and drought, respectively, can correspond to the *same* concentration of sugar solutions and to the same thickness of the hypodermis. Analogously different grades of productivity can correspond to a same value for photosynthetic activity. In fact, given the existence of a direct relationship between length of the interval from setting to maturity and the entity of the yield, at equal photosynthetic activity, the corresponding degree of productivity will be higher the greater the duration of the said interval.

I will illustrate this, referring to two varieties of dwarf bean

Variety.	Interval length flowering–maturity, days.	Gm. of seed per plant.	Photo-synthetic intensity, mg.
Monachino di Mugello .	47	16	17·0
Turco di Magione . .	38	12	17·2

(the photosynthetic activity is measured by the mg. of CO_2 assimilated by 100 sq. cm. of leaf surface in an hour).

With equal photosynthetic activity the product therefore increases, as was easily foreseeable, as the duration of the interval between flowering and maturity also increases.

It may be deduced that the characteristics correlated with productivity and resistance cannot be considered in themselves alone, isolating them from the physio-morphological complex of the plant, but must be isolated within the said complex in relation to the function of all the other characteristics and components of productivity and of resistance, respectively.

An important step in the solution of this problem has been made when, instead of trying to find the direct link between the ecological characteristics and the characteristics of productivity and resistance, the velocity–mass–structure system is interposed between these characteristics, and the corresponding values of productivity and resistance.

The Conception of Velocity–Mass–Structure

In the representation of the relationships between the development and yield of cultivated plants on the one hand, and the conditions of the natural and artificial (physical and agrotechnic) environment on the other, the concept of the two fundamental intrinsic situations casts a bright light on the problem.

These fundamental situations may be represented by the symbols vMS and Vms, where :

$$v = \text{small velocity}$$
$$M = \text{great mass}$$
$$S = \text{macrocellular structure}$$
$$V = \text{great velocity}$$
$$m = \text{small mass}$$
$$s = \text{microcellular structure}$$

Between velocity, mass and structure there exists a most important order of relationships which marks the irreversible character of the specifically dynamic system directed towards future realisations. The velocity is without doubt the initial and most important act of the plant's life, in that it determines a movement which subsequently brings with it all the successive organic and physio-morphological structures up to the completion of the biological cycle. By mass, we mean the whole body of the plant in the various successive moments of the cycle of development. By structure is meant the dimension of the cellular elements into which the mass is subdivided.

The velocity, whose function is exclusively one of *cause*, although in a somewhat new and specific sense, can in no way be influenced by the mass and structure. We could affirm that velocity is a direct manifestation of the germinal plasma, being therefore the only one of the three values which can, and in a certain sense also independently from extrinsic or ambiental factors, be integrally transmitted from one generation to the next, thus being hereditary in a perfect manner.

The mass has a character both of *cause* and of *effect* : it is an effect in respect of velocity while acting as cause in respect of structure, since the more a mass tends to expand, the more the dimensions of the cellular elements tend to increase, even if not in altogether direct proportion, while to a contraction of the mass corresponds a decrease in the cellular elements.

In weighing up the statics and dynamics of the system considered, structure cannot evidently influence the two preceding values, and is exclusively a direct or indirect effect of these. Rather shall we say that the macro- and micro-cellular structures represent the two basic complexes of the effects of the causal values of velocity and mass.

The vMS system is identifiable with the tendency of the plant to utilise more and more, and in the greatest measure with regard to its development, the ambiental availabilities at its disposal. This system carries with it a great part of the morphological and physiological characteristics of productivity.

The Vms system is identifiable with the tendency of the plant to adapt itself to unfavourable conditions of environment, completing its normal development even in a regime of more and more limited natural or artificial availability.

This system carries with it a great part of the morphological and physiological characteristics of resistance.

Velocity of Development

On general lines we can affirm in relation with the velocity of development :

(1) The shorter the duration of the vegetative period, the easier will it be for the plant to find a favourable interval in the year which will permit it to better itself in the ambiental framework of a given locality. At the same time, however, the plant will be unable to accumulate a large amount of dry matter, and the yield will be rather low. A high velocity must therefore tend to hardiness.

(2) When the vegetative period is very long, on the other hand, the difficulties of the plant's adaptation become accentuated because, with the worsening of ambiental conditions and with the subsequent contraction of the interval available to reach its complete development, the accomplishment of the biological cycle in the time available becomes more difficult. However, the increase in length of the vegetative period makes it possible in long lasting favourable conditions, to utilise greater quantities of the ambiental availabilities for a longer time and, consequently, other conditions remaining constant, the yield increases. A small velocity must therefore tend towards productivity.

The results of certain experiments carried out at Perugia with numerous varieties of potato in the two years 1940 and 1941 are interesting, as they were in great contrast to their meteorological situations.

In 1940 conditions proved to be particularly favourable throughout the whole summer period, thanks to the abundant and well-distributed rains, so that late varieties were able to complete their life cycle in favourable conditions, taking advantage of a larger amount of environmental availabilities.

In 1941 on the other hand, drought was prolonged up to the end of the vegetative period, and having begun to make itself felt early, it acted negatively on the yield, and the more so, the more the lateness (i.e. the longer the length of the vegetative period) of the type of potato considered. In this case the higher yields should presumably have been obtained with the earlier, even though less productive, plants.

For the experiment the varieties considered were divided into three groups : early, intermediate and late.

(1) *Early :* duration of interval from planting to harvest 133 days at the most.

(2) *Intermediate :* duration of interval from a minimum of 134 days to a maximum of 153 days.

(3) *Late :* duration of interval from planting to harvest of tubers equal to or above 154 days.

For each of these groups I supply the mean product in quintals/ha. for 1940 and 1941 :

Potato Variety Trials
1940

No. of varieties.	Group.	Mean yield in quintals/ha.
33	Early	224·25
112	Intermediate	275·50
75	Late	285·50

As was to be foreseen, the best results were obtained with the latest varieties, which, thanks to the favourable conditions until the autumn, had naturally been able to make better use of ambiental availabilities, thus giving a decidedly superior yield to that obtained from the early varieties. The earlies, owing to the great velocity of development and the brevity of their cycle, were only able to utilise a relatively limited part of the natural thermic and moisture availabilities in the environment.

For 1941 we find exactly the opposite :

Potato Variety Trials
1941

No. of varieties.	Group.	Mean yield in quintals/ha.
34	Early	121·50
115	Intermediate	106·50
71	Late	81·25

The best results were obtained with the earliest varieties, which, thanks to their great velocity of development, completed their cycle before drought could have any great negative influence on the yield.

This negative action by drought is naturally the more pronounced the longer the duration of the vegetative period; the late varieties owing to their small velocity of development, are, in fact, cut down by drought long before the completion of their cycle, and therefore furnish a much smaller crop (minute tubers).

.   .   .   .   .

While in the Mediterranean region, drought represents the factor limiting the duration of the useful period in which the potato can complete its development, in the Scandinavian region and the nearer we get to the polar frontier of the area of distribution for this plant, it is the low temperatures, or, better, the brief duration of the frostless season, which confines the development of the tubers within shorter and shorter intervals.

Knut Vik's research in Norway in this field is instructive. He set out to demonstrate the effect of temperature on the development and yield in the tubers of several varieties of potato (early, intermediate and late) which were sown in a great number of places and under the most varied temperature conditions, with the purpose of studying the relationship between thermic availabilities and yield. For each place, the sum of mean daily temperatures from June to September was determined.

The said places were then grouped into four categories in relation to the sum total of temperatures :

(1) Sum of temperatures up to 1,400° C.
(2) Sum of temperatures from 1,400° to 1,600° C.
(3) Sum of temperatures from 1,600° to 1,800° C.
(4) Sum of temperatures from 1,800° upwards.

The early varieties develop more rapidly than the late, so that within the same interval of time the substances accumulated in the tubers are greater than those stored up by the late varieties in the same time.

However, if the growing season is prolonged beyond certain limits, the late varieties end up by having accumulated more substance than that found in the early varieties, and this because the latter rapidly reach their maximum development and are then no longer able to utilise further the temperature at their disposal. The late varieties, however, continue their normal development and increase their tuber production by utilising those temperatures.

The following table gives in quintals/ha. the yields of the three varieties : *Magnum bonum* (late), *Early Puritan* (early) and *Marius* (intermediate) in comparative form for the four groups of experimental stations.

Variety of potato.	Group of stations and sum of temperatures.			
	I. 1200°–1400°.	II. 1400°–1600°.	III. 1600°–1800°.	IV. 1800° and over.
Magnum bonum	140·2	192·0	226·1	247·5
Early Puritan .	214·2	224·9	237·0	233·7
Marius . .	189·0	234·7	240·7	227·2

In the first group, the places less favoured with regard to temperature, " Early Puritan " (early) holds first place. In the stations of the second and third groups, " Marius " (intermediate) is to be preferred while, lastly, in the most favoured hot regions of the fourth group with a long period of vegetation, the late variety " Magnum bonum ", thanks to its small velocity of development and to the consequently longer duration of the cycle, can make better use of the high ambiental availabilities, and comes decidedly into first place, at the same time furnishing the highest absolute yields.

The Optimal Velocity of Development from an Ecological Viewpoint

There must exist for every form, in relation to the modalities of development, an optimal velocity and two limiting velocities —too small a velocity or too great—with reference to the yield.

By optimal velocity is meant that velocity which permits the plant, once completed its cycle, to push its productivity to a maximum, furnishing the highest yield possible; in this case there is perfect harmony between the development of the plant and the environment.

A regime which produces an acceleration (anticipation in the appearance of a phase) or a slowing up (with delay in the manifestation of a phase) will, in certain circumstances, be able negatively to influence the crop.

As a demonstration of this, we may well take the differences observed during the geographical trials between different varieties of wheat in their capacity of adaptation to a regime of high and gradually ascending temperatures (equatorial limit) and to one of low and gradually decreasing temperatures (polar limit).

(a) *Equatorial Limit.*—Moving south, with an increase in temperature and with the intensification of the phenomenon which accentuate transpiration, the length of the sub-period from earing to maturity decreases up to a certain limit (approx. 30 days). A further decrease in the sub-period harms the processes of metabolism, thus bringing to a halt the normal development of the plant (hot spells). With reference to a given variety, in a regime of very high temperature, the longer the interval between earing and maturity, the higher shall we consider the plant's capacity of adaptation in developing normally near the equatorial limit of culture of the species.

The variety " Timilia " (Italy) has the maximum extension of the sub-period at a mean temperature of 23·1° C. From earing to normal maturity is 43 days, and its high capacity of resistance to the phenomena tending to curtail the duration of the said interval becomes evident. For " Gelchsheimer " (Central Europe) we find a duration of 39 days and for " Börsum " (Scandinavia) the period drops to 35 days, so that this last variety will reach the limit for abnormal maturity before the others, being the least suitable in a regime of thermic excesses.

In fact, in the stations where we find hot spells, " Börsum " presented a maximum value for shrivelling of 12·0, " Gelchsheimer " follows with 9·0, while " Timilia " was able to develop regularly, and its seed showed no sign of shrivelling. To give an idea of the negative potentiality of the phenomenon, it suffices to compare the yield furnished by " Timilia " with that of " Börsum " : 18·9 and 1·2 quintals per ha., respectively (Tunis).

The graduation in shrivelling is represented by a scale ranging between 0·0 (no shrivelling) and 5·0 (grain completely shrivelled) Four determinations were made : Algiers irrigated, Algiers dry, Tunis irrigated, Tunis dry, and the sum of the four grades in shrivelling was taken as an indication of greater or smaller susceptibility to hot spell (total maximum 20).

(b) *Polar Limit.*—Moving north towards the pole, the interval between earing and maturity, with decrease in temperature, is increased to a maximum (around 75 days) beyond which the plant remains at the herbaceous state and the grain no longer matures. The shorter this interval with reference to a given variety in regime of very low temperatures, and therefore the greater the velocity of development, the more marked are we to consider the capacity of the variety to prosper near to the polar limit of culture—that is, in a regime of thermic deficiency. " Börsum " proves to be the most suitable, since it completes its development from earing to maturity in 61 days at a mean temperature of 13·9° C., while "Timilia " needs no fewer than 70 days, so becoming the least adaptable to a condition of thermic deficiency. " Gelchsheimer " occupies an intermediate position with 66 days.

Basing ourselves on the stations of Linköping, Skara, Forus and Lulea, where maturity did not reach perfection on account of cold, and adopting a scale from 0 (normal development of kernel) to 5 (maximum shrinkage of grain from cold), we have : 3·3 for " Timilia ", 3·0 for " Gelchsheimer " and 1·7 only for " Börsum ", which we have already quoted as being the most suitable in regimes of thermic deficiency in general.

Non-uniform Contraction of the Cycle's Duration

In constantly favourable ambiental conditions productivity would appear to be directly correlated with the duration of the vegetative period, as we have seen. Under these conditions in fact, the late forms, which have at their disposal a longer interval of time in which to utilise the ambiental availabilities, will give (other conditions remaining constant) a yield superior to that obtainable from early varieties.

The degree of greater or lesser earliness and of greater or lesser lateness is measured by the length of the interval from sprouting to the completed maturity of the fruits. However, just as the contraction of the mass can, as we shall see later on, be effected in different measure in respect of one part or another of the plant, so, analogously, can the contraction in the duration of the cycle be effected in different proportions according to the sub-period of the vegetative period considered.

" Mentana " is an early wheat, and has a relatively brief cycle of development. In Romagna it is sown 20 days after the medium-early varieties ("Gentil Rosso", "Rieti", etc.) and reaches maturity 15 days before them, so that there is a contraction in the life-cycle of " Mentana " of no less than 5 weeks when compared with the medium-early varieties.

It could be argued that such a behaviour must perforce be correlated with a low productivity, while actually, as is well known, this variety figures among the most productive.

The explanation for this is not to be sought in the total earliness (number of days between sowing and harvest), but in the extraordinary earliness in earing, characteristic of this variety. In Romagna, " Mentana " matures in the middle of June, and in general ears as from the 25th April : so it is that the sub-period from earing to the harvest has a duration of approximately 50 days (which is generally encountered much further north, between northern Germany and southern Sweden).

In reality, " Mentana " is therefore a variety having a rapid development, and with a tendency therefore to contract its cycle from sowing to the earing phase. Its development between earing and the harvest is, however, slower than for other varieties. In identical ambiental conditions, " Gentil Rosso " (medium-early) ears on the 17th May, and matures on the 25th June, so that the fourth sub-period lasts only 40 days, 10 days less than " Mentana ".

Now, the length of the fourth sub-period, from earing to harvest, constitutes an ecological characteristic directly cor-

Stages in Growth of " Mentana " Wheat. Perugia

	Year.		
	1938.	1939.	1940.
Earing . . .	26th May	19th May	2nd May
Harvest . . .	22nd June	25th June	25th June
Length of interval .	28 days	37 days	54 days
Yield in quintals .	8·9	24·9	35·0

related with productivity, as has been ascertained with experiments in Perugia with " Mentana ".

In Umbria (Perugia), in contrast to the observations made in Romagna, " Mentana " is not satisfactory. In the three years considered it gave a maximum yield of 35 quintals only in 1940, as against a general mean of 20·8 for seventy varieties from all the other Italian regions.

In 1939 it gave a crop of 24·9 quintals, slightly inferior to the general mean of 25·9 quintals, while " Quagliarella Bianca " was in first place with 42 quintals.

Lastly, in 1938 " Mentana's " yield fell to 8·9 quintals, while the general mean oscillated around 15 quintals, and the soft Sicilian wheat, " Majurcuni ", was at the top of the list with 28 quintals.

Only once out of three years, therefore, did " Mentana " prove to be superior to other wheats, and this happened in 1940, when it was fully able to show its earliness in earing, which took place on 2nd May, and the interval between earing and the harvest was consequently prolonged to no less than 54 days. In 1938, a year in which there was a minimum yield, maturity was effected at the same time as in other years, while, on the other hand, earing was greatly delayed and only took place on 26th May; the fourth sub-period was thus reduced to 28 days.

To furnish an explanation of these phenomena, the mean temperatures per 10-day period in the months March–May are given below for the two extreme years, 1938 and 1940.

Mean Temperatures in ° C. for 10-day Period

		1938.	1940.
March :	First 10-day period . . .	8·9	4·2
	Second ,, . . .	7·8	8·6
	Third ,, . . .	11·0	9·2
April :	First ,, . . .	8·3	7·2
	Second ,, . . .	7·5	10·7
	Third ,, . . .	6·5	13·6
May :	First ,, . . .	10·6	12·6
	Second ,, . . .	14·0	14·0
	Third ,, . . .	13·5	16·1

In 1940 the temperatures in spring rose gradually, so that the different grades of earliness for each variety in respect of earing were able to show themselves regularly, and, in fact, we find this date corresponding to the 2nd May for the earliest varieties, and 27th May for the latest, a total difference of 25 days.

In 1938, however, temperatures remained very low for the whole of April, and then began to rise suddenly and rapidly in the month of May. As a consequence of this, the thermic threshold for earing was reached very late, so that all the varieties, early and late alike, eared practically at the same time : maturity took place at the usual time, and the contraction of the sub-period was therefore all the more accentuated the more late earing the variety considered.

In Romagna, spring temperatures increase gradually, while in the territory of Perugia conditions similar to those of 1938 are frequent. It is evident that in Umbria " Mentana " cannot show its characteristic earliness in earing, and since this phase is greatly retarded and the interval between earing and harvest more or less contracted, the yield will naturally not be very high.

The positive correlation between the duration of the fourth sub-period and yield is thus definitely established. " Mentana's " capacity of prolonging the duration of the fourth sub-period without doubt constitutes an interesting physiological characteristic correlated with a high grade of productivity, and this in spite of it being an early variety, taken over its whole cycle from sprouting to harvest.

.   .   .   .   .   .

The intensity with which any characteristic manifests itself evidently depends on the relationship between intrinsic (biological) and extrinsic (ambiental) factors. When the conditions of the physical environment are unfavourable, as was seen in Perugia for the years 1938 and 1939, the manifestation of the plant's characteristics remains as if veiled and hidden in spite of the favourable genotypical complex.

With reference to the intensity of manifestation of the plant's characteristics, we therefore have the following four possible combinations :

(1) Positive genotypical situation and positive environmental conditions.

(2) Positive genotypical situation and negative environmental conditions.

(3) Negative genotypical situation and positive environmental conditions.

(4) Negative genotypical situation and negative environmental conditions.

The characteristic considered, earliness, will naturally reach its greatest intensity in the first case, and the lowest in the fourth, while in the second and third combinations we shall have intermediate effects.

Baltadori's research confirms that in the evaluation of the mass–velocity binomial it is not the total duration of the cycle which is of importance, but the length of the sub-period comprised between setting and maturity of fruits and seed. Here are the results of his experiment relating to wheat, maize and bean (dwarf and runner) :

	Duration of fourth sub-period, days.	Mean yield, quintals/ha.
Wheat (320 varieties)	46	39·64
	50	41·87
	55	44·40
Maize (234 varieties)	48	22·72
	56	23·34
	62	24·26
Dwarf bean (154 varieties)	32	11·50
	48	12·44
	64	16·45
Runner bean (224 varieties)	44	14·77
	60	16·80
	76	19·57
	92	20·39

In the evaluation of the velocity in respect of yield it is therefore more convenient to base ourselves on the sub-period comprised between flowering and maturity, than on the duration of the whole cycle from sprouting to completed maturity.

Having seen the importance of the duration of this sub-period for all plants, it becomes clear that when making our choice, in all cases, without exception, we shall have to aim at the type which presents the maximum duration compatible with the conditions of the environment.

Y

In particular cases, however—of wheat, for example—an anticipation in earing beyond certain limits can expose the plant to the deleterious action of cold spells in the very delicate phases of pollination and setting. This happens in Umbria when farmers adopt types of wheat which ear with too great anticipation.

On the other hand, the regime of high temperatures at the beginning of summer in the Mediterranean region marks a limit beyond which one cannot go without incurring hot spells : a late maturity, in this case, will prove to be negative.

Early maturing varieties are also necessary on the polar limit of expansion for wheat, because a delay could expose the still immature plants to the first autumnal frosts, while a premature earing exposes the plants to the late spring frosts.

In this last case the plant is as if seized in a grip of ice, which forces it to thrive within greatly restricted phenological limits in order to safeguard its existence : a long duration of the fourth sub-period in such conditions is thus decidedly negative.

In every locality it is therefore convenient to choose the maximum length of the interval earing–maturity provided it is compatible with the conditions of the atmospheric environment (frost and hot spells).

·   ·   ·   ·   ·

MASS

As regards mass and the adaptation to the physical environment, we can in general affirm that :

(1) The larger the mass expansion, the greater the plant's ability to utilise the ambiental factors at its disposal up to a maximum corresponding to the highest yield possible for the said plant. The capacity of increasing its mass should therefore be correlated with productivity.

(2) The more reduced is the mass, the better will the plant be able to adapt itself to the progressive impoverishment of the environment, and this until the limit of economic convenience has been reached.

The capacity of contracting its mass should thus be correlated with hardiness.

I do not wish here to weary the reader with examples which literature and nature can abundantly supply.

In fact, both among herbaceous and among woody plants are always found small and large-sized forms; large and minute fruits and leaves with reduced or greatly expanded surfaces to which, according to the cases, correspond different degrees of productivity and hardiness.

To give an idea of the extensive possibilities of variation in the mass of a plant, I refer on the one hand to a plant of wheat obtained by Vivenza which possessed no fewer than 342 culms, and on the other to a plant (spring variety) from Assergi which I picked up on the Gran Sasso and which it is difficult to accept as being wheat, so slender and wretched was it, in appearance similar to a spontaneous graminacea from an open meadow : the culm is 19 cm. high, 0·56 mm. in diameter, has a single ear and a single grain.

The different parts or organs of the plant do not contract in the same way, or in the same measure, so that the dwarf specimen is clearly distinguished from a normal individual not only for the smaller size, but also for the narrower leaf surfaces, the thicker culm and, with regard to the histology of the plant, a noticeable thickness of the hypodermis and of the epidermis, with relatively voluminous parenchymatous cells.

These voluminous dimensions of the parenchymatous cells are due to the fact that the possibility of contraction of cells and soma are different, and that the latter is able to contract when the cells have already reached the smallest dimensions possible. From this moment, to a further diminishment of the body of the plant, a corresponding decrease in the volume of the cells will be impossible, and there will be a curtailment in their number, so that the cellular elements will appear to be relatively large in respect of the soma.

Here are the figures for a normal, and for a dwarf plant :

	Normal.	Dwarf.	Relationship
Thickness of the parenchyma (in microms) . . .	294	126	2·3 : 1·0
Dimensions of parenchymatous cells (microms) .	78	43	1·8 : 1·0

The only grain normally developed in the dwarf plant is related to the normal in the proportion of 1·0 : 1·7. In fact, the grain of the dwarf plant weighs 0·03 gm., while the weight of the normal is 0·05 gm.

All the modifications which the vegetable form has undergone represent the extreme conditions of equilibrium—the result, I would almost say, of the effort which the organism has made in a greatly impoverished environment to reach the reproductive phase at its limiting position : the formation of a single seed.

And now let us consider the other extreme : Vivenza's giant plant with 342 ears furnished with regularly developed grains to the number of approximately 7,000 : and we cannot exclude the possibility that by making ambiental conditions still more suitable it might be possible to obtain even more gigantic specimens, it being in no case possible to affirm with certainty that the absolute limit has been reached.

The practical limit in relation to ambiental availability in normal conditions of culture is in any case largely surpassed, and Vivenza's splendid specimen, when compared to the small plant picked at the foot of the Gran Sasso, gives us an adequate idea of the extreme capacities of adaptation in extraordinarily favourable and extremely unfavourable ambiental conditions.

The enormous gap separating the two forms is a manifest proof of the elasticity of the organism " wheat ", and a measure of the truly exceptional range of mass variations. Between the two forms stand the following relationships :

Ratio of weight of the dwarf–giant plants 1 : 15,000
Ratio of number of grains in dwarf–giant plants 1 : 7,000.

These figures naturally vary from one species to another.

For the two plants of the " Borlotto di Vigevano " variety of bean, the extremely contracted form reduced to a single legume containing a single seed and the powerfully developed form, we find :

Ratio of weight of the dwarf–giant plants 1 : 56.
Ratio of number of seeds in dwarf–giant plants 1 : 227.

It is to be noted that the single seed of the dwarf plant has a weight superior to that encountered in those of the giant plant—1·25 gm. against 0·91 gm.

Mass variations can be found in a harmonic and proportional manner in all parts of the plant, so that in wheat, for example, to an increase or decrease in culms and leaves there corresponds a proportional increase, or decrease, in the size of the ear and in the grain.

But, as we shall see in the next page, variations in mass can take place in different measure and proportion with reference to the single parts of the plant—a fact which naturally becomes of practical importance when the harvest is not concerned with the whole plant, but rather with a part or an organ of it, that part being the principal reason for which the plant is cultivated. Thus for wheat it is the grain. We can now state that in relation to formation and development of the kernel, the mass of leaves (which assure the photosynthetic process)—and certainly the culms—is partially superfluous. The attempt to reduce culm and leaves (by genetics) and obtain the maximum development of the ear and grains is therefore justifiable.

" Biancone dell' Elba ", a productive variety with a notable total mass, shows, as we shall see, a great reduction of the foliar mass; " Mentana " in its turn, is productive and supplied with large, handsome ears, but its culms are low and its yield in straw is poor.

To demonstrate with measured values what has on general lines been affirmed, I shall discuss only the mass values for two varieties of wheat : " Frassineto " (a selection of " Gentil Rosso " from Tuscany) and " Bianchetta " (from Puglie), in favourable ambiental conditions (rich ambiental availabilities) and in unfavourable ambiental conditions (scarce ambiental availabilities), but always within the limits of reality from an agricultural point of view.

	Frassineto.		Bianchetta.	
	Favourable conditions.	Un-favourable conditions.	Favourable conditions.	Un-favourable conditions.
Weight of culm-ear in gms. . .	29·1	13·3	18·5	15·2
Yield in quintals per ha. . . .	54·6	6·3	27·9	8·1

These two varieties are very suitable as an example, in that they differ little in their velocity of development : the only variable is the mass which we have identified with the weight of the culm-ear at the beginning of milk maturity.

" Frassineto " possesses a capacity of expansion of the mass in relation to function of the yield, which is decidedly superior to " Bianchetta ", and it is for this reason that in zones with good ambiental conditions " Frassineto " furnishes a product superior to " Bianchetta ". In unfavourable conditions, however, " Bianchetta " yields more, because, considering its smaller size, it manages to complete its development normally, supplying a yield which is inferior to that obtained in very favourable conditions, but satisfactory all the same. " Frassineto ", which by nature tends further to expand its body, will find a notable hindrance for its development in unfavourable situations, and this can only have a negative effect on production and, in effect, in these conditions it yields less than " Bianchetta ".

Non-uniform Contraction of the Mass

The contraction in mass is, as already said, directly correlated with hardiness, since the plant is able to form its own organs and complete its development even when ambiental availabilities are very limited. This contraction can take place in the same measure, in equal proportions, for all parts of the plant (culm, leaves and fruits), but it can also vary, either in the positive or in the negative sense, from one organ to another.

The wheat " Coccitta " offers a good example of non-uniform contraction of the mass in a negative direction. The reduction, in fact, is the most evident with reference to the ear, which is always very small (Fig. 40). Even in the best environmental conditions, when culms and leaves react with considerable increases in size, the ear does not correspond, and remains as small as those observed in highly unfavourable conditions.

We will now examine in some detail a typical case of positive non-uniform contraction of the body.

The year 1941 was characterised by an intense summer drought, and served well for the study of resistance to water deficiency in three varieties of dwarf and early (small in size and with a brief cycle) maize selected by the Institute of Agri-

Fig. 40. "Coccitta" (*left*) and "Rieti" (*right*) Wheats.

cultural Ecology of the University of Perugia. During the
vegetative period, rainfall was distributed thus :

From sprouting up to the critical period . .	79·5 mm.
During the critical period	0·0 ,,
From the end of the critical period to milk maturity	0·0 ,,
From milk maturity to complete maturity . .	70·5 ,,

Rainfall deficiencies during the critical period, when the
plant's requirements are greatest, are obvious. Now, in these
adverse conditions, the three varieties of maize gave yields
which, against the 16 quintals per hectare of the local variety,
proved to be very high, thus revealing a notable degree of
resistance to drought :

Nano di Mugello	26·58 quintals per ha.
Locale di Somma Passo . .	28·45 ,, ,,
Locale di Roccalbegna . .	29·20 ,, ,,

These varieties, with reference to what was said above concerning velocity and mass as a function of productivity and
resistance, present a much-shortened cycle and a considerable
contraction in their mass.

For comparison, I give below the lengths of the vegetative
period and the weight of the whole plant dessicated in the open
air for the three dwarf varieties and for the Umbrian local
variety—more productive but less resistant :

	Length of vege- tative period, days.	Total weight of plant, gm.
Umbrian local . . .	130	855
Nano del Mugello . . .	107	360
Somma Passo . . .	106	212
Roccalbegna . . .	108	380

However, what is of particular interest is the study of the
relationships between the weight of the ear and that of the plant.
While in fact the relationship between weight of ear and that
of the rest of the plant is 1 : 1 for normal maizes such as the local
Umbrian, for the dwarf the weight of the cob decidedly prevails
over that of the plant, until with the " Somma Passo " variety,
the relationship of 2 : 1 is reached (in certain extreme groups of
individuals 4 : 1 has been observed).

	Weight of ear, gm.	Weight of plant, gm.
Umbrian local . . .	425	430
Nano di Mugello . . .	240	120
Somma Passo . . .	135	77
Roccalbegna	240	140

The contraction of the mass, considered as a mode of adaptation to an unfavourable environment, is not therefore verified in the present case in an equal and uniform manner for the whole plant; in the dwarf varieties of maize the cob is proportionately much less reduced.

Contracting the stem and leaves to the minimum compatible with photosynthetic requirements, the plant utilises for the formation of the cob the scarce ambiental availabilities to the best possible advantage, thanks to the reduction in transpiration. This particular construction therefore constitutes an interesting ecological characteristic correlated with resistance to drought.

TWO CONSTANTS WHICH REGULATE THE RELATIONSHIPS OF MASS AND VELOCITY IN THE DEVELOPMENT OF PLANTS

In these experiments with maize the cycle of the plant is divided into two portions, A and B.

A = from germination to the appearance of the leaves.
B = from leafing to the phase of maximum weight.

Two varieties were considered : " Nostrano dell' Isola " (late) and " Nano di Mugello " (early). Now, the velocity of growth of the early variety in the interval A is inferior to the velocity of growth of the late maize, while in the interval B we find precisely the opposite : the velocity of growth of the early variety is decidedly greater than that of the late type.

As a consequence of this, the interval A is longer for early maize and shorter for late, while the duration of period B is greater for the late variety and shorter for the early.

Expressing the period's extent in hours, we find the following :

Variety.	A.	B.
Nostrano dell' Isola (late) . .	80 hrs.	2,688 hrs.
Nano di Mugello (early) . .	97 ,,	2,232 ,,

If the duration (expressed in hours) of the two intervals A and B are multiplied together, the products are almost identical.

Variety		A.	B.
Nostrano dell' Isola (late)	. . .	$80 \times 2{,}688$	$= 215 \times 10^2$
Nano di Mugello (early)	. . .	$97 \times 2{,}232$	$= 216 \times 10^2$

Indicating by V (for " Nostrano dell' Isola ") and V' (for " Nano di Mugello ") the length of period A, and by v (for " Nostrano dell' Isola ") and v' (for " Nano di Mugello ") the length of period B, we have :

$$V \times v = V' \times v' = \text{constant}.$$

For mass, expressing the weight in grams, we find :

Variety.		A.	B.
Nostrano dell' Isola (late)	. . .	$0{\cdot}22$	795
Nano di Mugello (early)	. . .	$0{\cdot}42$	412

Here, too by multiplying the values corresponding to the two intervals we obtain almost identical figures.

Variety		A.	B.
Nostrano dell' Isola (late)	. . .	$0{\cdot}22 \times 795$	$= 175$
Nano di Mugello (early)	. . .	$0{\cdot}42 \times 412$	$= 173$

Indicating by M (for " Nostrano dell' Isola ") and M' (for " Nano di Mugello ") the mass (weight) corresponding to A, and by m and m', respectively, the mass corresponding to B, we have :

$$M \times m = M' \times m' = \text{constant}.$$

Again values are obtained which, taking into consideration the inevitable errors of observation, can be considered practically equal. In effect, the two values given in the first table differ by less than 1%, and those given in the second differ by less than $1{\cdot}08\%$.

Taking the mean for the two values, both for the first and for the second couple, respectively, we find : $C^* = 215{\cdot}772$; $C^{**} = 173{\cdot}97$, which are the two constants for maize discovered by me.

From these values Puma has made further determinations which have also led to the discovery of a constant for total energy taken in the sense of Planck's elementary quanta of action.

Indicating by t_1 and t_2 the times taken by the first variety, the late (in the two sub-periods A and B, respectively) and by T_1 and T_2 the analogous times for the second variety (early), we have with reference to Azzi's first constant, which can be indicated with $C*$

$$(1) \quad t_1 \, t_2 = T_1 \, T_2 = C*$$

Similarly, if we indicate with m_1 and m_2 the increase in mass in the first variety, in the intervals A and B and with M_1 and M_2 those corresponding to the second variety, we shall have:

$$(2) \quad m_1 \, m_2 = M_1 \, M_2 = C***$$

Where $C***$ is a constant: the quotient of the second Azzi constant $C**$ by the square of the constant of gravity.

Dividing (2) by (1) we have the following:

$$(3) \quad \frac{m_1 \, m_2}{t_1 \, t_2} = \frac{M_1 \, M_2}{T_1 \, T_2} = \frac{C***}{C*}$$

Where the last term which expresses the relationship between two constants is, in its turn, a constant which can be represented by C_1. Equation (3), when by ν_2; ν_1; ν'_1; ν'_2 we indicate the inverse of the times: t_1; t_2; T_1; T_2, can be expressed as below in (4)

$$(4) \quad (m_1\nu_1)(m_2\nu_2) = (M_1\nu'_1)(M_2\nu'_2) = C_1$$

Let us now consider Planck's elementary quantum of action, which is generally represented by the letter h.

It is well known that in mechanics the action displayed by a moving mass is the product of the mass by its velocity and by the distance covered. Let us assume as a unit of measure for mass an arbitrary mass m_o; as unit for measure of linear spaces a segment Δ_s, and as unit of measure of velocity, that of the light in vacuum, c; thus the expression of h will be

$$(5) \quad h = k \, m_o \, c \, \Delta_s$$

where k is a pure number.

As a consequence of the aforesaid choice of units of measure, the masses M_1 and M_2 will be equal to m_o multiplied by certain coefficients, which we shall, respectively, call n_1 and n_2; N_1 and N_2, so that (4) may be written thus :

$$(6) \quad (n_1\, m_o\, \nu_1)(n_2\, m_o\, \nu_2) = (N_1\, m_o\, \nu'_1)(N_2\, m_o\, \nu'_2) = C_1$$

Let us now multiply all the factors inside brackets by the constant quantity $k\, c\, \Delta_s$; bearing in mind (5), we have :

$$(7) \quad (n_1\, h_1\, \nu_1)(n_2\, h_2\, \nu_2) = (N_1\, h_1\, \nu'_1)(N_2\, h_2\, \nu'_2) = C_2$$

where C_2 is a constant obtained from C_1 by multiplying by the square of $k\, c\, \Delta_s$.

Now, mechanics, and more especially atomic physics, teach us that the products of Planck's constant h by a frequency (inverse of the time) gives *energy*; therefore $n_1\, h_1\, \nu_1$ (i.e. the first factor of the first term in (7)) is the energy corresponding to the mass m_1. Similarly for the other factors which appear within the first two terms in (7). As already stated, however, the values m_1; m_2; M_1; M_2 represent the " increases " in mass for the two varieties at the end of each of the two intervals A and B.

It then became necessary to refer to intermediate values. These intermediate values are connected with increases by coefficients of proportionality which are practically the same for one variety as for the other. If we refer, therefore, not to the *final increases* m_1; m_2; M_1; M_2, but to the intermediate values, the two terms of (7) would each come to be multiplied by a same coefficient and so from (7) equal values would still be obtained.

If, therefore, we indicate with w_1; w_2 and W_1; W_2 the corresponding energies of the first and second varieties in the intervals A and B, we shall obtain

$$w_1\, w_2 = W_1\, W_2 = C_3$$

Also : the product of total energies corresponding to the two sub-periods A and B is constant—that is, it has the same value both for the early variety of maize as for the late.

. . . . . .

In order to explain these phenomena, with particular reference to the inversion of the velocity of development observed for the late and for the early varieties in the passage from sub-period A to sub-period B, we must separate the two moments, or values :

(1) the initial velocity of development;
(2) the constants.

The initial velocity of development is exclusively concerned with the germinal plasma, while the constant regulating of the relationships of mass and velocity controls the soma : the two moments are completely separate and in no way interdependent.

The initial morphogenetic mass, in the centres of origin of a species (this in agreement with the ideas of Vavilov), may be represented in the form of an essentially heterogeneous complex, and therefore in a most unstable state of equilibrium. More-over, with reference to each single characteristic of the plant, it would be logical to admit the existence of a series of values in the hereditary material, able to regulate the transmission for all grades of intensity in the manifestation of the said char-acteristic. So, for all that concerns velocity of development we shall, by the harmonic law of continuous variability, pass from the maximum to the minimum velocity through all the intermediate graduations.

With reference to the intervals A and B taken separately, the early type " Nano di Mugello " grows slowly in A and rapidly in B, while, vice versa, the late develops rapidly in A and slowly in B. In other words, the velocity of development would appear to vary in the two intervals without any plausible motive for so doing.

In reality, the intrinsic velocity of each variety cannot vary from a hereditary point of view, and the two varieties would develop with velocities corresponding to the initial impulse, were it not for a factor which is not concerned with the proper-ties of the plasma and which is not a particular characteristic, but a general one concerning all the forms of maize without distinction, and not each one separately. This factor is pre-cisely that constant which regulates the relationships of mass and velocity of development. If, in fact, each of the two varieties carried on in its development with the initial velocity, it follows that late forms would transform themselves in very early ones, and the plant would consequently undergo an excessive contraction, while the early varieties would become late to a maximum degree and the mass would greatly expand. Having calculated the proportions, we would find :

	Total duration of cycle, hours.	Dry weight of plant, gm.
Nostrano dell' Isola . . .	1,841	215
Nano di Mugello . . .	3,259	1,518

Outside the group of local Italian maize varieties there exist in different countries plenty of varieties with much lower and higher initial velocities than those obtained for " Nostrano dell' Isola " and " Trenodi di Campiglia ".

In these cases more accentuated contraction of the mass and gigantic expansion could be produced, incompatible with the normal architecture of the species, giving rise to teratological manifestations.

These two resolutions, both negative, for excess of expansion and of contraction of the mass, are inhibited by the constant which acts as a mould. The type growing quickly in period A becomes slow-growing in period B, and vice versa, for the type growing slowly in period A becomes quick-growing in period B. It is this constant which allows the integral utilisation of all the values of the hereditary material, part of which would otherwise be lost.

I would not like to reach any conclusion at this point; however, since from experiments at present being carried out, and still referring to very early and very late varieties, similar observations are being made, one is apt to envisage the existence of a law which is valid for the whole vegetable world. The law is, in any case, established for wheat, and it would also appear so for the bean.

There is yet another point to which I would like to draw the attention of the reader : the facts illustrated here cannot, for the evident contradiction of the situations in A and B, be easily explained on the basis of the habitual cause–effect scheme. The natural explanation of these phenomena would, on the other hand, be found in the new " theory of Vital

Phenomena " elaborated by Fantappié, for whom these phenomena (or at least those most typical which he calls "synthropic ") would show themselves subject to a principle of finality (anticipated potential) in clear contrast with the principle of causality of the physical or "entropic " phenomena (retarded potential).

The results obtained from our research would thus come to confirm materially the existence of synthropic phenomena, discovered by Fantappié in 1942 by purely theoretical methods through the mathematical equations of the very recent studies of quantic and relativistic physics.

VARIATIONS IN STRUCTURE

Macrocellular and Microcellular Structure

After having illustrated the concepts relative to velocity and mass, there remains to be considered the third element on which the system is based—the structure, which represents the sum total of the effects determined by velocity and mass. In the experiments made to clear up this point we chose two varieties of soft wheat, " Gelchsheimer " (German) and " Coccitta " (Sicily). " Gelchsheimer " in very favourable ambiental conditions produces up to and beyond 48 quintals per hectare, thus demonstrating its high degree of productivity (P_5). In conditions which are unfavourable through rainfall deficiencies the crop falls to 8 quintals, its susceptibility to drought and thermic excesses so being proved (rHD_3). " Coccitta ", on the other hand, produces 22 quintals in favourable conditions of the environment, and therefore has a very low productivity (P_1), but in a dry–hot regime its yield is about 11 quintals, so that its high resistance to this group of adversities is demonstrated (rHD_5).

The experiment conducted for the study of the macro- and micro-cellular structure was carried out in ten plots, in the first of which the conditions were made as favourable as possible, it being obvious that in this case an expansion of the soma is also accompanied by maximum dimensions in the cellular elements. For successive series, environmental availabilities were gradually reduced, until at the tenth series we find decidedly unfavourable conditions in which the defensive microcellular structure will have to be at its greatest intensity.

We said "defensive microcellular structure", which is equivalent to saying that the microcellular structure induces hardiness—i.e. a complex of resistances, which can, at least in part, be attributed to the relatively minor quantity of sensitive material (plasma) and to the relatively greater quantity of inert substances present (great thickness of cellular walls), a material which is less sensitive to both drought and frost.

In many cases, in fact, the ash content and the percentage of dry matter, which is higher the more minute the cells and thicker the cell walls, are in direct relation to the resistance to drought and low temperatures, as we shall see later.

In the following table for the ten series and the two varieties considered are given the mean diameters of the parenchymatous cells, the thickness of the parenchyma and the product of these two figures, which, when divided by 1,000, gives what has been called the "histologic index" (see Fig. 41).

Series.	"Gelchsheimer."	"Coccitta."
(1)	$73 \times 567 = 41\cdot3$	$60 \times 410 = 24\cdot6$
(2)	$62 \times 514 = 31\cdot9$	$55 \times 374 = 20\cdot6$
(3)	$58 \times 501 = 29\cdot0$	$53 \times 354 = 18\cdot8$
(4)	$57 \times 431 = 24\cdot6$	$52 \times 318 = 16\cdot5$
(5)	$52 \times 318 = 16\cdot5$	$51 \times 311 = 15\cdot9$
(6)	$50 \times 284 = 14\cdot2$	$48 \times 275 = 13\cdot2$
(7)	$49 \times 275 = 13\cdot5$	$33 \times 238 = 7\cdot9$
(8)	$47 \times 224 = 10\cdot5$	$34 \times 199 = 6\cdot8$
(9)	$45 \times 196 = 8\cdot8$	$31 \times 138 = 4\cdot3$
(10)	$42 \times 174 = 7\cdot3$	$30 \times 137 = 4\cdot1$

On the right-hand side of the graph, in the first quadrant, is traced the tangent (whose length is equal to the radius of the circle considered), which is divided into fifty equal parts, so that a scale of values for the histologic index in the favourable series from fifteen to sixty-five, is represented : this will include, within reasonable limits of probability, all the possible cases.

For each of the two varieties a rectilinear segment is now drawn, which, departing from the centre (intermediate situations), joins together the values which successively correspond to ever more favourable situations up to the two values of 41·3 ("Gelchsheimer") and 24·6 ("Coccitta"), the two yields encountered for the most favourable situations possible. These two segments form two angles with the horizontal, whose amplitude is directly proportional to the plant's tendency towards a macrocellular structure; this tendency is much more marked in " Gelchsheimer " than in " Coccitta " : 28° and 11°, respectively. The tendency towards the assumption of a macrocellular structure is therefore measured by the angular

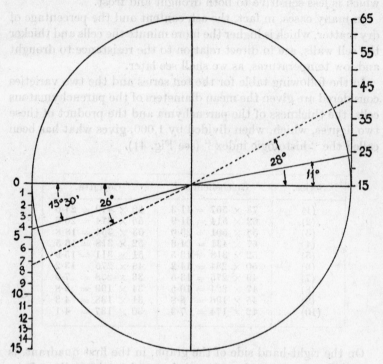

FIG. 41. TENDENCY TO MACRO- AND MICRO-CELLULAR STRUCTURE.

coefficient or trigonometric tangent of the straight line which joins the histologic values corresponding to the different situations from the centre of the circle to the scale of values.

If here we also adopt the quinary system of grading, we get five values representing the tendency towards a macrocellular structure (see Table on page 337).

On the left of the circle, and in the third quadrant (still on the tangent equal to the radius of the circle, and this time divided into fifteen parts), is drawn the scale representing the

Tendency.	Angular value.
tS_1 = very weak	0– 9
tS_2 = weak	9–18
tS_3 = intermediate . . .	18–27
tS_4 = strong	27–36
tS_5 = very strong . . .	36–45

less favourable situations from 0 to 15, chosen so as to include, within reasonable limits, all the possible cases.

For each of the two varieties is now marked a rectilinear segment which, departing from the centre, joins together the values successively corresponding to ever more unfavourable situations up to the two values 7·3 (" Gelchsheimer ") and 4·1 (" Coccitta "), which are precisely the index to be found in the most unfavourable situations.

These two segments give us two angles whose amplitude is this time inversely proportional to the tendency towards a microcellular structure, these being of 15° 30′ for " Coccitta " and 26° for " Gelchsheimer ". In fact, the smaller, under identical adverse conditions, are the dimensions of the cells, and therefore the more restricted the angle, the greater and more marked will be the plant's tendency to assume a microcellular structure and a resistance to adversities in general. Here, too, can be distinguished five graduations for the tendency towards the microcellular structure.

Tendency.	Angular Value.
ts_5 = very strong	0– 9
ts_4 = strong	9–18
ts_3 = intermediate . . .	18–27
ts_2 = weak	27–36
ts_1 = very weak . . .	36–45

From the above the fact emerges that, in certain cases at least, a characteristic is not to be represented by an absolute value, but by an angular value representing the tendency it has of manifesting itself.

Representation by means of a fixed and determined measurement, as is sometimes found in biometry, gives a picture of the characteristic at a single point—that is, in relation to only

z

one of the many aspects and values which it may assume under greatly varied ambiental conditions. In this way the characteristic is represented in a static form, as if belonging to a deceased organism. In effect, a characteristic cannot be measured with reference to a single ambiental situation, but must be expressed in respect of the complete series of ambiental situations, from the most to the least favourable at its (the characteristic's) appearance, so as to integrate all the aspects which the characteristic itself can assume.

" Gelchsheimer ", for instance, has a histologic index of 24·6 in the fourth series, and this is identical with that which " Coccitta " presents in Series No. 1. If, therefore, without keeping due account of the continuous series of bio-ambiental reactions, we had chosen " Gelchsheimer " plants in situations corresponding to the fourth series and " Coccitta " plants corresponding to the first series, we could conclude that these two varieties have the same histologic index and an equal tendency towards the macrocellular structure. It is true that we must here recall a rather noticeable error in which, certainly, a careful research worker would not have fallen. But if, in order to eliminate this error, we should even consider the complete series of variations and represent, with the average figure obtained, the histologic index of the two varieties, no advantage could derive from such procedure. In fact, the averages thus obtained do not mark any sensible difference between the two varieties; these averages gravitate, in fact, around the intermediate series " 5 " and " 6 ", which are very similar for both varieties.

The different tendencies in the two varieties towards a macrocellular or a microcellular structure show themselves in two opposite directions the more we depart from intermediate situations, until the most visible manifestation appears in agreement with series " 1 " (for the macrocellular structure) and series " 10 " (for the microcellular structure), respectively.

We therefore consider ourselves entitled to affirm that from a dynamic point of view—the only one with which the phenomena of life is to be considered—at least certain characteristics cannot be statistically represented by well-defined mean values or with a value corresponding to one of the many which the characteristic can present, but may be established with an angular measure which permits us to evaluate the tendency towards the two extreme situations, which in their ultimate effects are the macro- and micro-cellular structures.

Here, now, are the angular values of the tendency towards the two types of macro- and micro-cellular structure for the two varieties considered :

Variety.	Macrocellular.	Microcellular.
Gelchsheimer . . .	28°	26°
Coccitta	11°	15° 30′

" Gelchsheimer " therefore shows a strong tendency towards the macrocellular structure (tS_4), while " Coccitta " has a weak tendency in this respect (tS_2); on the contrary, in respect of the tendency towards a microcellular structure, " Coccitta " is on top with ts_4, while " Gelchsheimer " has an intermediate tendency ts_3. " Gelchsheimer " should thus be considered more productive but less hardy, while " Coccitta " is hardier but less productive. The yields obtained in very favourable and very unfavourable ambiental conditions correspond satisfactorily on the whole to the characteristics described here for the two varieties considered.

Non-Uniform Variations in Cellular Dimensions (in structure)

As we have seen for velocity and mass, so also do we find with regard to structure, that the dimensions of cells vary in a non-uniform manner throughout the soma; it is quite possible that in extreme cases certain parts of the plant may be found tending towards macrocellular structure, others towards microcellular structure. An example of this is " Biancone dell' Elba ", which, as we shall see later, has on the whole xerophytic habits, although having a not particularly thickened parenchyma in the culm, and with cells that are at least as voluminous as those found in " Rieti " and " Gentil Rosso ". The foliar laminae, however, have a decidedly microcellular structure.

To avoid repetition, I refer to page 357, where, in speaking of the specific resistance offered to hot spells by " Biancone dell' Elba ", the relative histologic figures are given.

CHAPTER XXI

THE PRACTICAL USE OF THE VELOCITY–MASS–STRUCTURE SYSTEM

FOR a measurement of the velocity of development we refer to the duration of the interval between earing and maturity, which is, as we have seen, directly correlated to productivity.[1]

Using as a basis a collection of Italian wheats in Perugia for the year 1938–39 which from a thermic point of view proved to be particularly suitable for a practical demonstration, we can attempt a first graduation for velocity.

V_5 = very great . . . . . 40 days and less
V_4 = great . . . . . . 40–45 days
V_3 = intermediate . . . 45–50 „
V_2 = small . . . . . 50–55 „
V_1 = very small . . . . . 55 days and more

For mass we distinguish five graduations or values based on the maximum weight of culm-ear and, quite naturally, in favourable ambiental conditions.

---

[1] The velocity of development considered as an intrinsic characteristic must be determined in conditions of the physical environment which are particularly favourable for the manifestation of this characteristic. This is verified when temperature increases slowly, or, better still, when it remains stationary for long periods. Particular varieties can, in such circumstances, clearly manifest their degree of earliness, since the dates of earing (and of maturing) of the earliest and latest varieties are spaced well apart.

In those years, however, when there is an abrupt and retarded passage from temperatures below the threshold for the earing phase or for maturity, to those which render possible the manifestation of these phases (earing and maturity respectively), we have an anticipation which becomes greater the later is the variety considered. There is therefore a crowding together, within a brief space of time, of the dates in which the phases appear for all varieties without distinction, a herding together which impedes an evaluation of the true degree of specific earliness of single varieties.

Making use of Vavilov's expression, we can say that : " In these cases environment dominates the genotype, while in conditions which are very favourable for the manifestation of the characteristic, it is the genotype that dominates the environment."

M_5 = very large . . . . . 28 gm. and more
M_4 = large . . . . . 28–24 gm.
M_3 = intermediate . . . . 24–20 „
M_2 = small . . . . . 20–16 „
M_1 = very small . . . . 16 gm. and less

The varieties which, in favourable ambiental conditions, have a reduced mass, are to be accepted as probably having a high degree of hardiness. The many experiments conducted to date effectively demonstrate that the varieties which in very favourable ambiental conditions do not greatly develop the culm-ear are those which, when found in highly adverse, poor ambiental conditions, are capable of contracting to a maximum degree their mass, giving a yield which will be very low but, at the same time, the maximum obtainable in such adverse conditions. The varieties which in highly favourable environmental conditions produce very large ears fail almost completely in negative situations.

What has been said for velocity and mass relative to the opportunity of measuring their specific grades in conditions which are very favourable for the manifestation of the characteristic may evidently also be applied to structure.

For structure we give the grading in relation to the histologic index as found in favourable ambiental conditions appropriate for increasing macrocellular structure :

S_5 = very high . . . . . 45 and more
S_4 = high 45–37
S_3 = intermediate 37–29
S_2 = low 29–21
S_1 = very low . . . . . 21 and less

The plant's tendency to macro- and micro-cellular structures should be expressed in angular values (as seen on page 337), and this undoubtedly furnishes a more exact and responsive measure of either one or the other condition. However, the said determination needs a great deal of work, while the simpler system adopted above (save for further and always possible corrections) may serve to arrive at a first approximation of this factor.

We can now summarise what has been said above in a general table representing the velocity–mass–structure system as a whole.

The Velocity–Mass–Structure System. Wheat

Series.	Velocity.	Days.	Mass.	Weight of culm-ear, gm.	Structure	Histo-logic Index.
(1)	V_1 = very small	$\geqslant 55$	M_5 = very large	$\geqslant 28$	S_5 = very high	> 45
(2)	V_2 = small	55–50	M_4 = large	28–24	S_4 = high	45–37
(3)	V_3 = intermediate	50–45	M_3 = intermediate	24–20	S_3 = intermediate	37–29
(4)	V_4 = great	45–40	M_2 = small	20–16	S_2 = low	29–21
(5)	V_5 = very great	$\leqslant 40$	M_1 = very small	$\leqslant 16$	S_1 = very low	$\leqslant 21$

The use of the table presents no difficulty for any determination it is required to make.

Let us suppose that in an experimental field, in absolutely favourable ambiental conditions, five varieties A, B, C, D and E (of which the characteristics of velocity–mass–structure have already been determined), have given the following yields : 46, 39, 28, 21, 15 quintals per hectare, respectively. If the velocity, mass and structure of variety A correspond to the first series, and those of varieties B, C, D, E to the second, third, fourth and fifth series, respectively, we may well say that the different behaviour of the varieties considered is due to clearly defined differences in the velocity–mass–structure values, and that in this case the velocity–mass–structure system explains the behaviour of each variety very well, singling out the intrinsic causes which have determined the respective yields. It is evident that a variety $V_5 M_1 S_1$, characterised by an evidently high grade of hardiness but low productivity, even in the most favourable ambiental conditions, will furnish a relatively low yield.

Passing now to another locality in which the ambiental complex happens to be decidedly negative, we find five more varieties, F, G, H, I, L, whose yields are of 13, 11, 9, 5 and 2 quintals per hectare, respectively. If for the F variety the values for velocity–mass–structure correspond to those of the fifth series, and those of the other varieties with ever-decreasing yields to the fourth, third, second and first series, respectively, we can say that in this case also the different behaviour of the single varieties measured by the yield produced is directly related to the law of velocity–mass–structure. In effect, a variety having the characteristics of the first series, and which is therefore extremely productive but not resistant, cannot but fail almost completely in totally unfavourable ambiental conditions.

Below are set out the results of a series of experiments undertaken, in this respect, with " Mentana " and with nine local varieties of Italian wheats of varying origin : " Cannavacante ", " Rieti di Montagna ", " Mistrittisa ", " Coccitta ", " Majorica Semiaristata ", " Romanello ", " Frassineto " (derived from " Gentil Rosso "), " Tosella Bianca " and " Bianchetta ".

For these varieties of wheat we give below the relative formulae with reference to the characteristics of velocity–mass–structure.

Mentana . . .	$V_1M_4S_5$	Mistrittisa . .	$V_3M_4S_2$
Frassineto . .	$V_1M_4S_5$	Romanello . .	$V_3M_2S_1$
Cannavacante .	$V_2M_5S_4$	Bianchetta . .	$V_3M_2S_1$
Majorica Semiaristata	$V_3M_2S_2$	Tosella Bianca .	$V_4M_1S_2$
Rieti di Montagna .	$V_3M_2S_2$	Coccitta . . .	$V_4M_1S_1$

In the following table are given the graduations of the yields for the varieties considered in two distinct years, one favourable from a meteorological point of view (and for optimal pedological, physiographical and agrotechnical conditions), the other unfavourable through intense drought (the plots were situated in decidedly unfavourable slope, soil and agrotechnical conditions).

For each year the yields are divided into three groups :

(*a*) relatively high yields;
(*b*) intermediate yields;
(*c*) relatively scarce yields.

Favourable year, quintals.			Unfavourable year, quintals.		
Mentana . . .	35·0		Coccitta . .	13·5	
Frassineto . .	31·8	31·4	Tosella Bianca .	13·0	13·1
Cannavacante .	27·5		Bianchetta . .	12·8	
Majorica Semiaristata .	25·0		Romanello . .	11·5	
Rieti di Montagna .	24·0		Mistrittisa . .	10·8	
Mistrittisa . .	22·9	23·0	Rieti di Montagna .	9·9	10·3
Romanello . .	20·1		Majorica Semiaristata	9·0	
Bianchetta . .	20·0		Cannavacante .	7·5	
Tosella Bianca .	18·3	18·4	Frassineto . .	7·2	6·9
Coccitta . .	17·0		Mentana . .	6·0	

In the favourable year the graduation of yields gives us also the graduation for productivity. Supposing that the velocity–mass–structure system is the cause of these different degrees of productivity, it is clear that the varieties which have furnished the highest product will have a formula corresponding to the first and second series. Those which have given the lowest yields will figure in the fourth and fifth series, while those with intermediate yields will have formulae between the second and the third or the third and the fourth series. The agreement between the formulae and the actual yields could not be more satisfactory.

In the unfavourable year, on the other hand, the graduation of yields should coincide with the graduation for hardiness.

In fact, the varieties which have furnished the highest yield have formulae comprised among the values of the fourth and fifth series, while those which have furnished the lowest yields are situated in the first and second series.

It is obvious that a variety having a slow development, large dimensions and a decided tendency towards a macrocellular structure, is particularly susceptible to adverse conditions of the environment, and this owing to the manifest contrast between the physio-morphological characteristics of the plant and those of the environment.

The behaviour of the varieties, considered in the most varied environmental conditions, therefore finds an explanation (the causes leading up to the yields) in the characteristics of velocity–mass–structure of the said varieties. These characteristics of velocity–mass–structure are therefore the cause of the different yields which a variety can give under the most varied environmental conditions.

. . . . .

The values for velocity–mass–structure are not held in a rigid system. It will be quite possible to have varieties of formula $V_2 M_5 S_4$ and others with, say, $V_5 M_2 S_2$, and so on. Theoretically, it is not even possible to exclude the quite exceptional existence of a V_2 (of the second series) combined with an M_2 of the fourth series. This is the case when, owing to its particular architecture, a variety is able to produce only a small ear as favourable as may be the conditions of the environment.

If temperature, once it has surpassed the threshold for earing, remains near the maturing threshold for a considerable period, the plant, having reached its maximum weight and achieved its complete development in a relatively short interval, will not be in a condition to utilise the availabilities during the rest of the fourth sub-period for a further increase of the mass and of the yield.   On the other hand, the further thermic availabilities cannot increase yield, but nevertheless are necessary to reach maturity.   In such conditions the relationship between high productivity and length of the fourth sub-period will not be observed.

In 1951, for instance, in spite of a duration of no less than 51 days from earing (7th May) to maturity (27th June), " Coccitta " developed a reduced mass (culm-ear 16 gm.), so that a small velocity V_2 was combined with a small mass M_2.

I repeat, however, that these are exceptional cases.   In general, and with reference to the great number of cases so far considered, the five series of our table represent a harmonious set of values which enable us to sum up schematically the most relevant relationships between productivity and hardiness in the following manner :

General conditions.	Productivity.	Hardiness.
Very favourable　　.　　.　　.	P_5	r_1
Favourable　　.　　.　　.　　.	P_4	r_2
Intermediate　.　　.　　.　　.	P_3	r_3
Unfavourable　.　　.　　.　　.	P_2	r_4
Very unfavourable　.　　.　　.	P_1	r_5

This is a first attempt which does not exclude, but rather necessitates, amendments and ultimate perfecting.   However, it already gives us the possibility of explaining the behaviour of the single varieties of wheat in the most varied conditions of the physical environment.   Naturally this is so in those cases, and they are in the majority, in which the said behaviour measured by the yield produced is in direct relation to the velocity–mass–structure system.

CHAPTER XXII

RESISTANCE TO COLD AND DROUGHT

IN studying the environment so far we have theoretically started from a point in which all the natural and artificial values are favourable to a maximum degree. We have then taken note of the successive worsening of the situation, implicitly admitting that such declines may be said to affect all the ambiental factors gradually, and in equal measure.

This is not always true. On the contrary, given that excess and deficiency of temperature and of rainfall are independent variables, they can be found in all their possible combinations. There are many localities in which optimal situations for rainfall are found, but where temperature has an intensely negative effect, either through excess or deficiency; conversely, in other zones optimal thermic conditions may be found accompanied by excess rainfall in certain cases, and by intense drought in others.

In these cases, quite naturally, it is no longer the sum of resistances, and therefore the hardiness, that interests us, but rather each, single, separate resistance.

I will now particularly refer to resistance to cold and resistance to drought.

Resistance to Cold

To an increase in the concentration of sugars in the cell sap there corresponds a lowering in the freezing point : hence the existence of a direct relationship between the resistance of the single varieties of a species to low temperature and the sugar content in the cell sap.

The following table gives the index-numbers relative to the percentage in sugar for different varieties of Swedish wheat, taking 100 as the sugar content of " Sammet ", the variety most resistant to cold.

The varieties of wheat are set out in order of decreasing resistance to low temperature.

346

The empirical graduation of resistance as found in the scale from 1 to 10 is based on observations made in open fields : the number of young plants which actually died during the winter through frost was recorded.

Wheat : Resistance to Cold and Sugar Content

Variety.	Grade of resistance.	Sugar content, index-no.
Sammet	10	100
Svea	9	97
Thule	7	70
Sol II	7	70
Pansar	6	60
Extra Squarehead . . .	5	50
Tystofte Smaa	4	40
Wilhelmina	3	30
Parl	2	20
Halland	1	10

The relationship between resistance to cold and sugar content could not be more perfect.

Similar relationships are found between resistance to the cold, and content in ash and dry matter. The high content in ash and in dry substances are in their turn related to a structure tending towards the microcellular state.

Resistance to Drought

Research carried out with the local varieties of wheat of " Val d'Ossola" (Alpine upper valleys), "Cologna" (Veneto), "Coccitta" (Sicily), and "Gargaresch" (Tripoli), showed that the development of the hypodermis and the microcellular structure appear obviously to be correlated with a resistance to water deficiencies.

Regarding productivity, " Val d'Ossola " comes first, followed by "Cologna", "Coccitta" and "Gargaresch", while for resistance to drought the graduation is exactly the opposite, so that " Gargaresch " takes first place, followed by " Coccitta ", " Cologna " and " Val d'Ossola ", which is the most susceptible to this adversity.

The table below gives the figures relating to yield in quintals of grain per hectare in very favourable ambiental conditions (Imola) and in very unfavourable ones, through rainfall deficiencies and thermic excesses (Tripoli).

Wheat Yields—Imola and Tripoli

Variety.	Yields, quintals per ha.	
	Favourable.	Unfavourable.
Val d'Ossola	35·0	2·0
Cologna	30·0	3·1
Coccitta	25·0	5·8
Gargaresch	20·0	6·3

As was to be expected in these cases, " productivity " and " resistance " are inversely related in respect of yield. We give below the thickness of the hypodermis and the cellular dimensions of the hypodermis and parenchyma for the different varieties.

Wheat—Sizes of Hypodermis and Cells

	Variety, microns.			
	Val d'Ossola.	Cologna.	Coccitta.	Gargaresch.
Width of hypoderm .	91	112	140	210
Dimensions of hypodermal cells . .	21 × 18	13 × 12	11 × 10	7 × 7
Dimensions of parenchymatic cells . .	126	84	71	54

The thickness of the hypodermis and the microcellular structure are thus directly correlated with resistance to drought, in contrast to the dimensions of the parenchymatic cells, which are correlated with productivity.

. . . . . .

With reference to resistance to thermic deficiencies and to drought, the common denominator in the cases described above is the microcellular structure which, with the decrease in plasma and the corresponding increase in inert substances, includes a minor susceptibility both to frost and to drought.

On the other hand, the microcellular structure is evidently correlated with the greater glucid concentration in the cell sap, a greater concentration which determines :

(1) resistance to the cold owing to the lowered freezing point;

(2) resistance to drought because of a decrease of the transpiration rate and increase in the absorption power of the roots when water reserves in the soil fall low.

In addition, a reduction of transpiration (correlated with resistance to drought) can also be useful on the polar limit of culture where, at the return of the good season, the atmosphere immediately warms up and accentuates the process of transpiration, while the ground remains frozen and does not permit the roots to supply the plant with the necessary water.

. . . . . .

Resistance to cold and to drought are therefore included within the velocity–mass–structure system, and so cannot constitute " separate resistances " in the true sense of the word.

The Particular Behavior of T. durum towards T. vulgare.

Bearing in mind what has been said above, let us now turn to hard wheats (*Tr. durum*) which present a different behaviour, and which we consider convenient to illustrate because it makes possible an explanation of the limit of distribution of this species over the surface of the earth.

In soft wheats, as we have already seen, resistance to cold tends to accompany resistance to drought in a single complex of hardiness.

In hard wheats, on the other hand, we find resistance to drought together with susceptibility to cold. From this derive peculiar characteristics in the order of bio-ambiental relationships, which we will now discuss briefly, referring successively to the damp–cold (*A*) sector and to the dry–hot (*B*) sector.

Damp–Cold Sector. The weak concentration of glucids in the cell sap (as found in hard wheats) can, in part at least, explain the susceptibility of *Tr. durum* to low temperatures; on the other hand, a high degree of humidity and excessive rainfall worsen the quality of the product, determining the softening of the kernels.

The ultra-violet rays, in which the atmosphere is particularly rich in the natural area of distribution for hard wheats, would appear to favour the synthesis of proteins, and therefore also of gluten. With a decrease in the intensity of short-wave radiations, the synthesis of proteic matter diminishes, while the kernel reacts *morphologically*, forming lax tissues and lacunas in which masses of starch accumulate. This determines the disappearance of the characteristic vitreous fracture of hard wheats, while the quality of the products decidedly worsens as a consequence of the lowering of the gluten content.

The forms of *Tr. durum* therefore cease with the advent of the first colds and the rains which lead to the softening.

Although it is obvious that the damp–cold complex is accompanied by a decrease in ultra-violet radiation, we cannot exclude that excess rains, together with low temperature, might, independently from the radiations, contribute directly to the formation of tissues rich in water, spongy, and therefore predisposed to softening.

In southern Italy and Sicily hard wheats dominate in the luminous and dry coastlines, while in the interior and on the mountain slopes, with the decrease in temperature and an increase in cloudiness, they yield their positions to the soft (" Maioriche ") and turgid (" Cintarola ", etc.) forms. The " Biancone dell' Elba " variety (*Tr. durum hordeiforme*) grown in Umbria degenerates, the kernel going completely starchy.

It is, indeed, true that a nucleus of *durum* is also found between southern Canada and the north-central sector of the United States. In these cases, however, the wheats are spring forms which, being sown in spring, naturally escape the winter colds, while throughout the brief and hot continental summer a high degree of luminosity and the almost total absence of rains favour the synthesis of proteic matter and the formation of gluten.

Dry–Hot Sector. Further to the morphological and physiological complex, the resistance to drought and to thermic excesses typical of hard wheats is accompanied by peculiar adaptations which reduce the loss due to transpiration at the time when the dangers from hot spell are greatest; a fact which emerges in our research on the " Biancone dell' Elba " (see page 356).

We wish in any case to draw the reader's attention to a characteristic of hard wheats which could be contributory in accentuating the resistance to drought.

The culm of many *durum* wheats is for long tracts (above and below the nodes) filled with a small column of pith which obliterates the lumen almost completely. This is formed by parenchymatic cells which take part in the circulation of water through the plant by osmosis, while in the proximity of the vessels the water passes directly through the tracheae.

The determination of the quantity of water which may, in this manner, be absorbed was carried out by the static method.

The tissue contained in a weighing-bottle is put in equilibrium with a limited atmosphere of water vapour, conditioned by a solution of 3.5% sulphuric acid at a temperature of $25° \pm 0.5°$ C.

The equilibrium is reached when there is no longer a passage of water from the atmosphere to the tissue and vice versa.

The tissue–water system at the state of equilibrium corresponds to a solution having an osmotic pressure of 15.5 atmospheres. The quantity of water absorbed by the tissue under such conditions was 98.9 gm. of water for 100 gm. of dry matter (dehydrated in 98% sulphuric acid).

It is therefore evident that a notable quantity of water may be accumulated in parenchymatic tissues by osmosis and, in relation with the water regime of the plant, returned to circulation and be utilised. And it is quite possible to suppose that this characteristic of the hard wheats can contribute to increase their resistance to drought.

The binomials " resistance to cold–resistance to drought " (for *Tr. vulgare*) and " susceptibility to cold ($+$dampness)– resistance to drought " (for *Tr. durum*) are the two motives which in the order of bio-ambiental relationships clearly separate the two species of *Triticum*. Soft wheats, by their greater capacity of adaptation, have thus spread in the four sectors : dry–hot, dry–cold, humid–hot, humid–cold; while hard wheats cease on the onset of the first rains and colds, typically remaining limited to the dry–hot sector.

From this it is not unreasonable to hope for the opportunity of giving greater consideration to the functional complex and the modalities of development within the framework of bio-ambiental relationships, so as to render the study more complete and facilitate comparison between the different forms.

CHAPTER XXIII

SEPARATE RESISTANCES

FROM the cases described we cannot, as yet, speak with certainty of separate resistances to cold and drought (for soft wheats).

However, if we now consider the resistance to rust, to hot spell and rainfall excesses (lodging), we shall find cases of separate resistances clearly defined.

Using the material collected from operations involving a large number of Italian and foreign wheats from 1930 until the beginning of the last world war, I wish now to consider the resistance to lodging, particularly as this decidedly represents an example of separate resistance.

The following varieties were examined :

Upplands Lantvete. Hardy and with a high resistance, both to cold and to drought, early, susceptible to lodging and a poor producer. It is principally found in the hilly zones of central Sweden, where climatic conditions are particularly harsh.

Saissette. Found in the dry–hot sectors of France, where it persists owing to its high resistance to drought and because of its notable earliness, which saves it from hot spell; it is, however, a poor producer and susceptible to lodging.

Bjeloklasa Osilesta Cervenka. Predominant in the districts of Pirdop and Ichtiman (Bulgaria). Highly susceptible to rust, it lodges easily and presents a very high degree of productivity. In fact, in favourable years it yields 35 and more quintals per hectare, in spite of the unfavourable topographical and agrogeological conditions of these zones.

Gentil Rosso. At the beginning of the century, and before the introduction of the Strampelli's hybrids, this was one of the most diffused varieties in central and northern Italy, because of its high productivity and the good quality of the flour. At the same time " Gentil Rosso " has an intermediate degree of resistance both to rust and lodging.

Rieti. Still considerably grown in limited hilly sectors of central Italy. Medium producer and tending to lodge, it is characterised by its very high resistance to rust. It has been used in a number of crosses in British East Africa and Peru for the production of races, particularly resistant to *Puccinia* spp.

Mentana. A hybrid obtained by Strampelli by crossing " Wilhelmina " × " Rieti " with " Aka Komughi ". It presents a complex of exceptionally favourable characteristics : very high productivity, very high resistance to lodging, resistant to rust. Early in its maturation it nearly always avoids hot spell, and at the same time, thanks to the extraordinary earliness in earing, the interval from earing to the harvest is very long : this is directly correlated with a high productivity.

Aka Komughi. Red wheat of Japan. It presents extreme earliness, and is highly resistant to lodging and to cryptogamous attacks : a scarce producer.

In the table below, for each of the seven varieties considered, are given the formulae relative to the characteristics of velocity-mass–structure and the degree of productivity and of resistance according to the scale : $n \times 4$ (see page 248) (20 = maximum degree of productivity and resistance, 1 = minimum degree of productivity and resistance).

Variety.	Produc-tivity.	Resistance to :		Formula of velocity-mass-structure.
		Lodging.	Rust.	
(1) Mentana . .	18	17	16	$V_1 M_4 S_5$
(2) Bjeloklasa Osilesta	16	6	5	$V_2 M_4 S_4$
(3) Gentil Rosso .	14	12	12	$V_2 M_4 S_3$
(4) Rieti . . .	13	4	17	$V_3 M_3 S_3$
(5) Upplands Lantvete	8	5	4	$V_4 M_2 S_2$
(6) Saissette . .	6	5	8	$V_4 M_1 S_2$
(7) Aka Komughi .	5	18	15	$V_5 M_1 S_1$

We give now the yields of these varieties in two years, one (in a very favourable complex) with favourable climatic conditions (1933), the other (1932) unfavourable through excessive rains which caused extended attacks of rust and lodging. The yields, in decreasing order, also give us a graduation in the values of productivity and resistance, particularly to lodging.

In the favourable year the graduation of yields is therefore in perfect accordance with the formula of velocity–mass–structure.

Favourable year, quintals.		Unfavourable year, quintals.	
(1) Mentana . .	35·1	(1) Mentana . .	18·1
(2) Bjeloklasa Osilesta	31·3	(2) Aka Komughi .	14·2
(3) Gentil Rosso .	27·0	(3) Gentil Rosso .	12·5
(4) Rieti . . .	24·6	(4) Rieti . . .	10·3
(5) Upplands Lantvete	19·0	(5) Bjeloklasa Osilesta	10·0
(6) Saissette . .	16·5	(6) Saissette . .	6·4
(7) Aka Komughi .	16·0	(7) Upplands Lantvete	5·9

In the unfavourable year, if the relationship was still valid, we should find an inversion in graduation which would undoubtedly place in the last positions the varieties with a high degree of productivity. In reality, the facts present a different picture. " Mentana ", in fact, remains in first place, inasmuch as high productivity is not in any way in contrast with a high resistance to lodging, while " Aka Komughi ", thanks to the solidity and elasticity of the culms, was only damaged in small measure, and so jumps into second place. " Bjeloklasa Osilesta ", a good producer but prone to lodging and susceptible to rust, goes into fifth place, while " Gentil Rosso " and " Rieti " occupy an intermediate position. " Rieti ", although an easy victim to lodging, defends itself and almost holds its position, by virtue of its specific resistance to rust. Leaving out " Aka Komughi ", passed—as we have seen—into second place, " Saissette " and " Upplands Lantvete " remain, as for favourable year, in last place because of their susceptibility to lodging and to rust and their low degree of productivity.

Productivity and resistance to lodging behave as independent characteristics and the most varied combinations among their different values is therefore possible.

Typically we find :

	Productivity.	Resistance.	Yields, quintals, in :	
			Favourable year.	Unfavourable year.
Mentana . .	+	+	35·1	18·1
Bjeloklasa Osilesta .	+	−	31·3	10·0
Aka Komughi .	−	+	16·0	14·2
Saissette . .	−	−	16·5	6·4

Resistance to lodging without doubt constitutes a case of "separate resistance". The presence in the hypoderm of elastic fibres and the solidity of the culms are in no way incompatible with a small velocity of development, a great expansion of the mass and with a macrocellular structure, a complex of characteristics which are undoubtedly correlative with a high degree of productivity.

. . . . .

I would now like to refer in some detail to a most interesting case of specific resistance to hot spell.

The " Biancone dell' Elba" Variety and its Specific Resistance to Hot Spells

When one speaks of resistance to hot spells, reference is always made to the earliness of the plant, which enables it to complete its cycle and mature the grain before the arrival of hot spells, the frequency of which increases the further we move on in summer. It is not therefore a true and proper resistance to hot spells, but rather an escape in time which enables the plant, so to speak, to subtract itself from the negative action of heat-strokes.

" Biancone " of the Isle of Elba, rather productive, is the only variety known to me to possess a high degree of specific resistance to hot spells.

Many years ago, certainly before 1930, Prof. Bellini and I had set out an experiment with this wheat in the territory of Grosseto. During that year the medium late and late wheats were badly hit by strong sirocco winds, which caused hot spells to appear. The yield was reduced to approximately 8–9 quintals per hectare for all varieties other than " Biancone " (see later).

Besides being scarce, the produce proved to be of poor quality owing to wrinkled and shrivelled grain, almost empty and practically reduced to a mass of cellulose, with very poor starch and gluten content. Under the action of the heat stroke the straw and glumes of " Biancone ", which was at the end of its milk maturity, also turned rapidly yellow, as did the other varieties. If the glumes were pulled apart, however, the still turgid and green grain could be seen inside.

The yield was 15–16 quintals per ha., thus demonstrating the specific resistance of this variety to hot spells.

Moreover, on the Isle of Elba, " Biancone " is considered a

good producer, so that, in spite of its not great resistance to lodging and rust, its cultivation is increasing, while the local " Biancolino " and the imported " Rieti No. 11 " is tending to disappear. The variety under consideration would therefore appear to have a high degree of productivity and a certain resistance to drought, besides having a specific resistance to hot spells : a set of characteristics which, on the whole, are a little out of the ordinary when one thinks of what has been said for the velocity–mass–structure system, and the general incompatibility between " productivity " and " hardiness ".

This particular behaviour of " Biancone " seems to correspond also to a peculiar habit of growth of this plant. The culm is long and thin, the ear large and procumbent, the internodes are very long, while the foliar laminae become smaller and smaller from the bottom upwards. A field sown with " Biancone " gives a general impression of a field of rye, owing to the marked reduction in the foliar apparatus and the accentuated length of the internodes. " Biancone " is late. In the year 1950, in Perugia, it eared on the 9th May, continuing in its slow development until the end of June, and brought its normally developed kernels to perfect maturity in spite of the high temperature. The length of the earing–harvest interval (directly correlated with productivity) was therefore 50 days.

For the stem and leaves at the beginning of the milky stage we have the following mean values (mean of 100 plants) :

Total weight of a green culm with leaves and ear . 21·2 gm.
Length of culm . . . . 185·0 cm.
Weight of foliar mass (per culm) . . . . 3·0 gm.
Foliar surface (per culm) . . . . . 127·0 cm.^{2}

For the structure we have :

	Mean diameter of parenchymatous cells, microns.	Mean thickness of parenchyma, microns.
Second internode from the bottom upwards	87·5	606·6
Third internode from the bottom upwards	102·3	542·5
Fourth internode from the bottom upwards	71·6	350·0
Mean	87·1	499·7

" Biancone " is therefore very late, with a decidedly slow development; it has a notable mass; macrocellular structure of the culm.   Its characteristics here are complex, for though they make a relatively high degree of productivity possible, they still do not furnish the elements which could explain its particular behaviour towards hot spells.

Hot spells, due to the simultaneous action of wind and high temperatures, can be harmful in a mere two or three hours. From reports we have for Italy, Spain, Russia and North Africa, numerous cases emerge in which the harvest was promising and well on the way towards maturity when the action of a hot wind for two or three hours interrupted the development of the grain and led to its shrivelling.

A hot spell is thus a phenomenon which takes the form of a crisis, and if the soma possesses particular means of over-coming it, the plant will be able to show its intrinsic, even high degree of productivity.   This would have been impos-sible in the presence of an adverse phenomenon such as drought, which cannot happen in one day, but needs a suffi-ciently long period with no rains to be realised and become harmful.

What, then, are the characteristics of resistance to hot spells ?

In relation to the total mass, " Biancone ", as can be deduced from the facts explained above, shows a considerable reduction of the foliar apparatus : in addition, the leaves tend to roll up longitudinally.   These characteristics undoubtedly induce a limited transpiration, and we could be tempted to attribute the resistance of the plant to hot spells to the reduction of the foliar laminae and foliar mass.   However, a more careful examination of " Biancone's " habit of growth leads to the discovery of a truly singular and special structure which explains the particular behaviour of this variety.

From an examination of the last three leaves towards the top of the plant we observe a peculiar fact.   For " Rieti ", as for all other wheats known to me, the third leaf from the top is less developed than the last but one, and generally the top leaf has a bigger surface.   For " Biancone " we observe exactly the opposite : the dimensions of the leaves decrease from the bottom upwards.

Beginning from the lower part, in fact, we find the following values for leaf surfaces :

Leaf Areas of Two Wheats—" Biancone " and " Rieti "

	Biancone.	Rieti.
	cm.²	cm.²
Third leaf from last (at the bottom) .	49·13	36·30
Last leaf but one (centre) . . .	42·65	54·00
Last leaf (at the top) . . .	35·88	63·29
Sum	127·66	153·59

The total leaf surface of " Biancone " is 83·11% of that of " Rieti "; the foliar mass of the first variety is thus considerably reduced, and the difference increases when we consider only the upper leaf, its surface being for " Biancone " almost only half that of " Rieti ".

As for structure, while insofar as the culm is concerned, " Biancone " is decidedly macrocellular, the last leaf at the top of this wheat presents a decidedly microcellular structure, as may be deduced from the following table, in which the figures for " Rieti " and " Biancone " are given for the topmost leaf :

	Rieti.	Biancone.
	microns	microns
(1) Thickness of cuticle . .	3–4	6–7
(2) Dimensions of epidermal cells :		
(a) Upper surface . .	18–21 × 33–38	16–19 × 22–25
(b) Lower surface . .	18–21 × 33–38	14–18 × 14–20
(3) Dimensions of parenchymatous cells	64–70	42–48
(4) Thickness of leaf :		
(a) Maximum . . .	323	201
(b) Minimum	252	141

As maturing progresses the leaves shrivel from the bottom upwards, and at last, when the danger from hot spell is greatest, only the topmost leaf remains functional. The small residual surface, on the other hand, is sufficient to assure the plant the continuation of the last weak assimilation processes, while transpiration, reduced to a minimum by the structure and extreme reduction of the leaf, enables the plant to win over the negative action, an action, violent but brief, brought about by the hot gusts of sirocco winds. Other varieties, owing to the greater width of the transpiring surface, suffer a break in the equilibrium of the water balance which leads to a decrease in turgidity and to sudden interruptions in the normal processes of development, with consequent shrivelling of the grain.

The characteristic of specific resistance to hot spells may therefore be described and interpreted as :

(1) The relative reduction of the foliar mass and the xerophylic structure, especially for the last leaf at the top, can undoubtedly contribute towards the resistance of the plant both to drought and to hot spells.

(2) The most interesting aspect, however, is without doubt to be sought in the progressive reduction of the leaf surfaces from the bottom upwards, so that the more imminent the danger from hot spells as the season advances, the narrower correspondingly becomes the transpiring surface; this enables the plant to withstand the sirocco winds without loss of turgidity of the grain.

(3) If the action of hot gusts of wind were prolonged " Biancone ", too, would not withstand them, but since the duration of the adverse phenomenon is generally limited to a few hours, the adjustments here described enable the plant to overcome the crisis without in any way sacrificing its productivity.

Productivity makes itself manifest and substantiates, we might well say, in the whole vegetative period, and with more evident results during the sub-period from earing to the completed maturation, which for " Biancone " is very long. Resistance to hot spells becomes evident only for a very limited space of time. For these reasons " Biancone's " specific resistance to hot spells is compatible with a relatively high degree of productivity.

We have here a clear case of separate resistances.

*   *   *   *   *

I have dwelt, perhaps with too much detail, on " Biancone's " particular structure and its specific resistance to hot spells.

The reason for this insistence is that we are faced with a most striking and typical case of " separate resistance " (hence compatability with a high degree of productivity).

Separate Characteristics of Resistances

Finally, we have to say something about separate characteristics of resistances attributable to small details of a physiological and morphological nature which can explain the specific resistance of a plant to determined adversities.

For instance, the " Manipeba " variety of manioca, considered the most resistant to drought in Brazil, although highly productive, has this characteristic because in droughty periods the plant allows all its leaves to fall, and the mass is consequently diminished : at the return of rainfall, " Manipeba " resumes normal growth, quickly forming its foliage again.

Many other plants in the tropics present this same characteristic. In the province of Caserta (Campania), as I was informed by Dr. Vollono, there is a variety of olive, the " Spogliatella ", which, similarly in the hottest summer periods, allows the greater part of its foliage to fall, so notably reducing water consumption.

We have traced the main lines of a method which permits individualisation of ecological characteristics, starting with the yield.

The preliminary phase is represented by the " reasoned yields ", which give the measure of the degree of productivity and of the degree of resistance.

The determination of the physiological and morphological characteristics, correlated with the different degrees of productivity and resistance, can pass through three succcessive phases :

(1) Determination of the characteristics of the velocity–mass–structure system. From what has already been said, it is clear that this determination is sufficient to explain the degree of productivity and the degree of hardiness (sum of resistances) for the majority of cases. Between " productivity " and " hardiness " there is incompatability.

(2) In certain cases, however, this determination is insufficient, and it then becomes necessary to study the

" separate resistances " as seen, for resistance to lodging and hot spells, which are not incompatible with a relatively high degree of productivity.

(3) In some few cases the determination of separate resistance is not sufficient in itself to explain the behaviour of a given variety. In such cases it is necessary to push the research further to discover some details of a morphological and physiological nature, often very small, but which prove to be the most apparent cause of a given degree of resistance—to drought, for instance. These characteristics are always the expression of the general architecture of the plant, but in practice behave as separate independent values. We thus have the separate characteristics of resistance to drought compatible with a relatively high degree of productivity. On the other hand, resistance to drought (as far as results determined by velocity–mass–structure go) is not compatible with a high degree of productivity.

. . . . .

The plant can be considered as a machine !

This is a first attempt to recognise and represent the different parts of this machine which produce starch, sugar, flour, alkaloids, wine, etc.; in effect, the beginning of " agricultural botany " !

The development of the plant seems to belong to a final cause which gradually takes shape, rather than to motives of cause and effect. It starts from but, morphologically, little differentiated material, which, through successive and ever more complex modifications, finds its final expression in the perfected and typical architecture of the plant.

The method proposed for the identification of the ecological characteristics finds its inspiration in a dynamic and finalistic principle which can be defined thus : " The complete organism, as a whole, is by no means the result of the sum of the details and of single characteristics, however conceived or represented, and which, in any case, are never preformed. These characteristics are associated with each other in an organic whole because the architecture of the plant represents that force which gradually determines its peculiar characteristics, and its own details of form and function."

PART FOUR

FACTORIAL COMBINATIONS AND DIFFERENTIAL ANALYSIS OF YIELD

CHAPTER XXIV

GENERAL DISCUSSION ON FACTORIAL COMBINATIONS

THE aims of agricultural experimentation could be roughly summarised as follows :

(1) Determination of the yield obtainable from new varieties.
(2) Increase in yield obtainable through the application of a new fertiliser, a different working of the soil, a new cultural expedient, etc.
(3) The effects of a new insecticide, or of a new anti-cryptogamic treatment on the yield of a particular plant.

What, in fact, is the actual procedure ?

Let us take, as an example, a new fertiliser formula.

Two groups of experimental plots are set out, to the first of which fertiliser is added, the second to which it is not.

The difference in mean yield obtained from the two groups of plots is taken as a measure of the effect on the plant of the new fertiliser. Of what value is this measure ? It may be accepted only in those cases in which soil and meteorological conditions are found to be identical with those existing during the trials. According to the laws of probability, such similar situations are rare. It is therefore evident that the experimental results, as obtained to-day, represent particular cases which do not allow the establishment of general rules for a practical application.

It is obvious that with generous applications of fertiliser there will always be an increase in product, so that, referring to two groups of plots, fertilised and non-fertilised, we shall in every case find a difference in the yields obtained : this could create the illusion that the problem of the greater or smaller advantage of using a certain fertiliser formula had been solved.

I have said the illusion. It is not, in effect, sufficient to demonstrate that there has been an increase in yield; it is indispensable to determine the entity of this increase under the most varied ambiental and agrotechnic conditions. This will enable us to judge and justify the greater or smaller advantage of employing the fertiliser in question.

The increases obtainable, if we take into consideration the interaction of all variables, differ widely in different cases.

In reality we cannot limit our determination to a difference between fertilised and non-fertilised plots : we have to determine as many differences as there are possible combinations of all the other factors (or at least the most important), natural and agrotechnic, influencing the yield.

But in this connection we are faced with a great difficulty. According to the official procedure in use to-day, the particular factor, the effects of which we wish to determine, must be made to vary within its extreme limits of variability, while all others are kept constant. Even if this becomes possible with a limited number of factors inside the laboratory, it is impossible in the open field where all factors vary freely.

This obstacle has been overcome by integrating the widespread geographical trials with the differential analysis of yields.

CHAPTER XXV

GEOGRAPHICAL TRIALS WITH MAIZE

UTILISING the principles of agricultural ecology, the Ministry of Agriculture (Italy) began in 1941 a series of widespread trials with maize. In these trials four variables are concerned :

(1) the plant ;
(2) the soil ;
(3) the entity of fertilisation ;
(4) meteorological conditions.

Plant. The two varieties " Nostrano dell' Isola ", very productive but not resistant, and " Trenodi di Campiglia ", very resistant to drought but not productive, were employed. We certainly cannot affirm that " Nostrano dell' Isola " is the most productive of Italian maize and " Trenodi di Campiglia " the more resistant. It is, however, undoubtedly true that the two varieties considered, if not in the extreme positions, are certainly (within the framework of local Italian maize varieties) close to the two extreme values of the series of combinations of the characteristics of " productivity " and " hardiness ".

Soil. In each region in which the trials were undertaken three soils with ratings of very good, intermediate and poor, for maize culture, were chosen for each of the two varieties. We have thus integrated the whole series of soils and, therefore, of possible yields as a function of the factor soil, within its extreme limits of variability.

Entity of Fertilisation. Each of the three plots was, in its turn, subdivided into two, one of which was given only 150 quintals per ha. of manure (low fertilisation), while for the other the following formula was adopted : dung, 400 quintals ; superphosphate, 6 quintals ; sulphate of ammonia, 2 quintals ; potassium sulphate, 2 quintals ; nitrate of calcium, 1·5 quintals (abundant fertilisation).

On the whole, and with reference to the three variables " plant ", " soil " and " quantity of fertiliser employed ", we have the following twelve combinations (six for each variety) :

No.	Variety.	Soil.	Fertilisation.
1	Nostrano dell' Isola	Good	Abundant
2	,, ,,	,,	Low
3	,, ,,	Intermediate	Abundant
4	,, ,,	,,	Low
5	,, ,,	Poor	Abundant
6	,, ,,	,,	Low
7	Trenodi di Campiglia	Good	Abundant
8	,, ,,	,,	Low
9	,, ,,	Intermediate	Abundant
10	,, ,,	,,	Low
11	,, ,,	Poor	Abundant
12	,, ,,	,,	Low

In these trials we used low and abundant fertilisation. In any further trials of this nature it would be better to adopt only the two opposed situations : manured and not manured.

Meteorological Conditions. There remains the fourth variable represented by the meteorological conditions, the effects of which cannot, of course, be calculated until the end of the trials. In the case of maize, as is well known, the dominant negative factor is usually (and it was particularly so in the year considered) summer drought. The stations are divided into two groups : no drought (favourable rainfall conditions) and drought (unfavourable rainfall conditions).

For each of the twelve combinations tabled above we will therefore have two variables : favourable meteorological situations and unfavourable meteorological situations. There are thus twenty-four combinations, for each of which we give the corresponding mean yield (see Fig. 42).

The twenty-four yields represent, with a good approximation, all the yields which the two varieties considered can furnish under the most varied soil, fertiliser and climatic conditions. Each of these factors was present under extreme situations, so enclosing the complete series of values relating to each factor within the most extreme limits of variability.

In every case the series of the yields will be completed with a satisfactory approximation by simple interpolation.

In the graph (Fig. 42) favourable situations (good soil, abundant fertiliser, sufficient rainfall) are indicated by a small white circle, and unfavourable ones (poor soil, scarce fertilisation, drought) by a small black circle, while intermediate soils are represented by a small circle half black and half white.

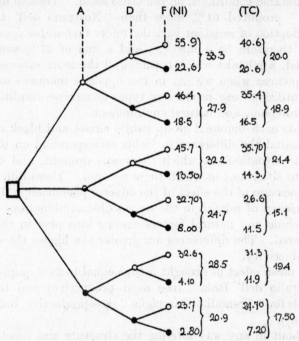

FIG. 42. EFFECT OF RAINFALL ON THE YIELD OF MAIZE.
A = Soil; D = Fertiliser; F = Rainfall; NI = "Nostrano dell' Isola";
TC = "Trenodi di Campiglia".

In the two extreme combinations of factors considered, the most and the least favourable, it is interesting to note the contrasting behaviour of the two varieties as a consequence of the different degrees of productivity and of resistance to drought.

Yields of Maize.   Italy 1941 Trials

	Favourable.	Un-favourable.
Nostrano dell' Isola . . .	55·90	2·80
Trenodi di Campiglia . . .	40·60	7·20
Nostrano dell' Isola (index-number)	100	39
Trenodi di Campiglia (index-number)	73	100

B B

In favourable conditions "Nostrano dell' Isola" (highly productive, small resistance) produces 27% more than "Trenodi di Campiglia" (highly resistant, low productivity). With unfavourable conditions, on the other hand, "Trenodi di Campiglia" produced 61% more than "Nostrano dell' Isola". The adoption of resistant varieties under favourable conditions would therefore be a mistake, and a loss of 27% would be incurred, a mistake which becomes all the more serious in its consequences when we act in the opposite manner—namely, when utilising very productive types in adverse conditions of the agrotechnic and natural environment.

Beside each binomial group (white circlet and black circlet) is indicated the difference in yields corresponding on the one hand to situations in which there was drought, and on the other to situations in which there was not. These differences are a measure of the effect of the adverse phenomenon, lack or insufficiency of rainfall in the six possible combinations of the agrotechnic and natural factors coming into play in the case considered. The differences are greater the higher the degree of productivity.

The mean effect of drought is thus equal to 27·9 quintals for "Nostrano dell' Isola" (the most productive) and to 18·7 quintals for "Trenodi di Campiglia" (less productive, but more resistant).

Without in any way altering the structure and function of the graph, we can now invert the position of the factors, speaking rather of an F–D–A order (rainfall, fertiliser, soil) than an A–D–F order (soil, fertiliser, rainfall).

At the side of each ternary group of values (yields in the three soil groups) is indicated the difference in yield between the two extreme types of soil (the best and the worst) (Fig. 43).

What has been seen for the factor drought is here repeated for soil, and its effect on yield is seen to be of 20 quintals for "Nostrano dell' Isola" and 9 quintals for "Trenodi di Campiglia".

Lastly we pass to the third order A–F–D (soil, rainfall, fertiliser) (Fig. 44).

In criticising the methods in use to-day for the evaluation and measurement of the effects of a particular fertiliser, we stated that when it is required to utilise the trial results outside the immediate boundary of the experiment, it becomes necessary to determine an organic series of differences between the fertilised and non-fertilised plots : they must be as many as the combinations of the other, or at least of the most important agrotechnic and natural factors which vary freely, and

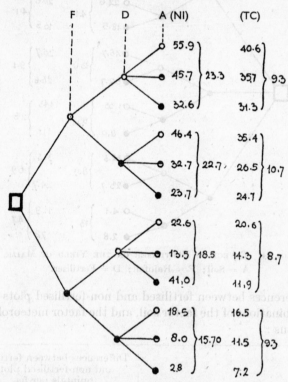

FIG. 43. EFFECT OF SOIL ON THE YIELD OF MAIZE.

F = Rainfall; D = Fertiliser; A = Soil; NI = "Nostrano dell' Isola"; TC = "Trenodi di Campiglia".

influence in different measures the entity of the yield. The two factors considered here, meteorological (drought, or absence of drought) and soil (very good, intermediate and very poor), give us six possible combinations, and in relation to each of these combinations we have six differences between fertilised and non-fertilised plots.

Taken from the graph (Fig. 44), I list in the following table

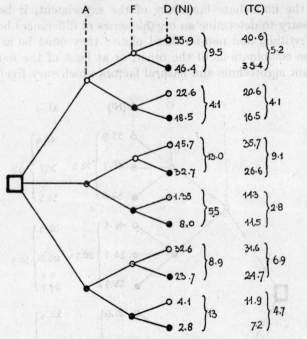

FIG. 44. EFFECT OF FERTILISER ON THE YIELD OF MAIZE.
A = Soil; F = Rainfall; D = Fertiliser.

the differences between fertilised and non-fertilised plots in the six combinations of the factor soil, and the factor meteorological conditions :

Soil and climate.	Differences between fertilised and non-fertilised plots, quintals per ha.	
	Nostrano dell' Isola.	Trenodi di Campiglia.
Very good soil :		
Sufficient rains . . .	9·5	5·2
Drought	4·1	4·1
Intermediate soil :		
Sufficient rains . . .	13·0	9·1
Drought	5·5	2·8
Poor soil :		
Sufficient rains . . .	8·9	6·9
Drought	1·3	4·7

The mean difference in yields observed in fertilised and non-fertilised plots for the six combinations is of 7·0 quintals for "Nostrano dell' Isola" and of 5·4 for "Trenodi di Campiglia". Here it is obvious that the differences between the positive and negative situations is greater for the variety having a higher degree of productivity.

The group of factors considered influence the yield in the following order : climate (rainfall), soil, fertiliser :

	Nostrano dell' Isola.	Trenodi di Campiglia.
	quintals per ha.	quintals per ha.
Rainfall . . .	27·9	18·7
Soil . . .	20·0	9·0
Fertiliser . . .	7·0	5·4

Each of these values (three for "Nostrano dell' Isola" and three for "Trenodi di Campiglia") represent the mean difference between positive and negative situations in relation to rainfall (absence of drought), to soil (very good–very poor soil), and to fertiliser (fertilised–non-fertilised).

As long as the variables at work are only soil and meteorological factors, while all the other variables have a common denominator, the six differences (for each variety) between fertilised and non-fertilised plots give us an organic series of values, and therefore a law which makes it possible to establish the action of fertiliser for any combination of natural and agrotechnic conditions, without incurring new experiments.

The case considered is very simple; in reality the number of factors which act on the yield is, in general, much larger. However, with very large numbers of variables the solution of the problem by our method is just as easy and quick, as we shall illustrate later.

From the point of view of the determination and utilisation of the results obtained, the proposed method offers the following practical advantages :

(1) Possibility of dividing the experimental work among many collaborators and of utilising the facts derived, independently of any limitations of space or time.

We have, in all, twelve plots in every research station or province; it is not necessary that a single person should be responsible for the twelve plots which can even be placed on twelve different farms and under the supervision of twelve different collaborators; this is provided that each one exactly follows the instructions given, so as not to invalidate the results of the experiment.

Operating in this manner, in twelve separate localities it may well be that several plots suffer from drought, while others have sufficient rainfall. Since, however, this situation may be observed in every province, the number of cases in which the phenomenon occurs tends to be practically constant and, in any case, each individual case with its particular yield must naturally be inserted into or united with its own group.

(2) Should blanks be drawn in certain cases, it will be possible to complete the trials carried out one year by repeating a limited number of experiments in opportunely chosen localities the year after, and this without having to repeat the trial completely.

No yields, as long as instructions are carried out, can be considered experimentally useless, for it is added to the mass of values previously recorded and makes successive approximations, in the statistical sense, all the more exact.

(3) With reference to the soil, to fertilisation and to the rain regime, any yield (it does not matter where and when determined, as long as the data relative to the entity of fertiliser employed, type of soil and rainfall sufficiency or insufficiency be stated in conformity with the instructions), finds its position in the general framework and can always be statistically utilised. Nothing is wasted, or lost !

(4) Without modifying the graph in its fundamental outline, it is always possible to determine the detailed effect of a particular variable, adapting, for instance, different amounts of the fertiliser used.

CHAPTER XXVI

ANALYSIS OF THE COMPONENTS OF YIELD

THE plan adopted for the geographical trials with maize may, by a very simple procedure as we shall now see, be developed into a general scheme to calculate and measure the effects of each of the multiple positive and negative causes influencing the yield.

In the formation of this scheme, topographical, agro-geological and agrotechnic situations must be considered separately; these may be pre-ordained, or are in any case known from the beginning of the trial and remain constant throughout it. These factors are different from the meteorological and biological (insects, diseases, etc.) factors, whose individual effect can be ascertained only at the end of the experiment.

Non-variable Situations. If, in the graph of the maize plant, we insert the couple "superficial working" (15 cm.) and "deep working" (30 cm.) of the soil in place of scarce and abundant fertilisation, we shall be able to measure the effects on yield of the working of the soil at two different depths using an identical procedure to that explained above.

However, instead of substituting, we can add the new pair of opposite factors into the table, so that :

Abundant fertilisation ⟨deep working of soil
shallow working of soil

Scarce fertilisation ⟨deep working of soil
shallow working of soil

Without in any way altering the graph and without in any way complicating the solution of the problem of the analysis of the yield, it is evident that we are now in the position of being able to develop the scheme, taking into consideration as many other components as we wish.

In a first attempt at general representation, we could adopt the following scheme for each single species (for herbaceous crops in general).

With regard to " soil ", as for all other variables, only the two extreme situations have been considered; good and poor :

(1) *Soil :* good and poor ;
(2) *Topographic situation :* flat and mountainous ;
(3) *Drainage :* well drained and badly drained ;
(4) *Irrigation :* irrigated and not irrigated ;
(5) *Working of soil :* deep and shallow ;
(6) *Fertilisation :* fertilised and not fertilised ;
(7) *Density of sowing :* normal and abnormal (seeds too close, or too far apart) ;
(8) *Preceding crop :* enriching or exhausting.

In order to avoid an excessive enlargement of the table, for typographical reasons, we have omitted couples Nos. 3, 4 and 7, limiting ourselves to a consideration of the soil (A), topography (B), working of the soil (C), fertilisation (D) and the preceding crop (E).

We thus have thirty-two situations in all, which can be obtained by combining the natural and agrotechnic factors under review in all possible ways (see Fig. 45), positive situations being marked with a white circlet, and negative ones with a black one.

We thus find a series of wholly positive values, as occurred with No. 1 :

(1) Enriching preceding culture.
(2) Abundant fertilisation.
(3) Deep working of the soil.
(4) Flat topographical conditions.
(5) Very good soil.

No. 12, on the other hand, gives the following combination :

(1) Exhausting preceding culture.
(2) No fertilisation.
(3) Deep working of soil.
(4) Hilly topography.
(5) Very good soil.

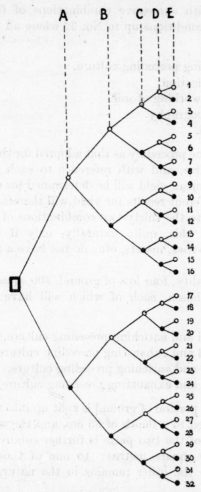

FIG. 45. TABLE OF THE COMBINATION OF NON-VARIABLE FACTORS.

A = Soil; B = Topography; C = Workability; D = Fertiliser; E = Preceding crop.

No. 23 corresponds to the following situation :

(1) Enriching preceding culture.
(2) No fertilisation.
(3) Shallow working of the soil.
(4) Flat topographical conditions.
(5) Poor soil.

And so on with successive combinations of favourable and unfavourable conditions up to No. 32 where all the factors are negative :

(1) Exhausting preceding culture.
(2) No fertilisation.
(3) Shallow working of soil.
(4) Hilly topography.
(5) Poor soil.

With the same procedure as that adopted for the geographical trials with maize, and with reference to each of these combinations, the mean yield will be determined for each situation. Thirty-two different results for yield will therefore be obtained corresponding to the thirty-two combinations of factors shown in the table : this, quite naturally, only if meteorological adversities, diseases, insects, etc., do not have a negative effect on the yield.

For each locality, four lots of ground, 400 square metres, will therefore be chosen, each of which will have the following requirements :

(1) Good soil and enriching preceding culture.
(2) Good soil and exhausting preceding culture.
(3) Poor soil and enriching preceding culture.
(4) Poor soil and exhausting preceding culture.

Each plot or portion of ground is split up into two parts, one of which is tilled to a depth of 35 cm. and the other to one of 15 cm. Each of the two parts is further subdivided into two plots each 100 square metres : to one of these is added a fertiliser, while the other remains in the natural state (non-manured).

These make sixteen plots in all, which, taken both on the flat and on the slopes, make a total of thirty-two plots for each trial in each separate region.

Variable Situations. The only variable factor which came into play in geographical trials with maize was rainfall (sufficient or insufficient rains).

It is, however, evident that with a similar procedure any number of variable factors could be considered without in any way modifying the structure and functions of the table.

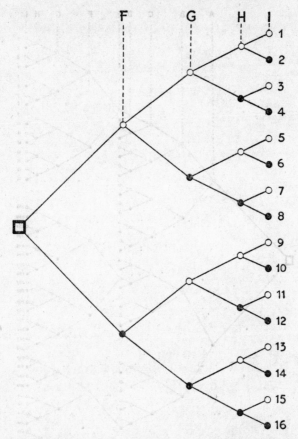

FIG. 46. TABLE OF COMBINATIONS OF THE VARIABLE FACTORS.
F = Rainfall; G = Rust; H = Rain in the fourth sub-period; I = Hot-spells.

With reference to wheat, we may consider :

(1) Drought (*F*).
(2) Rust (*G*).
(3) Excess rainfall (*H*).
(4) Hot spells (*I*).

Each of these factors can present a negative action (represented by the black circlet = drought, for instance) or a positive one (white circlet—e.g., absence of drought or, in other words, favourable rains) (Fig. 46).

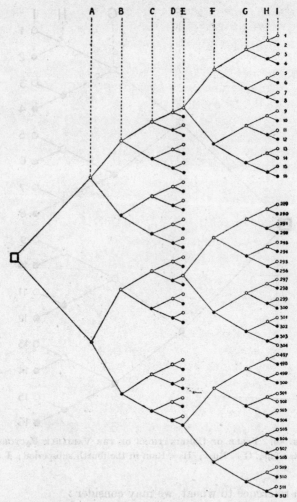

Fig. 47. General Table of all the Possible Combinations of the Factors Considered.

Here we thus find a group of sixteen possible combinations which can repeat itself for each of the thirty-two combinations of the non-variable factors; for the complex as a whole, of fixed and variable factors, we find a total of 512 possible combinations, to each of which there will correspond a particular yield (Fig. 47). The figure represents a reduced scheme of the general table which is quite adequate, however, as a demonstration of the above situation. The yield corresponding to No. 1 is therefore obtained when all factors are positive :

(1) No hot spell.
(2) No excess rainfall in the month after earing.
(3) No trace of rust.
(4) Favourable rainfall before earing.
(5) Enriching preceding culture.
(6) Abundant fertilisation.
(7) Deep working of the soil.
(8) Flat topographical situation.
(9) Very good soil.

The yield corresponding to No. 512 is, on the other hand, obtained when all factors are negative :

(1) Hot spell.
(2) Excess rainfall (from earing to harvest).
(3) Attacks of rust.
(4) Drought in the month before earing.
(5) Exhausting preceding culture.
(6) No fertilisation.
(7) Shallow working of the soil.
(8) Hilly topographical situation.
(9) Poor soil.

The table is in itself such a clear illustration that no further word of explanation is necessary. Let us take any number at random, say, 299 : we shall find that the corresponding yield is obtained under the following conditions :

(1) Absence of hot spell.
(2) Excess rainfall from earing to harvest.
(3) No attack from rust.
(4) Drought in the month preceding earing.
(5) Enriching preceding culture.
(6) No fertilisation.
(7) Deep working of the soil.
(8) Flat topographical situation.
(9) Poor soil.

382

AGRICULTURAL ECOLOGY

However, besides furnishing us with the yields obtainable from a particular variety under the most varied conditions of the natural and agrotechnic environment, the scheme enables us to separate and define the effect on yield of each individual variable, or of a number of factors, however chosen and grouped together.

The actual solution of the problem of the effect of single variables, be it a few or a number tending towards infinity, thus becomes easy and simple through the very construction of our scheme.

Let us calculate the loss imputable to a single factor, and let us suppose that the factor is a hot spell. All that we need do is to look for that series having white circlets and only a

TABL

	HGIF	HGIf	HgIf	HGif	hGIf	HGiF	HgiF	hGiF
ABCDE	46·8	32·1	21·5	18·0	19·5	27·5	21·8	23·0
ABCDe	40·1	29·1	18·8	15·4	17·0	23·9	17·6	21·3
ABcDE	37·9	27·0	18·0	13·9	15·8	23·5	19·8	20·1
ABCdE	32·1	20·8	15·4	14·1	13·1	18·9	16·1	17·0
ABcDe	32·3	23·1	14·4	13·4	14·5	19·9	14·2	15·0
ABCde	26·8	17·6	12·7	10·3	11·9	14·7	13·0	14·2
ABcdE	26·1	17·1	13·1	9·5	11·5	13·8	13·1	13·5
ABcde	21·9	13·0	8·6	8·2	9·8	10·4	7·3	10·2
AbCDE	38·3	25·7	19·0	14·6	18·4	24·5	17·1	22·9
AbCDe	31·2	20·1	17·6	12·0	14·4	19·5	12·0	19·0
AbcDE	29·1	18·4	17·1	11·1	13·4	19·5	13·0	16·6
AbCdE	20·4	14·2	10·9	8·8	8·6	17·8	9·2	11·3
AbcDe	23·8	14·4	13·3	9·1	10·6	13·7	10·6	13·2
AbCde	16·5	10·6	8·6	6·3	8·8	9·2	7·4	9·0
AbcdE	16·9	10·4	8·6	5·9	6·0	9·6	7·0	7·7
Abcde	12·5	7·2	5·6	4·9	5·2	6·9	5·7	6·4
aBCDE	25·8	17·1	13·7	10·2	12·9	13·0	11·7	12·7
aBCDe	14·1	8·5	7·6	5·7	5·1	7·6	6·0	7·5
aBcDE	20·5	13·4	10·4	8·5	10·0	10·4	9·3	10·0
aBCdE	17·4	11·4	9·2	8·0	8·3	8·6	7·4	8·2
aBcDe	13·4	8·8	6·6	4·1	4·1	7·1	4·8	6·2
aBCde	9·3	4·9	4·2	3·3	3·0	4·8	3·5	4·6
aBcdE	13·7	9·0	7·6	4·9	6·4	6·8	5·9	6·3
aBcde	7·1	3·7	2·6	2·6	2·1	3·7	2·7	3·5
abCDE	23·5	14·9	12·4	9·5	10·8	17·0	13·6	14·0
abCDe	14·8	9·1	8·5	5·9	7·4	9·2	8·0	9·2
abcDE	17·7	11·2	9·5	8·0	7·9	12·7	10·4	11·3
abCdE	17·2	11·0	8·9	6·0	6·3	11·2	9·2	9·9
abcDe	13·0	6·9	6·4	5·3	5·4	7·0	6·6	6·8
abCde	10·7	5·6	5·1	3·9	4·3	6·5	4·8	5·0
abcdE	13·6	7·4	6·0	5·2	4·6	8·8	6·6	6·9
abcde	6·2	3·7	3·2	2·6	3·2	4·1	3·9	3·8

black one corresponding to hot spell. Such is Series No. 2. The difference in yield existing between that established for Series No. 1 and that established for Series No. 2 is the measure of the loss imputable to a hot spell.

For the negative combination poor soil, no fertilisation and presence of hot spell by analogy we shall look for the series in which all other circlets are white and those corresponding to the letters A, D, I are black. This corresponds to Series No. 290, and the difference in the yield registered for Series No. 1 and for Series No. 290, measures the loss brought about by the joint action of the three negative situations. And so on for other factors or groups of factors.

In order, therefore, to establish the negative effect of physical

HgIF	hGIF	hgIF	hGif	Hgif	hgIf	hgiF	hgif	
22·5	29·0	20·6	12·6	17·2	14·8	14·9	10·0	ABCDE
20·8	26·7	17·3	11·5	14·5	12·3	12·7	9·2	ABCDe
20·5	23·9	16·2	10·8	13·4	11·9	13·0	7·8	ABcDE
17·1	18·8	14·7	11·0	9·9	9·2	9·6	7·8	ABCdE
15·6	20·5	13·3	9·6	11·5	9·8	11·1	6·0	ABcDe
14·5	17·3	11·8	7·4	7·8	7·8	8·1	6·2	ABCde
14·2	15·5	11·1	7·6	7·8	7·4	8·2	6·0	ABcdE
10·0	14·3	7·4	6·5	6·6	6·2	6·5	4·6	ABcde
21·3	27·5	19·9	11·3	12·7	10·6	11·3	7·4	AbCDE
18·0	23·2	16·3	8·6	10·2	7·4	9·6	5·8	AbCDe
18·4	20·8	15·1	8·4	9·6	7·9	8·3	5·7	AbcDE
13·8	12·8	10·5	5·9	7·9	6·1	6·4	4·1	AbCdE
14·1	17·6	12·4	7·0	7·6	6·6	7·1	4·7	AbcDe
11·0	10·3	8·0	5·1	6·1	4·6	5·5	3·3	AbCde
10·7	9·5	7·6	4·3	5·2	4·1	4·6	3·1	AbcdE
9·2	8·0	6·5	3·7	4·7	3·1	3·7	2·5	Abcde
15·2	17·5	14·2	9·5	9·5	8·0	8·9	5·2	aBCDE
8·5	8·7	6·8	4·7	4·6	4·5	4·5	2·6	aBCDe
11·9	14·0	11·4	7·2	7·2	6·9	7·2	4·2	aBcDE
11·5	11·1	10·2	5·7	5·6	6·3	6·6	3·2	aBCdE
6·7	7·1	3·9	3·8	3·9	3·6	4·5	2·1	aBcDe
5·4	4·9	4·2	2·5	2·4	2·4	2·5	1·5	aBCde
9·2	8·7	8·6	4·5	3·7	4·0	4·2	2·7	aBcdE
3·9	3·8	3·5	1·9	1·9	1·7	1·7	1·2	aBcde
17·0	17·7	11·8	7·3	8·9	7·9	8·4	6·0	abCDE
12·4	11·1	8·2	4·7	5·6	4·6	5·2	3·3	abCDe
13·9	14·0	10·0	6·0	7·0	6·4	7·2	4·2	abcDE
12·5	12·2	9·6	5·9	6·4	5·0	6·0	3·8	abCdE
8·2	8·7	6·7	3·6	4·5	3·4	4·2	2·2	abcDe
6·4	6·6	5·0	2·7	3·7	1·9	2·8	1·0	abCde
8·5	8·9	6·3	3·5	3·6	3·2	4·2	2·2	abcdE
4·5	5·2	3·9	2·1	2·6	1·2	2·3	0·8	abcde

or of agrotechnic factors, taken separately or in the most varied combinations, all that has to be done is to choose that series among the 512 where the factor or factors in question are represented by one or more black circlets, and therefore in a negative position, while all other factors are positive.

The difference between the yield corresponding to this series and that corresponding to the first (where all fixed and variable factors are in a positive position) will give us the measure of the negative effects imputable to that particular factor or group of factors.

Without this pattern, without this framework, which we have originated, all these separate and disjointed combinations would naturally appear as a confused tangle, a skein so intricate that the thought of analysing the scientific and technical problem of bio-ambiental relationship might be considered as being out of the question.

Suppose, in fact, that the rectilinear segments within the framework of the scheme—the black circlets, the white ones, the numbers (corresponding to the different yields)—were all small pieces of wood, separated and placed on a plane as indicated in the scheme, and imagine that a gust of wind came and whirled them all up together. The yields, indicated by numbers, separated from their causes or components, would lose their value and become a meaningless jumble. We should then have a state of anarchy of the yields! Once the paths which connect them break up and become confused, we are no longer able to undertake that analytical examination so amply illustrated above, that gave us a means of measuring the action of any factor or group of factors by isolating it not from the whole, but within the whole, and thereby appearing as a function of all the other natural and agrotechnic factors acting on yield.

In the year 1953–54, a series of experiments with the soft wheat variety " Mentana " were carried out in order to obtain for the first time the yields corresponding to the 512 combinations for the nine factors in favourable and unfavourable situations. The results obtained are being elaborated in order to establish the rules which govern the hitherto unknown relationships of the nine factors.

For the reader's interest I have set out in Table A on pages 382, 383 the total results of the experiment.

The reader when considering attentively the table will probably be struck by the singular harmony of all the figures. There is no contradiction in terms and the reason is that following our method each yield is controlled and defined by all the others so that the table becomes a well organised unitary complex. This clearly indicates the exactitude and the significance of the scheme in relation with experimental research.

Below are given some examples concerning the results of the elaboration of the experimental figures.

When, in a positive complex of factors, one of them becomes negative, we observe a consequent diminishment of the yield. The gradual passage of other factors to a negative position increases the losses but not proportionally to the number of the factors involved. In fact with the decrease of the yield the effect of the negative action is progressively reduced.

When, on the contrary, in a negative complex of factors, one of them becomes positive, we observe a consequent increase of the yield. The gradual passage of other factors to a positive position will progressively increase the yield. In fact with the increase of the mass of the product the effect of the positive action is progressively greater.

Considering separately the fixed and variable factors we obtain the following tables.

For the fixed factors :

No. of factors.	Quintals per ha. total.	Quintals per ha. for each factor.
Negative.	*Losses.*	*Losses.*
1	12·8	12·8
2	23·1	11·5
3	30·1	10·0
4	35·3	8·8
5	40·6	8·0
Positive.	*Gains.*	*Gains.*
1	5·2	5·2
2	8·7	4·3
3	20·6	6·8
4	28·3	7·1
5	40·6	8·0

C C

In the third column we give the values of the quotient obtained by dividing the total loss by the number of factors involved. The figures confirm what has been already stated (page 385).

The same situation is observed in relation with the variables factors.

No. of factors.	Quintals per ha.	Quintals per ha. for each factor.
Negative.	Losses.	Losses.
1	19·0	19·0
2	26·1	13·0
3	30·2	10·1
4	36·8	9·2
Positive.	Gains.	Gains.
1	4·9	4·9
2	10·7	5·3
3	17·7	5·8
4	36·8	9·2

Below we give the losses due to each factor acting negatively (in relation with the maximum yield of 46·8 quintals per ha. obtained when all the factors are favourable).

Exhausting preceding culture (e) . = 6·7 quintal per ha.
Hilly topography (b) . . . = 8·5
Shallow working of the soil (c) . . = 8·9 ,, ,,
No fertilisation (d) . . . . = 14·7 ,, ,,
Poor soil (a) . . . . . = 21·0 ,, ,,
Drought (f) . . . . . = 14·7 ,, ,,
Lodging (h) . . . . . = 17·8 ,, ,,
Hot spell (i) . . . . . = 19·3 ,, ,,
Rust (g) . . . . . = 24·3 ,, ,,

When two factors act contemporarily (in a negative position) three cases may occur :

(1) The total gains or the total losses are equal to the sum of the proportional gains or losses due to the two factors involved.

For example, the couple : shallow working of the soil and lodging, acting simultaneously, give a loss of 26·7 quintals per ha., while shallow working alone gives a loss of 8·9 and lodging alone of 17·8, a total of 26·7 quintals per ha.

(2) The negative action is accentuated.

For instance, the couple : poor soil and exhausting preceding culture, acting contemporarily give a loss of 37·2 quintals per ha., while poor soil alone causes a loss of 21·0 quintals and exhausting preceding culture a loss of 6·7 quintals, a total of 27·7 quintals per ha.

(3) The negative action is diminished.

For example, the couple : rust and hot spell, acting simultanously give a loss of 25·0 quintals per ha. while rust alone causes a loss of 24·3 and hot spell of 19·3, a total of 43·6 quintals per ha.

We consider now three factors acting contemporarily : soil, fertiliser and rotation.   We observe that :

(1) In the good soils the negative effect of the lack of fertiliser overcome the negative effect of the rotation. In fact we have :

Quint.
per ha.

good soil + enriching preceding culture + fertiliser   = 46·8
good soil + *exhausting preceding culture* + fertiliser   = 40·1

difference   6·7

good soil + enriching preceding culture + fertiliser   = 46·8
good soil + enriching preceding culture + *no fertiliser* = 32·1

difference   14·7

(2) In the poor soils, on the other hand, the negative effect of rotation overcomes the negative effect of the lack of fertiliser.

Quint.
per ha.

poor soil + enriching preceding culture + fertiliser   = 25·8
poor soil + *exhausting preceding culture* + fertiliser   = 14·1

difference   11·7

poor soil + enriching preceding culture + fertiliser   = 25·8
poor soil + enriching preceding culture + *no fertiliser* = 17·4

difference   8·4

Following the elaboration here indicated it is possible to study the relationships for an ever increasing number of factors.

Before the study of bio-ambiental relationships had been resolved by our system in a precise manner, we were in a situation comparable to alchemy as it is related to chemistry.

Our method is based on distinguishing the relatively few elementary situations, just as the simple bodies in chemistry are relatively few.

In just the same way as an innumerable number of compounds are derived from the combination of the elements, so from the combination of the few elementary situations are derived those many and varied ambiental combinations which, in the past, made the representation of environment an inextricable tangle of values and relationships.

In the case particularly referred to, from the nine elementary situations are derived the 512 compound ones, arranged in such a way as to be easily identifiable and controlled in all their aspects and for all the elements composing them.

CHAPTER XXVII

UTILISATION OF ANALYTICAL RESULTS FOR THE SOLUTION OF ECOLOGICAL PROBLEMS

THE exactitude of the first conclusion derived from the application of this method is thus demonstrated—namely, the determination of the effects which the single variable or group of variables have on the yield.

Examining now the second part of the problem, we wish to demonstrate how geographical trials permit us to pass from the spacial to the temporal section of the phenomenon, calculating with good approximation the mean results which will be obtained when adopting one variety or another, one or other fertilisation programme, etc., at any place where that particular fertiliser had never been previously adopted, and the new variety never cultivated.

To do this we shall first examine the distribution of rainfall during the critical period for maize in space (numerous localities spread over a very wide area), and in time (a period of years for a single locality).

Distribution of Rainfall in Space

Rainfall may be split up into classes of 5 mm. each : 0·0 mm., 0·1–5·0 mm., 5·1–10 mm., 10·1–15·0 mm., and so on.

The table on p. 390 gives the rainfall figures for a hundred stations spread over Italy for 1932 for the month corresponding to the critical period.

In the second column is found a frequency of four for the 0·0 mm. value, implying that in four of the 100 stations considered there was no precipitation whatsoever during the critical period.

For the 30·1–35·0 mm. value there is a frequency of 13, showing that in thirteen out of the 100 stations there were between 30·1 and 35 mm. of rainfall in the critical period, and so on.

389

Values.	Frequency.	Values.	Frequency.
0·0	4	100·1–105	1
0·1– 5	3	105·1–110	2
5·1– 10	8	110·1–115	2
10·1– 15	7	115·1–120	1
15·1– 20	5	120·1–125	—
20·1– 25	9	125·1–130	1
25·1– 30	4	130·1–135	1
30·1– 35	13	135·1–140	1
35·1– 40	8	140·1–145	—
40·1– 45	2	145·1–150	—
45·1– 50	2	150·1–155	—
50·1– 55	3	155·1–160	—
55·1– 60	2	160·1–165	—
60·1– 65	2	165·1–170	—
65·1– 70	3	170·1–175	—
70·1– 75	2	175·1–180	2
75·1– 80	4	180·1–185	1
80·1– 85	2	185·1–190	—
85·1– 90	1	190·1–195	—
90·1– 95	1	195·1–200	—
95·1–100	2	200 and more	1

The sum of all the frequencies will naturally add up to 100—the total number of stations.

It is quite clear that the loss imputable to drought will be the higher the lower (in general) is the quantity of rain fallen during the critical period. Since, however, all the values are represented from 0·0 to 40·1–45 mm., the mean of all yields in stations with rainfall below the equivalent (46 mm.) will, with sufficient approximation, give the measure of the mean yield which the variety considered supplies under unfavourable pluviometric conditions.

From 46 mm. upward, the yield increases with the increasing of rainfall. However, following the same procedure adopted for drought, we can obtain the mean yield which the variety taken into consideration gives in favourable pluviometric conditions. For such purpose we calculate the mean of the products in the stations with precipitation superior to the equivalent for drought (practically from the class 45·1–55·0 upward).

With regard to rainfall in the critical period we find there are two situations only in relation to yield : in regime of drought and in regime of sufficient rainfall.

Similarly, the effects of excess rainfall, excess and deficient temperatures, of insects, diseases, etc., may be considered by means of the same procedure.

For rust, for instance, we find a mean yield in all stations in which rust did not appear and a mean yield in all those in which it made its attacks, from the lightest to the most virulent.

Distribution of Rainfall in Time

Below in the table we give the frequency of the classes of rainfall values in 5 millimetre groups during the critical period of maize for the Central Observatory of Florence for a century.

In the preceding case it was " space " that was considered : we had 100 observing stations spread over a wide surface for a year; in this second case, in which " time " is our subject, 100 years are considered for a single station.

For this station (Florence), as emerges from an examination of the table, almost all the values are represented continuously (with a few exceptions corresponding to the higher values) from 0·0 up to 110·1–115·0 mm.

Class, mm.	Frequency.	Class, mm.	Frequency.
0·0	3	75·1– 80	3
0·1– 5	9	80·1– 85	2
5·1–10	9	85·1– 90	—
10·1–15	12	90·1– 95	3
15·1–20	9	95·1–100	—
20·1–25	9	100·1–105	2
25·1–30	4	105·1–110	1
30·1–35	3	110·1–115	2
35·1–40	7	115·1–120	—
40·1–45	3	120·1–125	—
45·1–50	3	125·1–130	—
50·1–55	3	130·1–135	—
55·1–60	3	135·1–140	—
60·1–65	4	140·1–145	—
65·1–70	2	145·1–150	1
70·1–75	3		

We may observe that practically all rainfall values are represented in the table, as had been seen when considering 100 stations in a single year.

In spite of the diversity in the frequencies of the single values for the temporal and spacial situations, the mean yield at all the stations in which total rainfall proved to be inferior to the drought equivalent can, in practice, at a first approximation, be considered quite close to the mean yields obtained in Florence in droughty years (within reasonable limits, all other conditions being equal).

Similar considerations can be made with regard to the mean yield obtained in favourable years.

.   .   .

These analogies offer the possibility of passing from the spacial to the temporal section of the phenomenon, and of applying the results of geographical trials to any station.

In adopting the expressions " mean yield " and " mean increase ", the above formulated concept becomes implicit : the adaptation of crops to the atmospheric environment is not in relation to weather, but to climate, which is " mean weather "

Hence it is the frequency in a 10-year period, of favourable and unfavourable situations through excess or deficiency, which must act as guide in the task of fitting crops to the environment.

It is now sufficient, for any place, to refer to a particular type of soil and determine the frequency of drought based on pluvio-metric registrations of the meteorological observatory.

As an example, I quote the territory of Imola (Romagna), where the rains which most particularly influence the yield of maize are those falling between the 21st June and 20th July, this being the critical period.

Since the drought equivalent is 46 mm., we note that the phenomenon repeats itself with a frequency of six times in 10 years, there being therefore 4 years with favourable meteoro-logical situations and 6 years with adverse ones.

In examining the situation, on the best soils for maize without fertilisation and with reference to the two varieties " Nostrano dell' Isola" and "Trenodi di Campiglia", we have (see Fig. 42) :

For " Nostrano dell' Isola "

$$46 \cdot 4 \times 4 = 185 \cdot 6$$
$$18 \cdot 5 \times 6 = \underline{111 \cdot 0}$$
$$\text{Mean :} \quad 29 \cdot 66$$

For " Trenodi di Campiglia "

$$35 \cdot 4 \times 4 = 141 \cdot 6$$
$$16 \cdot 5 \times 6 = \underline{99 \cdot 0}$$
$$\text{Mean :} \quad 24 \cdot 06$$

We may affirm that on the best soils of this territory, " Nos-trano dell' Isola ", though never having been cultivated there before, would give the approximate mean yields above indicated thus having the right of preference over " Trenodi di Cam-piglia ".

Let us see what happens in the less suitable soils :

For " Nostrano dell' Isola " we have :

$$23 \cdot 7 \times 4 = 94 \cdot 8$$
$$2 \cdot 8 \times 6 = \underline{16 \cdot 8}$$
$$\text{Mean}: \quad 11 \cdot 16$$

For " Trenodi di Campiglia " :

$$24 \cdot 7 \times 4 = 98 \cdot 8$$
$$7 \cdot 2 \times 6 = \underline{43 \cdot 2}$$
$$\text{Mean}: \quad 14 \cdot 2$$

In the worst soils of the territory, " Trenodi di Campiglia " would thus be preferred to " Nostrano dell' Isola ".

· · · · ·

We have examined a very simple case with an extremely limited number of variables : one only, in fact, with regard to the atmospheric environment, absence or presence of drought. But even with a much higher number of variables, the solution of the problem dealing with passage from a spacial to a temporal aspect is just as easy and quick.

Given that the meteorological adversities in play are the four (see Fig. 46) considered with reference to wheat, it is clear that the combinations in the table integrate the situation for any place. All that is to be done is to multiply the yields of the corresponding series by the frequencies of the adversities at that place, frequencies which are derived from the equivalents.

If for a given place chosen at random we find, for instance,

4 favourable years,
2 with rust, drought and hot spells,
1 with excess rainfall,
2 with drought and hot spells,
1 with rust and excess rainfall,

in order to calculate the mean yield obtainable, the yields corresponding to series 1, 14, 3, 10, 7 (see fig. 46) are multiplied by the frequencies above, the products so obtained are summed and divided by ten.

With reference to the variety " Mentana " (see Table A) we have the following corresponding yields.

Conditions.	Frequency per 10 years.	Yield in quintals, ha.	
		Year.	10 years.
Favourable	4	46·8	187·2
Rust, drought and hot spells .	2	17·2	34·4
Excess rainfall . . .	1	29·0	29·0
Drought and hot spells . .	2	18·0	36·0
Rust and excess rainfall . .	1	20·6	20·6
Average yield = 30·72 quintals, ha.		Total	307·2

The average yield of " Mentana ", all other factors being favourable, is therefore 30·72 quintals per ha.

. . . . . .

The results of geographical trials integrated with the differential analysis of yields therefore give the possibility of :

(1) determining the yields which a variety can give in all the possible combinations of the natural and agrotechnic environmental factors, each one left to vary freely within the extreme limits of variability ;

(2) isolating and measuring the effect on yield of any factor or group of factors, agrotechnic and natural, as a function of the environment as a whole ;

(3) determining the mean yield of a variety in a locality in which that particular variety had never before been cultivated ; the mean increase in yield obtainable with the adoption of a new fertiliser formula, or a few system of working the soil, etc., which had not previously been the subject of experiment at that station.

Agricultural Ecology thus offers a concrete basis for the organisation of agricultural experimentation and for the solution of problems concerned with a better adaptation of crops to the physical environment.

METHODOLOGY

In Agricultural Ecology, the yield constitutes the point of departure for all research carried out on the climate, soil and plant in order to realise the most favourable bio-ambiental relationship.

The environment with its components acts as a whole (active-unit) on the plant which, in its turn, reacts as an independent physio-morphological complex (reacting-unit). The order of relationships between these two groups of values is measured by the yield.

For an evaluation of the atmospheric environment, we adopt the equivalents which enable us to represent and summarise climate by the frequencies of normal and abnormal situations through excess or deficiency of rain, temperature, etc. Since to these three situations there correspond three different mean yields, it may be said that climate is represented as a function of the said yield.

Requirements in temperature and rainfall vary greatly from one plant to another. It suffices to recall that in order to obtain perfect maturity of the " Deglet-nur " date, it is essential that during the sub-period, maximum temperatures do not fall below 45° C.—temperature which would scorch an entire grape or olive harvest.

The equivalents therefore must be determined for each plant separately.

This is not all : for the same plant, requirements vary in the different sub-periods, so that while for the maturing of wheat the deficiency equivalent from maturity to harvest is 14° C., during the period of winter rest a mean temperature of 10° C. for the winter forms turns out to be decidedly excessive. This is so because the wheat for its complete development requires (at that time) low temperatures which reduce the velocity of growth to a minimum. If this state is lacking, as clearly emerges from research on vernalisation, the plant will later grow in a purely vegetative sense without earing or, at any rate, formation of the reproductive organs will be greatly delayed, exposing the crop to the dangers of hot spells, and to a consequent decrease of the yield.

The equivalents must therefore be determined for each of the sub-periods into which the cycle of the plant is divided.

By the use of the equivalents, integrated by an evaluation of losses through excess or deficiency, we obtain the " climatic formulae " which summarises the positive or negative atmospheric values in the various zones for each single crop.

In the study of soils for Ecology we first of all differentiate the various soils and (agrotechnic and climatic conditions being equal) distinguish one from the other on the basis of their behaviour towards each crop. Once the soil units have been determined, the problems relative to the discernment of soils is studied through two successive phases :

First Phase. In each locality those pedological components are studied which can furnish an explanation for the behaviour of local soils towards the single cultures (determination of chemical capacity, water balance, workability and structure).

395

On the basis of these reports, a measure of the positive and negative pedological values, with reference to each culture, is obtained in every zone.

Second Phase. Once the classification of soil-units is undertaken on all or part of the area of distribution of each crop, we can turn to the problems concerned with the study of the pedological characteristics in their totality and in relation to the individual crop cultures separately.

Referring to wheat, for instance, 50 soil-units considered optimal and 50 which are considered very unsuitable for this culture, are chosen. From this material we may then determine :

(*a*) the attributes common to all very good soils;
(*b*) the attributes common to all unsuitable soils.

By means of this procedure the solution of the problem of the relation-ship between soils and the various crops is made much easier. This has been made possible for the first time by the definition and determination of the soil-unit.

. . . . . .

The series of soils repeated along the climatic axis enables us to repre-sent the physical environment in its whole (climatic–soil units), perfectly co-ordinating the meteorological and pedological factors, and thus offering that measured representation of the physical environment which is indispensable to the agronomist, the economist and the genetic-ist in order to face those problems—and they are in the majority—for the solution of which an understanding of the physical environment is essential.

. . . . . .

However important the effect of the factors of the physical environ-ment may be, it is evident that they do not represent the only com-ponents of the yield; this is also affected, and in notable measure, by artificial and agrotechnic factors (cultural provision). To reach the yield therefore through the study of its components, it is necessary to study the problem of a global influence by all environmental factors, natural and artificial, indiscriminately, in order to determine the effect of each one of them. Up to the present day a great obstacle had prevented this determination, an obstacle which may be summarised by the following conception : " In order to determine the effects of any one factor, it must be made to vary within its extreme limits, all other factors remaining constant," and this in an open field is impossible.

With the geographical trials and the differential analysis of yields such an obstacle has been overcome, and it becomes easy to evaluate the possible yields in the most varied ambiental conditions and to isolate the action of each factor or group of factors not outside the complex but within it—i.e., as a function of all the other factors which act on the yield.

. . . . . .

After having considered the environmental factors, we now pass to the study of the properties of the plant, the reacting-unit, recalling that the yield is the result of two main components : productivity and resistance. Here also it is the environment which serves to consolidate and bring these characteristics to our attention.

In a first approximation we have implicitly admitted that in par-ticularly favourable environmental conditions the yield grading for a group of varieties gives us a grading of productivity. Conversely, the grading of yields in particularly unfavourable environmental conditions corresponds to a hardiness grading (sum of resistances).

Such representation may almost seem ingenuous, it might provoke discussion or criticism, but it is undoubted that the procedure is rational and meets fully the requirements of a first good approximation of the degrees of productivity and hardiness.

We thus reach, at a first stage, the " reasoned yields " which enable us to measure the degrees of productivity and resistance on the basis of the effects of ambiental factors on the crop.

The causes now need to be explained.

The relativity of yield was first time affirmed by the present author. Yield is not an absolute value, but the result of the relation between the two fundamental components of the same yield : " productivity " and " resistance " (hardiness). We call ecological characteristics the morphological and physiological values which result from and are correlated with the different degrees of " productivity " and " resistance ".

In the determination of such ecological characteristics the system velocity–mass–structure is of fundamental importance.

Small velocity, great expansion of the mass and macrocellular structure constitute a system correlated with productivity, while the great velocity, small mass and microcellular system is correlated with resistance (" hardiness ").

From a series of preliminary determinations it is now clear that an evaluation of the characteristics of velocity–mass–structure serves to explain, in at least 70% of cases, the behaviour of any one variety in the most varied environmental conditions. Such an evaluation is made even clearer schematically by the fact that between productivity and hardiness, beyond certain limits at least, there exists a natural incompatability.

In certain cases, however, this incompatability does not appear, so that the system velocity–mass–structure can no longer explain the behaviour of the plant. This is the general case when from a consideration of hardiness we pass to one of separate resistances.

With reference to rust, for instance, to lodging and to hot spells, a higher degree of resistance may even be encountered with a small velocity of development, great mass and macrocellular structure to which corresponds high productivity.

With the evaluation of separate resistances added to the velocity–mass–structure system, we shall be able to explain the behaviour of the single varieties in, perhaps, 95% of the cases.

We have left a hypothetical margin of 5% for those very few cases which cannot yet be explained by the velocity–mass–structure system, nor by a study of separate resistances, and this makes it necessary to continue the investigation until even the smallest detail of a physiological and morphological nature has been explained : small details which are in such cases of dominating importance in bio-ambiental relationships. We have already mentioned the " Manipeba " variety of manioca, which loses its leaves in periods of drought, and is thus enabled temporarily to resist drought, even though it has a high degree of productivity.

Taking as our starting point the " reasoned yields " which are a synthesis of the complex of bio-ambiental relationships, we reach our determination of ecological characteristics by three successive steps :

(1) the velocity–mass–structure system;
(2) the separate resistances;
(3) the separate characteristics of resistance.

These ecological characteristics can, as we have seen, be for the whole body of the plant, or for small details of a structural or functional nature which are in any and every way an expression of the fundamental architecture of the plant.

Here, too, as for the factors of the environmental complex, the single characteristics may be isolated not outside but within the body of the plant itself—i.e., as a function of all the other intrinsic characteristics.

.   .   .   .   .

In our treatise the dominating action of the environment in the binomial plant-environment has made itself more and more evident.

The manifestation of any characteristic, morphological or physiological, is the result of a reaction between a determined value of the hereditary material and a determined value of the environment. Between the genotype and the complex of characteristics which integrate the framework of the complete being, development inserts itself, and during this development ambiental factors influence the living organism and can, in certain cases, in contrast to the characteristics of the hereditary material, render impossible or reduce the manifestation of a certain characteristic.

But if, passing over the individual development and going outside the limits imposed by one generation, we survey the whole process of evolution of the species within the phylogenetical framework, we cannot but remark upon the powerful moulding or modelling action of the environment, which, in every zone, eliminates those individuals which are less suitable, and which in the end permit the survival only of those forms which respond to the requirements of an equilibrium between being and environment.

We could almost use as a comparison the evolution of the relief during which the fluvial erosion chisels and successively moulds the morphological traits of the mainland until, at last, the whole mass of rock above the profile of equilibrium of the river system has been demolished and brought away.

Environment in the course of time acts as a formless stream of energy which, however, develops an undoubtedly formative action on living beings : it directs and selects the successive adaptations which, within the architectonic limits for each species, indicate the main lines of the natural evolution of the living forms.

GLOSSARY

Meteorological Equivalents

By meteorological equivalents—thermic and pluviometric—are meant the degrees of temperature or mm. of rainfall which separate normal from abnormal conditions through deficiency or excess of rainfall or temperature, respectively.

(The equivalents allow us to represent climate by the frequencies of normal and abnormal situations.)

Growth

Growth is the increase in mass, even when this is accompanied by slow or imperfect development.

Development

The development of a plant is the series of morphological and physiological transformations which mark the evolution of its biological cycle in a continuous manner, from germination (or budding) to the complete maturity of fruits or seeds.

Phases of Development

By phases of development of a plant must be understood the modifications of a morphological and physiological nature which, in a brief space of time, greatly alter the plant and so make it vary its water and temperature requirements in the different sub-periods of the biologic cycle.

Sub-period of Development

The sub-period of development of a plant is the interval of time within two successive phases, during which the needs of the plant remain constant, or vary in a single direction.

Critical Periods

By critical periods of a plant in relation to an environmental factor is intended the interval in the biological cycle during which the plant presents the greatest susceptibility towards this factor with regard to its effects on yield, both positive and negative.

Period of Rest (lethargy : active or passive)

The interval of the vegetative period during which the plant is practically indifferent to the action of a given factor, either positive or negative.

Climoscope

A table in which the meteorological values are divided into groups corresponding to the single sub-periods of the vegetative cycle of the plant.

Climatic Formulae

These are given by the symbols for excess and deficiency of rain and temperature with the indications relative to sub-periods and frequencies.

Axis of Frequency

The straight line joining the values of frequency from 0 to 100% for each of the following adverse phenomena :

Deficient rainfall	.	.	.	.	DP
Excess rainfall	.	.	.	.	EP
Deficient temperature	.	.	.	.	DT
Excess temperature	:	.	.	.	ET

Curve of Frequency

The curve joining together all the points in which, with reference to a certain adverse environmental factor, the same frequency is observed.

Zone of Frequency

The area found between two successive curves of frequency.

Climatic Axes

The straight lines formed by the two axes of frequency for deficiency and excess, joined together at zero. We will thus have a climatic axis for rains and a climatic axis for temperatures.

Thermo-pluviometric Diagram

The diagram which integrates the area of distribution of a plant. It is formed by the two climatic axes crossing each other perpendicularly on the zero and by a series of circles and parallels traced in correspondence with the frequency values (from 0 to 10) for excess and deficiency of rain and temperature.

Area of Distribution

The area of distribution of a plant is the complex of the points in which it is, or in which it may be, cultivated.

Physiographic Zone

A portion of the thermo-pluviometric diagram or a part of the area of distribution of a plant, in which similar bio-atmospheric conditions are found.

Valley-unit

From a climatological point of view, we call " valley-unit " the complex of geo-morphological situations (dimension, form and orientation) of a valley or of a basin of a river, which give to the air masses enclosed within it particular characteristics which distinguish them from the masses of air of the surrounding atmosphere. The valley-unit links the general climatic conditions with the complex of micro-climatic details.

Soil-unit

In Ecology we distinguish the soils one from the other on the basis of their behaviour towards cultivated plants, and behaviour measured by yield. Each soil therefore constitutes a particular value which cannot be further subdivided and which we call " soil-unit ".

(The soil-unit integrates and summarises in the form of a resultant all the pedological components, all the causes therefore known and unknown which determine the special behaviour of the soil under consideration, towards each cultivated plant.)

Yield

Yield is the expression of a relationship between plant and environment which integrates all the actions, positive and negative, which have
acted on the plant during its development.   The yield of the different
forms and varieties of cultivated plants is not an absolute value, but
the result of a compromise between productivity and resistance to the
negative factors of the environment.

Productivity

The productivity of a plant [1] is its capacity to utilise the environmental means at its disposal, so that in favourable ambiental conditions
the increase of these availabilities corresponds to successive increases in
product up to a maximum yield, the entity of which is in direct relationship to the degree of productivity.

Resistance

The resistance of a plant to a certain adverse factor is its capacity of
developing in the unfavourable conditions determined by this factor,
and this in such a way that, to an intensification of the negative cause,
there corresponds successive decreases in yield decreases which will be
smaller the higher the degree of resistance.

Hardiness

By hardiness we mean the sum of resistances—that is to say, the
capacity of the plant to develop in adverse agrotechnic and natural
conditions, reacting to the gradual worsening of the environmental
situation with decreases in product decreases which will be smaller the
higher is the degree of hardiness.

Ecological Characteristics

The morphological and physiological values correlated with the
different degrees of productivity and resistance, the two fundamental
components of yield.
(These characteristics can affect the whole body of the plant, or manifest themselves in certain organs or even in small details of structure,
composition or aspect.)

Ecotype

By ecotype we mean the aggregation of individuals which, independently of different botanical characteristics, present the same
complex of morphological and physiological values, making them particularly suited to the environmental conditions of a particular physiographic zone ; to which conditions, in the course of time, through
somatic and genetical selection, they have adapted themselves perfectly.

Law of Velocity–Mass–Structure

Velocity of development, mass and structure are in direct relationship to the productivity and hardiness of a plant in the sense that a
small velocity, great expansion of the mass and macrocellular structure
seem to summarise and convey all the characteristics of productivity ;
while high velocity, contraction of the mass and microcellular structure

---

[1] When we speak of " plant " we naturally refer to the different
varieties of a species which are distinguished one from the other by the
different degrees of productivity and resistance.

seem to summarise and convey the characteristics of hardiness. (Between productivity and hardiness an evident incompatability manifests itself beyond certain limits.)

Separate Resistances

Resistances which are compatible with a high grade of productivity.

Separate Characteristics of Resistance

By these are intended small details of a morphological, physiological or bio-chemical nature which, notwithstanding their limited value, represent the real cause or at least the most evident cause, of a particular degree of productivity and of resistance.

Differential Analysis of Yields

The method which gives the possibility of defining and measuring the action of any variable acting on yield as a function of all the other variables which affect it.

BIBLIOGRAPHY

Chapter I

AZZI, G. Effect of meteorological factors on the yield of maize in Umbria (Italian). *Il Coltivatore*, No. 34, Casale Monf. 1927.

AZZI, G. The meteorological equivalents and agricultural climatology (Italian) *La Meteorologia Pratica* Vol. XIV, No. 1, Perugia 1933.

AZZI, G. Geometrical demonstration of the stability of equivalents (Italian). *Rivista di Ecologia* Vol. II, No. 3, Perugia 1952.

DE ALMEIDA FIGUEIBO, F. Research on agricultural meteorology undertaken in the experimental plots of the Institute of Agronomy of Lisbon (Portuguese). *Boletin de Associacão Agricultura Portoguesa* An. XXI, Lisbon 1919.

Chapter II

AZZI, G. The phenological seasons in Italy (Italian). *Rivista Meteorico-Agraria*, An. 35, No. 14, Rome 1914.

AZZI, G. The development of the vine in Brazil in a regime of constantly high temperatures (Italian). *La Meteorologia Pratica*, An. 19, No. 2, 1938.

BALTADORI, A. The pluviometric equivalents of the fig-tree (Italian). *Annali della Facoltà di Agraria*, Vol. 8, Perugia 1952.

BRICCOLI, M. The climate of olive-tree in Italy (Italian). *Nuovi Annali dell' Agricoltura*, Vol. 5, Rome 1925.

BRICCOLI, M. Effect of rainfall on the development of the fruits of the almond (Italian). *Nuova Agricoltura*, No. 2, Rome 1928.

BROUNOV, P. I. The importance of climate and weather in agriculture—Organisation of agricultural meteorological stations (Russian). Tipographie Vincke, St. Petersburg 1904.

DE GASPERI, L. The phenology of the vine in Italy (Italian). *La Meteorologia Pratica*, An. 15, No. 3, 1934.

DELOLME, A. Yield per hectare of peanut in Senegal (French). *Oléagineux*, An. 3, No. 5, Paris 1948.

HENRY, Y., and DE VISME. Rice culture in Indochine (French). Imprimerie d'Extrème-Orient, Hanoi 1928.

HOPKINS, D. A. The laws which regulate the march of periodical phenomena in life can influence agronomical research and agricultural practice. *Monthly Weather Review*, U.S. Dept. of Agr., Supplement No. 9, Washington 1918.

KRASSITCHKOV, A. Influence of the meteorological factors on the development and yields of apple-tree, on the basis of the data collected by the Meteorological–Agricultural Station annexed to the School of Pomology of Pensa (Russian). *Works of Agricultural Meteorology*, Fasc. 13, St. Petersburg 1914.

MARCUCCI, G. B. The cryptophases in agricultural economy. Physio-morphological observations on the pre-budding and pre-flowering of the olive-tree (Italian). *Olivicoltura*, No. 3, Rome 1948.

QAFZEZI. N. Experimental researches on the water requirements of beans (Albanian) in *Bujqësija*, Nos. 20–21, Tirana 1942.

ROCCHI, M. The development of fruits of the cucurbitacea and the water balance (Italian). *La Meteorologia Pratica*, An. 7, No. 2, 1936.

SCHNELLE, F. Phenological characteristics of typical climatic regions of Europe (German). *Petermann's Geographische Mitteilungen*, Vol. 91, No. 3, Berlin 1935.

SCHNELLE, F. Introduction to the problem of Agricultural Meteorology (German). *Schriften über Neuzeitlichen Landbau*, Heft No. 11, Bonn 1948.

SCHNELLE, F. The meteorological phenological conditions in relation to catch crops in the region of Hessen (German). *Landwirtschaftlicher Informationsdienst*, Sonderheft, Frankfurt 1948.

SEMADENI, K. I. Relationships between yields in apples and rainfall in the period 1901–1908 (Russian). *Works in Agricultural Meteorology*, Fasc. 5, 1909.

Chapter III

AZZI, G. Experimental researches on the critical period of wheat in relation to rainfall (Italian). *Nuovi Annali del Ministero dell' Agricoltura*, An. 1, No. 2, Rome 1921.

AZZI, G. Effect of variations of water content of the soil in the critical period of wheat (Italian). *Il Coltivatore*, An. 18, No. 28, 1922.

AZZI, G. The equivalent for drought during the critical period of maize (Italian). *La Meteorologia Pratica*, An. 23, Nos. 5–6, 1942.

BALTADORI, A. The physical environment and the culture of maize in the region of Perugia (Italian). *La Meteorologia Pratica*, An. 23, No. 4, 1942.

BALTADORI, A. Determination of the meteorological equivalents and the distribution of the asymmetric cases in the mixed zone (Italian). *Rivista di Ecologia*, Vol. 2, No. 1, 1952.

DIONIGI, A. Active and passive lethargy (Italian). *Rivista di Patologia Vegetale*, An. 31, Pavia 1941.

KIRIAKOV, K. Effect of the variations of the water regime on the growth, development and yield of maize (Italian). *La Meteorologia Pratica*, An. 19, No. 6, 1938.

MALIBOGA, A. Influence of the drought of soil at different moments of the vegetative period on the growth and yield of cereals (Russian). *Bulletin of Applied Botany and Selection*, Vol. 17, Leningrad 1927.

Chapter IV

BALTADORI, A. The meteorological factors and the production of lucerne in the region of Perugia (Italian). *Annali della Facoltà di Agraria*, Vol. 4, Perugia 1947.

BALTADORI, A. The meteorological factors and the production of clover in the region of Perugia (Italian). *Annali della Facoltà di Agraria*, Vol. 4, Perugia 1947.

BALTADORI, A. The meteorological factors and the yield of hay in the region of Perugia (Italian). *Annali della Facoltà di Agraria*, Vol. 4, Perugia 1947.

BRICCOLI, M. Experimental researches on the water requirements of the potato (Italian). *La Meteorologia Pratica*, An. 21, No. 1, Perugia 1940.

DE GASPERI L. Effect of meteorological factors on the quantity and quality of the product of sugar-beet (Italian). *Annali di Tecnica Agraria*, An. 6, Fasc. 4, Naples 1933.

MARCHI, V. Experimental researches on the water balance of clover (Italian). *La Meteorologia Pratica*, An. 24, No. 5, Perugia 1943.

MILIANI, R. Influence of environmental factors on the production of alfalfa (Italian). *Italia Agricola*, An. 69, No. 2, Piacenza 1932.

MILIANI, R. Determination of the meteorological equivalents for drought for hemp (Italian). *La Meteorologia Pratica*, An. 24, No. 1, Perugia 1943.

MUSMARRA, A. Meteorological equivalents for drought in relation to the critical period of the bean in Sicily (Italian). *La Meteorologia Pratica*, An. 24, No. 5, Perugia 1943.

MUSMARRA, A. The physical environment and the culture of the caper-bush (Italian). *La Meteorologia Pratica*, An. 24, No. 5, Perugia 1943.

OMODEO, C. Rainfall and production of alfalfa in Umbria (Italian). *La Meteorologia Pratica*, An. 22, No. 3, Perugia 1941.

OMODEO, C. Experimental researches on the water requirements of flax (Italian). *La Meteorologia Pratica*, An. 21, No. 5, Perugia 1941.

ROGANOVITCH, B. Areas of the culture of cotton in Yugoslavia (Serbo-croatian). 376 pages, Serb State Press, Belgrade 1951.

VIGGIANI, G. Effect of temperature and rainfall on the yield of leguminous fodder crops in the province of Perugia (Italian). *Rivista di Zootecnia*, An. 3, Firenze 1926.

VIGGIANI, G. Experimental determination of the ecological constants of the potato (Italian). *Bollettino della Società dei Naturalisti in Napoli*, Vol. 39, An. 41, Naples 1927.

VIGGIANI, G. Experimental determination of the ecological constants for the potato, 2nd contribution (Italian). *Annali del R. Istituto Sup. Agrario di Portici*, Serie 3, Vol. 3, Naples 1928.

Chapter V

BALTADORI, A. The meteorological equivalents and the water balance of wheat. (Italian). *Bollettino della Società Italiana di Biologia Sperimentale*, Vol. 26, Fasc. 2, Naples 1950.

BRICCOLI, M. The soil moisture and the rainfall in Perugia (Italian). *Rivista di Ecologia*, Vol. 1, Nos. 5–6, Perugia 1950.

BROUNOV, P. I. Crops and weather (French). St. Petersburg 1912.

CAVALAGLIO, F. Effect of some factors on the water balance of the soil (Italian). *Annali della Facoltà di Agraria*, Vol. 8, Perugia 1952.

CONTI, M. Ecological limits of the wheat culture in Argentina (Spanish). *Facoldad de Agronomia y Veterinaria*, Bollettino No. 7, Buenos Aires 1930.

DE GASPERI, L. Effect of meteorological factors on the tillage of wheats (Italian). *La Meteorologia Pratica*, An. 14, No. 2, Perugia 1933.

GAETANI, L. Effect of rainfall and temperature on the yield of wheat in the territory of Imola (Italian). *La Meteorologia Pratica*, An. 17, No. 5, Perugia 1936.

GAETANI, L. The climate of Capitanata in relation to cereal culture (Italian). *La Meteorologia Pratica*, An. 18, No. 1, Perugia 1937.

GESLIN, H., and JONARD, P.   The maturation of wheat and climate :
characteristic curve of the development of wheat from a physical
point of view (French).   *Comptes Rendus des Séances de l'Académie
d'Agriculture de France,* séances des 27–28 mars 1946, Paris
1946.

MILIANI, R.   Determination of the meteorological equivalents for
hot spell (Italian).   *La Meteorologia Pratica,* An. 12, No. 6,
Subiaco 1931.

MILIANI, R.   Influence of low temperatures on the development
and maturation of winter wheats (Italian).   *La Meteorologia
Pratica,* An. 13, No. 4, Subiaco 1932.

MILIANI, R.   Effect of temperature and humidity on tillering of
spring wheats (Italian).   *Il Coltivatore,* No. 16, Casale Monf.
1932.

OMODEO, C.   Rainfall and yield of wheat in the territory of Perugia
(Italian).   *La Meteorologia Pratica,* An. 21, No. 2, Perugia
1940.

ROCCHI, M.   Influence of meteorological factors on the diffusion of
rust (Italian).   *La Meteorologia Pratica,* An. 17, No. 2, Perugia
1936.

VIGGIANI, G.   Climate of wheat in Lucania (South Italy) (Italian).
Terra Lucana, Potenza 1927.

Chapter VI

AZZI, G.   Effect of meteorological factors on the development and
yield of the vine in the territory of Perugia (Italian).   *Il Coltivatore,* No. 34, Casale Monf. 1927.

AZZI, G.   The physical environment and the cultivation of the olive-
tree (Italian).   *Atti del Congresso Nazionale di Olivicoltura,*
Bari 1938.

BASTIANONI, M.   Thermic equivalents of *Arbustus Unedo* (Italian).
Annali della Facoltà di Agraria, Vol. 11, Perugia 1955.

BODENHEIMER, F. S.   The importance of climate in agricultural
entomology (German).   *Zeitschrift für Angewandte Entomologie,*
Berlin 1926.

BODENHEIMER, F. S.   Factors limiting the area of distribution of a
species (German).   *Biologischen Zentralblatt,* Vol. 47, Heft 1,
Erlangen 1927.

BODENHEIMER, F. S.   Limits of diffusion of " *Calendra oryzae* " and
" *C. granaria* " L. (German).   *Zeitschrift für Wissenschaftliche
insektenbiologie,* Vol. 31, No. 3–4, Berlin 1927.

BRICCOLI, M.   Preliminary note on the climate and area of distribution of the chestnut (Italian).   *La Meteorologia Pratica,* An. 15,
No. 3, Perugia 1934.

DE GASPERI, L.   Rainfall and the reserves of water in the soil in
relation to the vine in Sicily (Italian).   *La Meteorologia Pratica,*
An. 15, No. 2, Perugia 1934.

DE GASPERI, L.   The meteorological factors in relation to the cultivation of the vine (Italian).   *La Meteorologia Pratica,* An. 15, No. 5,
Perugia 1934.

FORMICA, F.   Vine production and meteorological factors in the
province of Bari (Italian).   *La Meteorologia Pratica,* An. 22,
No. 5–6, Perugia 1941.

FORMICA, F.   The meteorological factors and the yield in olives in
the province of Bari (Italian).   *La Meteorologia Pratica,* An.
22, No. 5–6, Perugia 1941.

GAETANI L. The yield in oil of olive-tree in dry and wet years (Italian). *Olivicoltura*, No. 5, Rome 1938.

MARCHI, V. Contribution to the study of the meteorological equivalents for the vine (Italian). *La Meteorologia Pratica*, An. 23, No. 2, Perugia 1942.

MILIANI, R. Ecological classification of olive-trees in Italy (Italian). *Annali di Tecnica Agraria*, An. 5, Fasc. 3, Napoli 1932.

OMODEO, C. Effect of meteorological factors on the yield of olive-tree in the hilly region of Perugia (Italian). *La Meteorologia Pratica*, An. 22, No. 1, Perugia 1941.

PIERCE, D. W. New concepts concerning the influence of humidity and of temperature on the development of insects. *Journal of Agricultural Research*, Vol. 5, No. 25, Washington 1918.

ROCCHI, M. Effect of meteorological factors on the development and diffusion of the olive-fly (Italian). *La Meteorologia Pratica*, An. 17, No. 3, Perugia 1936.

ROCCHI, M. The olive-tree in the physical environment of Romagna (Italian). *Italia Agricola*, An. 73, No. 9, Rome 1936.

VIGIANI D. Effect of meteorological factors on the production of chestnut (Italian). *Atti della R. Accademia dei Georgofili*, 6th series, January–February, Florence 1941.

VOLLONO F. Influence of the meteorological factors on the yield of the olive in the province of Naples (Italian). *Olivicolture*, An. 17, No. 9, Rome 1941.

Chapter VII

AZZI, G. Research on the phenomena of photoperiodism (Italian). *Italia Agricola*, An. 64, No. 6, Piacenza 1927.

AZZI, G. Temperature and length of day in relation with the development of wheat (Italian). *La Meteorologia Pratica*, An. 17, No. 6, Perugia 1936.

AZZI, G. Effect of the moon on the development of the onion (Italian). *La Meteorologia Pratica*, An. 18, No. 1, Perugia 1937.

BALTADORI, A. The expansion limits of wheat in relation to temperature and photoperiodism (Italian). *Rivista di Ecologia*, Vol. 1, No. 5–6, Perugia 1950.

CARTON, P. Considerations on the action of light on plants, ecological factors " intensity of light " and " length of day ", " vernalisation ", particularly for tropical countries (French). *Bulletin Géneral de la Direction de l'Instruction Publique de l'Indochine*, Hanoi 1934.

GAETANI, L. Researches on photoperiodism (Italian). *La Meteorologia Pratica*, An. 18, No. 6, Perugia 1937.

GARNER, W. W., and ALLARD, H. A. Effect of the relative length of day and night and other factors of environment on growth and reproduction in plants. *Journal of Agricultural Research*, An. 18, No. 11, Washington 1920.

KIRIAKOV, K. Specific behaviour of three varieties of maize in relation to photoperiodism (Italian). *La Meteorologia Pratica*, An. 20, No. 2, Perugia 1920.

LYSENKO, T. D. Agrobiology (Russian). 639 pages, State Press for Agricultural Literature, Moscow 1948.

RASUMOV, V. I. Effect of the relative length of day on the development of potato tubers (Russian). *Bulletin of Applied Botany*, An. 27, No. 5, Leningrad 1931.

SALVATORI, B. Regression from the polar limit of expansion of wheat in absence of photoperiodic stimulus (Italian). *Rivista di Ecologia*, Vol. 3, No. 1, Perugia 1953.

Chapter VIII

Azzi, G. Agricultural Ecology (Italian). 204 pages, Edition Dante Alighieri, Città di Castello 1944.

Chapter IX

Azzi, G. Agricultural Ecology (Italian). 237 pages, Edition Tipografia Editrice Torinese, Turin 1928.

Azzi, G. The ecological framework of wheat in Brazil (Portuguese). *Ministerio da Agricoltura* D.N.P.V., serie *Triticea*, No. 3, Rio de Janeiro 1937.

Azzi, G. The meteorological equivalents as basis for agricultural climatology (Italian). *Rivista di Ecologia*, Vol. 2, No. 1, Perugia 1952.

Livingston, B. E. A single index to represent both moisture and temperature conditions as related to plants. *Physiological Researches*, Vol. 1, No. 9, Baltimore 1916.

Livingston, B. E. Physiological temperature indices for the study of plant growth in relation to climatic conditions. *Physiological Researches*, Vol. 1, No. 8, Baltimore 1916.

Livingston, B. E., and Livingston, G. J. Temperature coefficients in plant geography and climatology. *Botanical Gazette*, Vol. 56, No. 5, Chicago 1913.

Chapter X

Azzi, G. The concept of limit in the distribution of cultivated plants (Italian). *Italia Agricola*, An. 65, No. 1, Piacenza 1928.

Baltadori, A. The orientation of slopes and the variation of the iodine value in olive oil (Italian) *Rivista di Ecologia*, Vol. 1, No. 1–2, Perugia 1949.

Briccoli, M. Importance of micro-climates from an agricultural view point (Italian). *Italia Agricola*, An. 67, No. 7, Piacenza 1930.

Briccoli, M. The resumption of development of olive-trees in Umbria after the heavy frosts of 1929 (Italian). *Rivista di Ecologia*, Vol. 3, No. 1, Perugia 1953.

Gaetani, L. The damage caused to the olive-trees in Umbria by the heavy frosts of 1929 (Italian). *La Meteorologia Pratica*, An. 19, No. 1, Perugia 1938.

Ivanov, S. Variations in the chemical composition of seeds of oleagenous plants in relation with the geographical factors (Russian). *Bulletin of Applied Botany and Genetics*, Vol. 16, No. 3, Leningrad 1928.

Omodeo, C. The climate of the olive in the region of the Alpine lakes (Italian). *La Meteorologia Pratica*, An. 21, No. 5–6, Perugia 1940.

Rocchi, M. The calorific power of olive oils in relation to altitude and orientation of slopes (Italian). *La Meteorologia Pratica*, An. 17, No. 4, Perugia 1936.

Rocchi, M. Effect of low temperatures on the development and maturation of fruits of the chestnut (Italian). *La Meteorologia Pratica*, An. 20, No. 3, 1939.

Vizzotto, Rino. Particular study on the damage of the olive-trees by the heavy frosts of 1929 (Italian). Thesis, Faculty of Agriculture, Perugia 1934.

Chapter XI

Azzi, G.   The cartographic representation of meteorological values in relation with the development of cultivated plants (Italian). *La Nuova Agricoltura*, Rome 1928.

Azzi, G.   Climate of wheat in Italy (Italian). *Nuovi Annali del Ministero di Agricoltura*, An. 2, No. 3, Rome 1922.

Azzi, G.   The climatic axes of wheat (Italian). *La Meteorologia Pratica* An. 20, No. 2, Perugia 1939.

Baltadori, A.   Effect of low temperatures on the wood of the vine (Italian). *La Meteorologia Pratica*, An. 23, No. 2, Perugia 1942.

Baltadori, A.   The variations of the vine's resistance to cold during winter (Italian). *Bollettino della Società Italiana di Biologia Sperimentale*, Vol. 20, Fasc. 11, Naples 1945.

Baltadori, A.   Resistance of vine to cold (Italian). *Annali della Facoltà di Agraria*, Vol. 3, Perugia 1946.

Baltadori, A.   Resistance of vine to cold and period of lethargy (Italian). *Bollettino della Società Italiana di Biologia Sperimentale*, Vol. 20, Fasc. 11, Naples 1945.

Baltadori, A.   Intensity of the lethargy and resistance of vine to cold (Italian). *Bollettino della Società Italiana di Biologia Sperimentale*, Vol. 23, Fasc. 1–2, Naples 1947.

Brounov, P. I.   With relation to the division of European Russia into geographical regions (Russian). *Studies Published by the Meteorological Bureau of the Scientific Committee for Agriculture of Russia*, St. Petersburg 1907.

Brounov, P. I.   Atlas of Agricultural Meteorology—Maps of global probability of drought in Russia (Russian). *Bureau of Agricultural Meteorology of the Ministry of Agriculture*, St. Petersburg 1913.

Marchi, V.   Influence of low temperatures and excess rainfall on the maturation of the grape (Italian). *La Meteorologia Pratica*, An. 23, No. 3, Perugia 1942.

Omodeo. C.   Climate and cultivation of vine in the territory of Perugia (Italian). *La Meteorologia Pratica*, An. 22, No. 2, Perugia 1941.

Rocchi, M.   The physiographical zones of the vine in Italy (Italian). *La Meteorologia Pratica*, An. 17, No. 4, Perugia 1936.

Chapter XII

Azzi, G.   Meteorological equivalents as a basis of agricultural climatology. This article is followed by commentaries of L. Fantappiè : Continuity, discontinuity and meteorological equivalents. A. Belluigi : Continuous and discontinuous, and G. Roncali : Mathematical aspects of the meteorological equivalents (Italian). *Rivista di Ecologia*, Vol. 2, No. 1, Perugia 1952.

Blair, T. A.   New methods for the calculation of the coefficient of correlation of the meteorological factors, the development and yield of winter wheats in Ohio. *Monthly Weather Review*, Vol. 47, No. 12, Washington 1919.

Moretti-Costanzi, S.   The use of the formula of correlation in relation to the meteorological equivalents (Italian). *La Meteorologia Pratica*, An. 20, No. 5, Perugia 1939.

Chapter XIII

Azzi, G.   Corporative agricultural technique (Italian). Pages 186, Tip. Arte della Stampa, Rome 1937.

D D

Azzi, G. Relation between soil and olive-tree under different climatic conditions (Italian). *La Meteorologia Pratica*, An. 19, No. 1, Perugia 1938.

Azzi, G. An effort to make an ecological classification of soils (Portuguese). Report presented to H. E. the Minister of Agriculture of the United States of Brazil, Rio de Janeiro 1939.

Briccoli, M. Ecological classification of soils in the territory of Perugia (Italian). Pages 102. Federazione Italiana dei Consorzi Agrari, Piacenza 1930.

Chiavarelli, M. Ecological classification of soils in the region of Cellere (Italian). *Italia Agricola*, An. 70, No. 10, Rome 1933.

Gaetani, L. The classification of soils and their chemical composition (Italian). *Annali di Tecnica Agraria*, An. 11, Fasc. 2, Naples 1938.

Miliani, R. Ecological classification of soils in the Imola region (Italian). Pages 111, Cooperativa Tip. Editrice P. Galeati, Imola 1932.

Rocchi, M. The water balance of different soils in relation to maize (Italian). *La Meteorologia Pratica*, An. 16, No. 1, Perugia 1935.

Rocchi, M. Soil humidity and tillability (Italian). *La Meteorologia Pratica*, An. 16, No. 2, Perugia 1935.

Rocchi, M. Determination of tillability in the series of soils of the Imola territory (Italian). *Italia Agricola*, An. 72, No. 1, Rome 1935.

Rocchi, M. Vine culture and the soils of the Isle of Ischia (Italian). *Il Coltivatore*, No. 12, Casale Monf. 1936.

Chapter XIV

Azzi, G. The climatic axes for maize and the repeated series of soils (Italian). *La Meteorologia Pratica*, An. 20, No. 4, Perugia 1939.

Azzi, G. The unitary representation of physical environment (soil and climate) (Italian). *Rivista di Ecologia*, Vol. 2, No. 3, 1952.

Chapter XV

Akerman, A. Pansar wheat in Southern Sweden (Swedish). *Sveriges Utsädeförenings Tidskrift*, An. 28, Fasc. 3, Malmö 1918.

Azzi, G. Regarding the degree of incompatibility between productivity and resistance to drought of beans (Italian). *La Meteorologia Pratica* An. 23, No. 1, Perugia 1942.

Briccoli, M. Determination of the degree of productivity and of resistance of wheats (Italian). *Annali di Tecnica Agraria*, An. 4, Fasc. 2, Naples 1931.

Dearing, Ch. Bettering of Muscadinia grapes by selection. *Journal of Heredity*, Vol. 8, No. 9, Washington 1917.

Dearing, Ch., and Husmann, G. The Muscadinia vine. *U.S. Department of Agriculture—Farmer's Bulletin*, No. 709, Washington 1916.

De Gasperi, L. The choice of varieties of wheat according to the conditions of climate and soil (Italian). *La Meteorologia Pratica*, An. 15, No. 2, Perugia 1934.

Gaetani, L. The yield of two varieties of early and tardy potatoes in the climatic and soil conditions of Umbria (Italian). *La Meteorologia Pratica*, An. 19, No. 2, Perugia 1938.

Gaetani, L. The insurgence of the characteristics of productivity and of resistance in relation with the nature of the soil (Italian). *Italia Agricola*, An. 75, No. 5, Rome 1938.

OPOLSKI, C. Considerations on wheat culture in the South East Indies (Dutch). *Wanasoeka*, Pengalengan 1922.

SAUNDERS, W. M. Types of apple-trees resistant to cold created for the N.W. sector of Canada. *Dominion of Canada, Department of Agriculture, Bulletin*, No. 68, Ottawa 1911.

VIGGIANI, G. Influence of temperature and rainfall on the production of the " Biancone " and " Riccia " varieties of potato (Italian). *Reale Istituto Superiore Agrario, Cattedra e Laboratorio delle Coltivazioni*, Naples 1927.

Chapter XVI

AKERMAN, A., and JACOBSON, J. Researches on the quality of Swedish wheats (Swedish). *Sveriges Utsädeförenings Tidskrift*, An. 45, Fasc. 1, Malmö 1935.

BALTADORI, A. The development of beans and their calorific power (Italian). *Bollettino della Società Italiana di Biologia Sperimentale*, Vol. 26, Fasc. 2, Naples 1950.

BOEUF, M. F. Results of research on the improvement of wheat, especially in relation to bread making (French). *La Tunisie Agricole*, An. 24, Tunis 1934.

BOEUF, M. F. Quality of Tunisian wheats (agronomic and industrial characteristics) (French). *Bulletin de la Direction Générale de l'Agriculture, du Commerce et de la Colonisation*, An. 28, No. 112, Tunis 1923.

BRICCOLI, M. The gluten content of wheat in relation to environmental conditions (Italian). *La Meteorologia Pratica*, An. 21, No. 1, Perugia 1940.

BRICCOLI, M. The chemical composition of the soil and the gluten content in the caryopsis of wheat (Italian). *Italia Agricola*, An. 78, No. 7, Rome 1941.

CAPRIOTTI, A. The agents of vine fermentation in Calabria (Italian). *Annali della Facoltà di Agraria*, Vol. 8, Perugia 1952.

CASTELLI, T. Consideration on the relationship between climate and agents of vine fermentation (French). *Revue des Fermentations et des Industries Alimentaires*, Vol. 7, No. 2, Brussells 1952.

CAVALAGLIO, F. Effect of the environmental factors on the formation of gluten (Italian). *Annali della Facoltà di Agraria*, Vol. 8, Perugia 1952.

DIMIČ, A. The calorific power of wheat in relation to the biological and environmental factors (Italian). *Italia Agricola*, An. 84, No. 10, Rome 1947.

GAETANI, L. The gluten content of the " Mentana " variety of wheat in relation to the nature of the soil (Italian). *Italia Agricola*, An. 75, No. 2, Rome 1938.

OMODEO, C. Influence of environmental factors on the calorific power of wheat (Italian). *La Meteorologia Pratica*, An. 22, No. 5–6, Perugia 1941.

SCHNELLE, F., and HEISER, F. Researches on the quality of wheat in the framework of the international geographical trials (German). *Mülenlaboratorium*, No. 3, 1935.

SCHNELLE, F., and HEISER, F. Influence of luminous radiations on the quality of wheat (German). *Künste Archiv*, Vol. 39, No. 121, 1935.

Chapter XVII

AZZI, G.   Generative yield (quality of seed for planting) pages 453–
464 of the " Treatise of Agricultural Ecology " (Italian).   Edition
Società Editrice Internazionale, Turin 1939.

BRICCOLI, M.   Natural selection and improvement of seed (Italian).
La Meteorologia Pratica, An. 15, No. 4, Perugia 1934.

DE GASPERI, L.   Effect of meteorological factors on the production
and quality of the seed (Italian).   *La Meteorologia Pratica*,
An. 14, No. 5–6, Perugia 1933.

MILIANI, R.   The germinability of the caryopsis of wheat in relation
with meteorological conditions during maturation (Italian).
Annali di Tecnica Agraria, An. 4, Fasc. 2, Naples 1932.

TALLARICO, G.   The caryopsis of wheat as food and as seed (Italian).
*Memorie della R. Accademia d'Italia, Classe di Scienze Fisiche,
Matematiche e Naturali*, Vol. 3, Rome 1931.

TALLARICO, G.   The conservation and the productivity of the seed
of wheat (Italian).   *Rendiconti della R. Accademia Nazionale dei
Lincei, Classe di Scienze Fisiche, Matematiche e Naturali*, Vol. 13,
sem. 2, Fasc. 2, Rome 1931.

TALLARICO, G.   Treatment of seed while still on the mother plant
(Italian).   *Rendiconti della R. Accademia dei Lincei, Classe delle
Scienze Fisiche, Matematiche e Naturali*, Vol. 13, sem. 1, Fasc. 2,
Rome 1931.

Chapter XVIII

BRICCOLI, M.   Trials on vernalisation with seed of local varieties of
wheat (Italian).   *Italia Agricola*, An. 76, No. 2, Rome 1939.

GASSNER, G.   Contribution to the study of forms of winter and spring
wheats (German).   *Zeitschrift für Botanik*, Vol. 10, Fasc. 8,
Iéna 1918.

KIRIAKOV K.   Vernalisation of maize as a mean of adaptation to
unfavourable conditions of environment (Italian).   *La Meteorologia Pratica*, An. 20, No. 1, Perugia 1939.

LYSENKO, T. D.   The theoretical basis of vernalisation (Russian).
Selskosgys, pages 153, Moscow 1925.

LYSENKO, T. D.   Vernalisation of Millet, maize, Indian millet and
soja (Russian).   *Bulten Jarovizazii*, No. 2–3, Odessa 1932.

LYSENKO, T. D., and PRESENT, J. J.   Selection and the stadial theory
of the development of plants (Russian).   Pages 63, Selskosgys,
Moscow 1935.

MARCHI, V.   Researches on vernalisation at high temperatures
(Italian).   *La Meteorologia Pratica*, An. 23, No. 2, Perugia 1942.

SALVATORI, B.   Behaviour of winter and spring forms of wheat in
relation with the shortening of day's length (Italian).   *Annali
della Facoltà di Agraria*, Vol. 10, Perugia 1954.

Chapter XIX

AZZI, G.   The ecological basis of the evolution of wheat (Italian).
Rivista di Ecologia, Vol. 2, No. 2, Perugia 1952.

AZZI, G., and PIROTTA, R.   The agricultural ecology (Italian).
Nuovi Annali dell'Agricoltura, An. 4, No. 2, Rome 1924.

BRICCOLI, M.   Differences in behaviour towards environmental
adversities by the lines of a same variety (Italian).   *Il Coltivatore*,
No. 11, Casale Monf. 1931.

DE CILLIS, E. The wheats of Italy (Italian). Pages 174, Tipografia della Camera dei Deputati, Rome 1927.

KÖRNICKE, F. Species and varieties of cereals (German). Verlag von Paul Parey, Berlin 1885.

OLIVA, A. The wheat in the mountain (Italian). *Atti della R. Accademia dei Georgofili*, Serie 6, Vol. 2, Florence 1936.

VAVILOV, N. I. The centre of origin of cultivated plants (Russian). *Bulletin of Applied Botany and Selection*, Vol. 16, Fasc. 2, Leningrad 1927.

VAVILOV, N. I. The theoretical bases of selection (Russian). Pages 1043, Selskosgys, Moscow 1935.

Chapter XX

AZZI, G. The variation in mass of wheat as a mean of adaptation to favourable and unfavourable conditions of the environment (Italian). *Italia Agricola*, An. 65, No. 2, Piacenza 1928.

AZZI, G. Two constants which regulate the relationships of mass and velocity in the development of plants. This article is followed by commentaries of L. FANTAPPIÈ : The laws of Azzi as possible indices of syntropic phenomena, and M. PUMA : Some physicomathematic considerations on Azzi's constants (Italian). *Historia Naturalis*, An. 3, No. 1, Rome 1949.

AZZI, G. Velocity–mass–structure system in relation to productivity and resistance of cultivated plants (Italian). *Rivista di Ecologia*, Vol. 1, No. 1–2, Perugia 1949.

AZZI, G. Resistance to lodging as a separate resistance (Italian). *Annali della Facoltà di Agraria*, Vol. 11, Perugia 1955.

BALTADORI, A. Velocity and mass in relation with yield in tubers of the potato (Italian). *La Meteorologia Pratica*, An. 23, No. 3, Perugia 1942.

BALTADORI, A. Productivity and duration of the sub-period from earing to maturation of wheat (Italian). *Bollettino della Società Italiana di Biologia Sperimentale*, Vol. 20, Fasc. 4–5, Naples 1945.

BALTADORI, A. The low of velocity and mass and yield of crops (Italian). *Bollettino della Società Italiana di Biologia Sperimentale*, Vol. 24, Fasc. 5, Naples 1948.

BALTADORI, A. Inversion of relationships of velocity and mass for wheat (Italian). *Bollettino della Società Italiana di Biologia Sperimentale*, Vol. 24, Fasc. 5, Perugia 1948.

BALTADORI, A. The thermic factor and the development of maize in the sub-period from germination to leafing (Italian). *Archivio di Scienze Biologiche*, Vol. 33, Bologna 1949.

BALTADORI, A. The method of Azzi in representing the characters with angular values (Italian). *Bollettino della Società Italiana di Biologia Sperimentale*, Vol. 26, Fasc. 2, Naples 1950.

BALTADORI, A. The velocity–mass–structure system and the yield in grain of wheat (Italian). *Annali della Facoltà di Agraria*, Vol. 8, Perugia 1952.

KNUT, VIK. Effect of meteorological factors on the yield of potatoes (Norwegian). *Aars Beretning On Norges Jordbrukshoiskola Akervekstforsok*, An. 20, Oslo 1914.

MILIANI, R. Earlyness as characteristic of adaptation in a dry and hot environment (Italian). *La Meteorologia Pratica*, An. 13, No. 3, Subiaco 1932.

OMODEO, C. Inversion of the time of earing in two different years of two spring varieties of wheat (Italian). *La Meteorologia Pratica*, An. 22, No. 3, Perugia 1941.

OMODEO, C.   An ecological characteristic of the " Mentana " wheat variety in relation with productivity (Italian). *La Meteorologia Pratica*, An. 22, No. 4, Perugia 1941.

ROGOZINSKI, A.   Earlyness of earing and maturity of wheat on the ecological point of view (Italian). *La Meteorologia Pratica*, An. 15, No. 1, Perugia 1934.

Chapter XXI

AZZI, G.   Methodology in the determination of the ecological characteristics (Italian). *Rivista di Biologia*, An. 44, No. 2, Perugia 1952.

CAVALAGLIO F.   Evaluation of the ecological characteristics of some Italian varieties of wheat (Italian). *Annali della Facoltà di Agraria*, Vol. 11, Perugia 1955.

Chapter XXII

AKERMAN, A.   Observations made at Svalöf, during winter 1921–1922, on the resistance of numerous varieties of wheat to winter adversities (Swedish). *Sveriges Utsädeförenings Tidskrift*, An. 27, Fasc. 5, Malmö 1922.

AKERMAN, A.   Experimental research on the resistance of plants to cold (Swedish). *Veröffeutlichungen der Kunt und Alice Wellenberg Stiftung* No. 10, Lund 1927.

AZZI, G.   A characteristic of the olive correlated with the resistance to drought (Italian). *Il Coltivatore*, Rome 1927.

BALTADORI, A.   Productivity and resistance to drought in relation to leaf surface (Italian). *Bollettino della Società Italiana di Biologia Sperimentale*, Vol. 26, Fasc. 2, Naples 1950.

KIRIAKOV, K.   The development of maize and the resistance to drought (Italian). *La Meteorologia Pratica*, An. 20, No. 3, Perugia 1939.

MARCHI, V.   A characteristic of maize correlated with resistance to drought (Italian). *La Meteorologia Pratica*, An. 23, No. 1, Perugia 1942.

SALMON, S., and FLEMING, F. L.   Turgescence and concentration of solutions in the cellular sap of graminacea in relation to resistance to cold. *Journal of Agricultural Research*, Vol. 13, No. 10, Washington 1918.

SINZ, E.   Correlation between the percentage of dry matter and the resistance to cold of certain varieties of wheat (German). *Journal für Landwirtschaft*, Vol. 62, Fasc. 4, Berlin 1914.

UPHOF, T. J. C.   Influence of temperature on the geographical distribution of certain species of *opuntia*. *Journal of Ecology*, Vol. 3, No. 1, London 1920.

WILSON, P., and HARRIS, A. J.   Resistance of plants to cold in relation with the lowering of freezing point of the cell sap. *Journal of Agricultural Research*, Vol. 7, No. 6, Washington 1916.

Chapter XXIII

AZZI, G.   The " Biancone dell' Elba " variety and its specific resistance to hot spell (Italian). *Rivista di Ecologia*, Vol. 1, No. 5–6, Perugia 1950.

AZZI, G.   Separate resistance to lodging (Italian). *Annali della Facoltà di Agraria*, Vol. 11, Perugia 1955.

Chapter XXIV

Azzi, G. The differential analysis of yields (Italian). *Agricoltura Fascista*, An. 14, Nos. 51–52, Rome 1942.

Chapter XXV

Azzi, G. The ecological basis of agricultural research (Italian). *La Meteorologia Pratica*, An. 23, No. 2, Perugia 1942.

Chapter XXVI

Azzi, G. The differential analysis of yields : determination of the effects of soils, of the slope, of fertilisation and the working of the soil on the yield of wheat (Italian). *Annali della Sperimentazione Agraria*, Rome 1952.

Bilancini, R. On a type of statistical analysis of the meteorological variables (Italian). *Rivista di Meteorologia Aeronautica*, An. 8, No. 4, Rome 1948.

Chapter XXVII

Azzi, G. Agricultural ecology (Italian). Pages 204, Edition Società Anonima Editrice Dante Alighieri, Città di Castello, Rome 1944.

INDEX